Dimensions Math®
Teacher's Guide 4B

Authors and Reviewers

Cassandra Turner

Allison Coates

Jenny Kempe

Bill Jackson

Tricia Salerno

Singapore Math Inc.

Published by Singapore Math Inc.

19535 SW 129th Avenue
Tualatin, OR 97062
www.singaporemath.com

Dimensions Math® Teacher's Guide 4B
ISBN 978-1-947226-39-5

First published 2020
Reprinted 2020 (twice)

Printed in China

Acknowledgments

Editing by the Singapore Math Inc. team.
Design and illustration by Cameron Wray with Carli Fronius.

Contents

Chapter		Lesson	Page

Chapter		Lesson	Page

Chapter		Lesson	Page

Dimensions Math® Curriculum

The **Dimensions Math®** series is a Pre-Kindergarten to Grade 5 series based on the pedagogy and methodology of math education in Singapore. The main goal of the **Dimensions Math®** series is to help students develop competence and confidence in mathematics.

The series follows the principles outlined in the Singapore Mathematics Framework below.

Pedagogical Approach and Methodology

- Through Concrete-Pictorial-Abstract development, students view the same concepts over time with increasing levels of abstraction.
- Thoughtful sequencing creates a sense of continuity. The content of each grade level builds on that of preceding grade levels. Similarly, lessons build on previous lessons within each grade.
- Group discussion of solution methods encourages expansive thinking.
- Interesting problems and activities provide varied opportunities to explore and apply skills.
- Hands-on tasks and sharing establish a culture of collaboration.
- Extra practice and extension activities encourage students to persevere through challenging problems.
- Variation in pictorial representation (number bonds, bar models, etc.) and concrete representation (straws, linking cubes, base ten blocks, discs, etc.) broaden student understanding.

Each topic is introduced, then thoughtfully developed through the use of a variety of learning experiences, problem solving, student discourse, and opportunities for mastery of skills. This combination of hands-on practice, in-depth exploration of topics, and mathematical variability in teaching methodology allows students to truly master mathematical concepts.

Singapore Mathematics Framework

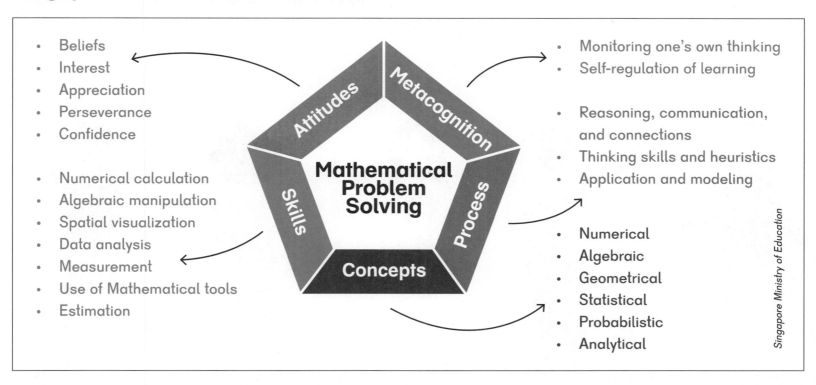

Dimensions Math® Program Materials

Textbooks

Textbooks are designed to help students build a solid foundation in mathematical thinking and efficient problem solving. Careful sequencing of topics, well-chosen problems, and simple graphics foster deep conceptual understanding and confidence. Mental math, problem solving, and correct computation are given balanced attention in all grades. As skills are mastered, students move to increasingly sophisticated concepts within and across grade levels.

Students work through the textbook lessons with the help of five friends: Emma, Alex, Sofia, Dion, and Mei. The characters appear throughout the series and help students develop metacognitive reasoning through questions, hints, and ideas.

A pencil icon ━━━━━▶ at the end of the textbook lessons links to exercises in the workbooks.

Workbooks

Workbooks provide additional problems that range from basic to challenging. These allow students to independently review and practice the skills they have learned.

Teacher's Guides

Teacher's Guides include lesson plans, mathematical background, games, helpful suggestions, and comprehensive resources for daily lessons.

Tests

Tests contain differentiated assessments to systematically evaluate student progress.

| Emma | Alex | Sofia | Dion | Mei |

Online Resources

The following can be downloaded from dimensionsmath.com.

- **Blackline Masters** used for various hands-on tasks.

- **Material Lists** for each chapter and lesson, so teachers and classroom helpers can prepare ahead of time.

- **Standards Alignments** for various states.

Using the Teacher's Guide

This guide is designed to assist in planning daily lessons. It should be considered a helping hand between the curriculum and the classroom. It provides introductory notes on mathematical content, key points, and suggestions for activities. It also includes ideas for differentiation within each lesson, and answers and solutions to textbook and workbook problems.

Each chapter of the guide begins with the following.

● Overview

Includes objectives and suggested number of class periods for each chapter.

● Notes

Highlights key learning points, provides background on math concepts, explains the purpose of certain activities, and helps teachers understand the flow of topics throughout the year.

● Materials

Lists materials, manipulatives, and Blackline Masters used in the Think and Learn sections of the guide. It also includes suggested storybooks. Many common classroom manipulatives are used throughout the curriculum. When a lesson refers to a whiteboard and markers, any writing materials can be used. Blackline Masters can be found at dimensionsmath.com.

The guide goes through the Chapter Openers, Daily Lessons, and Practices of each chapter, and cumulative reviews in the following general format.

● Chapter Opener

Provides talking points for discussion to prepare students for the math concepts to be introduced.

● Think

Offers structure for teachers to guide student inquiry. Provides various methods and activities to solve initial textbook problems or tasks.

● Learn

Guides teachers to analyze student methods from Think to arrive at the main concepts of the lesson through discussion and study of the pictorial representations in the textbook.

● Do

Expands on specific problems with strategies, additional practice, and remediation.

● <u>Activities</u>

Allows students to practice concepts through individual, small group, and whole group hands-on tasks and games, including suggestions for outdoor play (most of which can be modified for a gymnasium or classroom).

Level of difficulty in the games and activities are denoted by the following symbols.

- ● Foundational activities
- ▲ On-level activities
- ★ Challenge or extension activities

● <u>Brain Works</u>

Provides opportunities for students to extend their mathematical thinking.

Discussion is a critical component of each lesson. Teachers are encouraged to let students discuss their reasoning. As each classroom is different, this guide does not anticipate all situations. The following questions can help students articulate their thinking and increase their mastery:

- Why? How do you know?
- Can you explain that?
- Can you draw a picture of that?
- Is your answer reasonable? How do you know?
- How is this task like the one we did before? How is it different?
- What is alike and what is different about…?
- Can you solve that a different way?
- Yes! You're right! How do you know it's true?
- What did you learn before that can help you solve this problem?
- Can you summarize what your classmate shared?
- What conclusion can you draw from the data?

Each lesson is designed to take one day. If your calendar allows, you may choose to spend more than one day on certain lessons. Throughout the guide, there are notes to extend on learning activities to make them more challenging. Lesson structures and activities do not have to conform exactly to what is shown in the guide. Teachers are encouraged to exercise their discretion in using this material in a way that best suits their classes.

Textbooks are designed to last multiple years. Textbook problems with a ⬛ (or a blank line for terms) are meant to invite active participation.

Dimensions Math® Scope & Sequence

PKA

Chapter 1
Match, Sort, and Classify

Red and Blue
Yellow and Green
Color Review
Soft and Hard
Rough, Bumpy, and Smooth
Sticky and Grainy
Size — Part 1
Size — Part 2
Sort Into Two Groups
Practice

Chapter 2
Compare Objects

Big and Small
Long and Short
Tall and Short
Heavy and Light
Practice

Chapter 3
Patterns

Movement Patterns
Sound Patterns
Create Patterns
Practice

Chapter 4
Numbers to 5 — Part 1

Count 1 to 5 — Part 1
Count 1 to 5 — Part 2
Count Back

Count On and Back
Count 1 Object
Count 2 Objects
Count Up to 3 Objects
Count Up to 4 Objects
Count Up to 5 Objects
How Many? — Part 1
How Many? — Part 2
How Many Now? — Part 1
How Many Now? — Part 2
Practice

Chapter 5
Numbers to 5 — Part 2

1, 2, 3
1, 2, 3, 4, 5 — Part 1
1, 2, 3, 4, 5 — Part 2
How Many? — Part 1
How Many? — Part 2
How Many Do You See?
How Many Do You See Now?
Practice

Chapter 6
Numbers to 10 — Part 1

0
Count to 10 — Part 1
Count to 10 — Part 2
Count Back
Order Numbers
Count Up to 6 Objects
Count Up to 7 Objects
Count Up to 8 Objects
Count Up to 9 Objects
Count Up to 10 Objects
— Part 1

Count Up to 10 Objects
— Part 2
How Many?
Practice

Chapter 7
Numbers to 10 — Part 2

6
7
8
9
10
0 to 10
Count and Match — Part 1
Count and Match — Part 2
Practice

PKB

Chapter 8
Ordinal Numbers

First
Second and Third
Fourth and Fifth
Practice

Chapter 9
Shapes and Solids

Cubes, Cylinders, and Spheres
Cubes
Positions
Build with Solids
Rectangles and Circles
Squares
Triangles

Dimensions Math® Scope & Sequence

Count Up to 10 Things — Part 2
Recognize the Numbers 6 to 10
Write the Numbers 6 and 7
Write the Numbers 8, 9, and 10
Write the Numbers 6 to 10
Count and Write the Numbers 1 to 10
Ordinal Positions
One More Than
Practice

Chapter 4
Shapes and Solids

Curved or Flat
Solid Shapes
Closed Shapes
Rectangles
Squares
Circles and Triangles
Where is It?
Hexagons
Sizes and Shapes
Combine Shapes
Graphs
Practice

Chapter 5
Compare Height, Length, Weight, and Capacity

Comparing Height
Comparing Length
Height and Length — Part 1
Height and Length — Part 2
Weight — Part 1

Weight — Part 2
Weight — Part 3
Capacity — Part 1
Capacity — Part 2
Practice

Chapter 6
Comparing Numbers Within 10

Same and More
More and Fewer
More and Less
Practice — Part 1
Practice — Part 2

KB

Chapter 7
Numbers to 20

Ten and Some More
Count Ten and Some More
Two Ways to Count
Numbers 16 to 20
Number Words 0 to 10
Number Words 11 to 15
Number Words 16 to 20
Number Order
1 More Than or Less Than
Practice — Part 1
Practice — Part 2

Chapter 8
Number Bonds

Putting Numbers Together — Part 1

Putting Numbers Together — Part 2
Parts Making a Whole
Look for a Part
Number Bonds for 2, 3, and 4
Number Bonds for 5
Number Bonds for 6
Number Bonds for 7
Number Bonds for 8
Number Bonds for 9
Number Bonds for 10
Practice — Part 1
Practice — Part 2
Practice — Part 3

Chapter 9
Addition

Introduction to Addition — Part 1
Introduction to Addition — Part 2
Introduction to Addition — Part 3
Addition
Count On — Part 1
Count On — Part 2
Add Up to 3 and 4
Add Up to 5 and 6
Add Up to 7 and 8
Add Up to 9 and 10
Addition Practice
Practice

Chapter 10
Subtraction

Take Away to Subtract — Part 1

Dimensions Math® Scope & Sequence

Compare Numbers to 20
Addition
Subtraction
Practice

Chapter 6
Addition to 20

Add by Making 10 — Part 1
Add by Making 10 — Part 2
Add by Making 10 — Part 3
Addition Facts to 20
Practice

Chapter 7
Subtraction Within 20

Subtract from 10 — Part 1
Subtract from 10 — Part 2
Subtract the Ones First
Word Problems
Subtraction Facts Within 20
Practice

Chapter 8
Shapes

Solid and Flat Shapes
Grouping Shapes
Making Shapes
Practice

Chapter 9
Ordinal Numbers

Naming Positions
Word Problems
Practice
Review 2

1B

Chapter 10
Length

Comparing Lengths Directly
Comparing Lengths Indirectly
Comparing Lengths with Units
Practice

Chapter 11
Comparing

Subtraction as Comparison
Making Comparison
    Subtraction Stories
Picture Graphs
Practice

Chapter 12
Numbers to 40

Numbers to 40
Tens and Ones
Counting by Tens and Ones
Comparing
Practice

Chapter 13
Addition and Subtraction Within 40

Add Ones
Subtract Ones
Make the Next Ten
Use Addition Facts
Subtract from Tens
Use Subtraction Facts
Add Three Numbers
Practice

Chapter 14
Grouping and Sharing

Adding Equal Groups
Sharing
Grouping
Practice

Chapter 15
Fractions

Halves
Fourths
Practice
Review 3

Chapter 16
Numbers to 100

Numbers to 100
Tens and Ones
Count by Ones or Tens
Compare Numbers to 100
Practice

Chapter 17
Addition and Subtraction Within 100

Add Ones — Part 1
Add Tens
Add Ones — Part 2
Add Tens and Ones — Part 1
Add Tens and Ones — Part 2
Subtract Ones — Part 1
Subtract from Tens
Subtract Ones — Part 2
Subtract Tens

Dimensions Math® Scope & Sequence

Dividing by 5 and 10
Practice C
Word Problems
Review 2

2B

Chapter 8
Mental Calculation

Adding Ones Mentally
Adding Tens Mentally
Making 100
Adding 97, 98, or 99
Practice A
Subtracting Ones Mentally
Subtracting Tens Mentally
Subtracting 97, 98, or 99
Practice B
Practice C

Chapter 9
Multiplication and Division of 3 and 4

The Multiplication Table of 3
Multiplication Facts of 3
Dividing by 3
Practice A
The Multiplication Table of 4
Multiplication Facts of 4
Dividing by 4
Practice B
Practice C

Chapter 10
Money

Making $1
Dollars and Cents
Making Change
Comparing Money
Practice A
Adding Money
Subtracting Money
Practice B

Chapter 11
Fractions

Halves and Fourths
Writing Unit Fractions
Writing Fractions
Fractions that Make 1 Whole
Comparing and Ordering
   Fractions
Practice
Review 3

Chapter 12
Time

Telling Time
Time Intervals
A.M. and P.M.
Practice

Chapter 13
Capacity

Comparing Capacity
Units of Capacity
Practice

Chapter 14
Graphs

Picture Graphs
Bar Graphs
Practice

Chapter 15
Shapes

Straight and Curved Sides
Polygons
Semicircles and Quarter-
   circles
Patterns
Solid Shapes
Practice
Review 4
Review 5

3A

Chapter 1
Numbers to 10,000

Numbers to 10,000
Place Value — Part 1
Place Value — Part 2
Comparing Numbers
The Number Line
Practice A
Number Patterns
Rounding to the Nearest
   Thousand
Rounding to the Nearest
   Hundred
Rounding to the Nearest Ten
Practice B

Dimensions Math® Scope & Sequence

The Multiplication Table of 9
Multiplying by 8 and 9
Dividing by 8 and 9
Practice B

Chapter 9
Fractions — Part 1

Fractions of a Whole
Fractions on a Number Line
Comparing Fractions with
    Like Denominators
Comparing Fractions with
    Like Numerators
Practice

Chapter 10
Fractions — Part 2

Equivalent Fractions
Finding Equivalent Fractions
Simplifying Fractions
Comparing Fractions — Part 1
Comparing Fractions — Part 2
Practice A
Adding and Subtracting
    Fractions — Part 1
Adding and Subtracting
    Fractions — Part 2
Practice B

Chapter 11
Measurement

Meters and Centimeters
Subtracting from Meters
Kilometers
Subtracting from Kilometers
Liters and Milliliters
Kilograms and Grams

Word Problems
Practice
Review 3

Chapter 12
Geometry

Circles
Angles
Right Angles
Triangles
Properties of Triangles
Properties of Quadrilaterals
Using a Compass
Practice

Chapter 13
Area and Perimeter

Area
Units of Area
Area of Rectangles
Area of Composite Figures
Practice A
Perimeter
Perimeter of Rectangles
Area and Perimeter
Practice B

Chapter 14
Time

Units of Time
Calculating Time — Part 1
Practice A
Calculating Time — Part 2
Calculating Time — Part 3
Calculating Time — Part 4
Practice B

Chapter 15
Money

Dollars and Cents
Making $10
Adding Money
Subtracting Money
Word Problems
Practice
Review 4
Review 5

4A

Chapter 1
Numbers to One Million

Numbers to 100,000
Numbers to 1,000,000
Number Patterns
Comparing and Ordering
    Numbers
Rounding 5-Digit Numbers
Rounding 6-Digit Numbers
Calculations and Place Value
Practice

Chapter 2
Addition and Subtraction

Addition
Subtraction
Other Ways to Add and
    Subtract — Part 1
Other Ways to Add and
    Subtract — Part 2
Word Problems

Dimensions Math® Scope & Sequence

Dimensions Math® Scope & Sequence

Suggested number of class periods: 9–10

	Lesson	Page	Resources		Objectives
	Chapter Opener	p. 5	TB:	p. 1	Investigate measurement.
1	Metric Units of Measurement	p. 6	TB: WB:	p. 2 p. 1	Solve problems involving addition, subtraction, and multiplication of measurements given in compound metric units of length, weight, and capacity.
2	Customary Units of Length	p. 9	TB: WB:	p. 7 p. 4	Express customary measurements of length (inches, feet, yards, miles) in compound units and single units.
3	Customary Units of Weight	p. 13	TB: WB:	p. 12 p. 8	Express customary units of weight (ounces, pounds) in compound units and single units.
4	Customary Units of Capacity	p. 16	TB: WB:	p. 16 p. 11	Express the capacity of objects using customary units (gallons, quarts, pints, cups, fluid ounces) in compound units and single units.
5	Units of Time	p. 20	TB: WB:	p. 20 p. 14	Express a measurement of time in compound units and in single units. Multiply time expressed in compound units.
6	Practice A	p. 23	TB: WB:	p. 23 p. 17	Practice concepts from the chapter.
7	Fractions and Measurement — Part 1	p. 25	TB: WB:	p. 25 p. 20	Express a smaller unit of measurement as a fraction of a larger unit of measurement.
8	Fractions and Measurement — Part 2	p. 27	TB: WB:	p. 28 p. 23	Convert a measurement given as a mixed number to compound units and single units. Express a smaller unit of measurement as a fraction of a larger unit of measurement that is not a whole number.
9	Practice B	p. 30	TB: WB:	p. 31 p. 26	Practice concepts from the chapter.
	Workbook Solutions	p. 32			

In Dimensions Math 3, students compared and estimated metric units of length, weight, and capacity using compound units and single units. In this chapter, students will solve computation problems and convert between different units of measure for length, capacity, and weight in customary units and time. These problems not only build measurement skills, but also help students practice the number sense and computational skills with fractions and whole numbers covered in Dimensions Math 4A. Students will not convert between customary and metric units.

Customary units are units of measurement commonly used in a particular country (such as inches, pounds, and gallons in the U.S.) or enterprise (such as nautical miles in sailing). In this series, students will work with the customary units above, although they may be familiar with other units of measurement.

New conversions formally introduced in this chapter include the following.

Length:

- 1,000 millimeters = 1 meter
- 12 inches = 1 foot
- 3 feet = 1 yard
- 5,280 feet = 1 mile

Weight:

- 16 ounces = 1 pound

Capacity:

- 8 fluid ounces = 1 cup
- 2 cups = 1 pint
- 4 cups = 1 quart
- 4 quarts = 1 gallon

Customary measurements for quantities of pounds and ounces report weight, while kilograms are a scientific measurement for mass. Mass is a measure of the amount of matter in an object. It does not depend on gravity. Pounds and ounces are a measure of weight. Weight is the quantity of force that gravity exerts on an object, given its mass. On Earth, a 1-kilogram mass weighs 2.2 pounds.

Note that the capacity of a container is the amount of liquid it can hold. The amount of fluid in a container is its liquid volume. This chapter only uses the term "capacity."

Conversions

In Lesson 1, students begin by learning two methods for computing with compound measurements in the metric system.

Method 1

Perform the computations on each of the compound units separately, then convert as needed.

$$2 \text{ kg } 700 \text{ g} \times 3$$

with a number bond splitting into 2 kg and 700 g

$2 \text{ kg} \times 3 = 6 \text{ kg}$
$700 \text{ g} \times 3 = 2{,}100 \text{ g} = 2 \text{ kg } 100\text{g}$
$6 \text{ kg} + 2 \text{ kg } 100 \text{ g} = 8 \text{ kg } 100 \text{ g}$

Method 2

Convert the compound measurement to a single measurement unit, perform the computation, and then express the answer in compound units.

$2 \text{ kg } 700 \text{ g} = 2{,}700 \text{ kg}$

$$\begin{array}{r} 2{,}700 \\ \times 3 \\ \hline 8{,}100 \end{array}$$

$8{,}100 \text{ g} = 8 \text{ kg } 100 \text{ g}$

Lessons 2—4 introduce strategies for converting between customary units of length, weight, or capacity using the methods from Lesson 1. This can be challenging for students as conversion rates in customary units of measurement vary, unlike in the metric system which uses base ten.

As students have not learned to divide by two-digit numbers yet, they can use multiplication to convert inches to feet, ounces to pounds, and hours to minutes:

1 ft ⟶ 12 in
2 ft ⟶ 2 × 12 in = 24 in
3 ft ⟶ 3 × 12 in = 36 in…

1 lb ⟶ 16 oz
2 lb ⟶ 2 × 16 oz = 32 oz
3 lb ⟶ 3 × 16 oz = 48 oz…

1 h ⟶ 60 min
2 h ⟶ 2 × 60 min = 120 min
3 h ⟶ 3 × 60 min = 180 min…

These can be recorded in a notebook or posted in the classroom for reference.

Students will use mental math strategies learned in earlier grades to help with computations. For example, rather than making the next ten or the next hundred when adding, they will now make the next unit of measurement. Examples include: make the next foot (12 inches) and make the next pound (16 ounces). Three example problems are shown to the right.

Example 1: 3 ft 7 in + 9 in

Method 1

Students can first add the inches: 7 + 9 = 16 and then convert 16 inches to 1 foot and 4 inches.

3 ft 7 in + 9 in = 3 ft 16 in = 4 ft 4 in

Method 2

They can consider how many inches it would take to make the next foot, and decompose the inches with this in mind.

3 ft 7 in + 9 in = 4 ft 4 in
/ \
5 in   4 in

Example 2: 3 lb 7 oz − 1 lb 9 oz

Students can think about subtracting the pounds first and then the ounces.

3 lb 7 oz − 1 lb 9 oz
/ \
7 oz   2 oz

3 lb − 1 lb = 2 lb
2 lb 7 oz − 7 oz − 2 oz = 1 lb 14 oz

In Lesson 5, students will convert between units of time:

1 hour = 60 minutes
1 minute = 60 seconds

Example 3: How long is 165 minutes in hours and minutes?

1 h ⟶ 60 min
2 h ⟶ 2 × 60 min = 120 min

165 min = 120 min + 45 min = 2 h 45 min

In Lessons 7–9, students will apply, to measurement, their knowledge of finding the product of a fraction and a whole number, and of a mixed number and a whole number.

Example: How many inches is $\frac{2}{3}$ of a foot?

1 ft $\longrightarrow$ 12 in
$\frac{2}{3}$ ft $\longrightarrow$ $\frac{2}{3}$ × 12 in = 8 in

Students will discover how to express a whole number as a fraction of a larger unit of measurement.

Example: 8 inches is what fraction of a foot?

$\frac{8 \text{ in}}{12 \text{ in}}$ $\longrightarrow$ $\frac{2}{3}$ of a foot

They will think about fraction of a set when converting to a smaller unit of measurement.

Once students understand these concepts, they will apply them to problems involving mixed numbers.

Example: How many seconds are in $3\frac{3}{5}$ minutes?

3 min $\longrightarrow$ 3 × 60 seconds = 180 seconds

$\frac{3}{5}$ min $\longrightarrow$ $\frac{3}{5}$ × 60 seconds = 36 seconds

180 seconds + 36 seconds = 216 seconds

There are 216 seconds in $3\frac{3}{5}$ minutes.

Materials

- 1-cup and 1-quart measuring cups
- 1-ft rulers
- 1-liter measuring cups
- 10-ft measuring tapes
- 3-ft stripes of paper, or ribbon
- Analog clock
- Chalk
- Empty Bottles
- Items that weight between 1–5 pounds
- Meter sticks
- Platform scales measuring customary units
- Platform scales measuring metric units
- Rulers with centimeter and inch markings
- Whiteboards
- Yardsticks

Blackline Masters

- Conversions of Measurement (BLM)
- Measurement Match Cards (BLM)
- Measurement Puzzle (BLM)

Activities

Fewer games and activities are included in this chapter as students will be using measuring tools. The included activities can be used after students complete the **Do** questions, or anytime additional practice is needed.

Objective

- Investigate measurement.

Lesson Materials

- 1-liter measuring cups
- Meter sticks
- Platform scales measuring metric units
- Yardsticks

Have students recall different units of measurement they have learned:

Inch	Gram	Second
Foot	Kilogram	Minute
Yard	Pound	Hour
Centimeter	Milliliter	Day
Meter	Liter	Week
Kilometer		Month

Students may know other units, such as: nautical mile, stone, fathom, degree Fahrenheit, dollar, cent, acre, furlong, cubit, and light year.

If a review of measurement is necessary, have students practice measuring different objects at stations for length, weight, and capacity using meter sticks, yardsticks, scales, and measuring cups.

If students easily recall units of measurement, continue to Lesson 1.

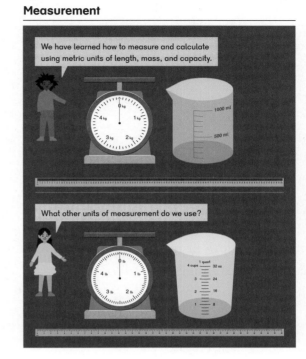

Chapter 10

Measurement

We have learned how to measure and calculate using metric units of length, mass, and capacity.

What other units of measurement do we use?

1

Lesson 1 Metric Units of Measurement

Objective

- Solve problems involving addition, subtraction, and multiplication of measurements given in compound metric units of length, weight, and capacity.

Lesson Materials

- Metric rulers with centimeters and millimeters
- Meter sticks

Think

Discuss the **Think** problem and Alex's comment. Students should recall that there are 100 centimeters in each meter.

Have students solve the problem independently and then discuss solutions.

Students may see that the fencing resembles a bar model.

Learn

Discuss the methods shown in **Learn** and have students compare their own methods with the methods shown in the textbook.

Method 1

Emma splits the length into meters and centimeters and multiplies each by 3. She converts the 240 cm into meters and centimeters and then adds the products.

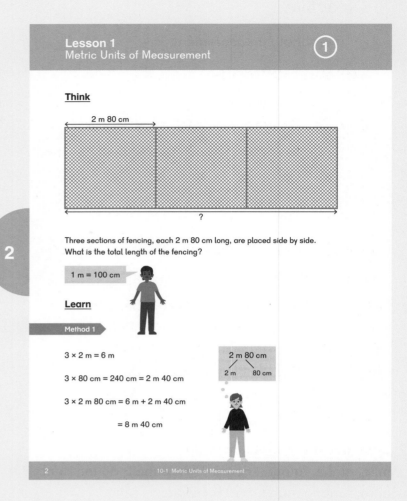

Teacher's Guide 4B Chapter 10 © 2019 Singapore Math Inc.

Method 2

Mei converts the length from compound units (m and cm) to all centimeters and then uses the multiplication algorithm to find the total length of the fencing. She then converts the total length back into compound units.

Dion introduces a new metric measurement, the millimeter, and its abbreviation (mm). Pass out metric rulers and have students identify and discuss how big a millimeter is.

Help students recall the other metric units of measurement they have learned for mass and capacity and their conversion rates, as listed on the textbook page: grams (g), kilograms (kg), liters (L), and milliliters (mL).

Do

1 — 4 For each question, discuss the problems and given examples with students.

2 Ensure students understand that 7 kg 4 g = 7,004 g, not 74 g or 704 g.

To solve (a), students may use different methods. They may use mental math and regrouping:

$$7 \text{ kg } 4 \text{ g} - 6 \text{ kg } 856 \text{ g} = 1{,}004 \text{ g} - 856 \text{ g}$$
$$6 \text{ kg} \quad 1{,}004 \text{ g}$$

Or they may use an algorithm:

$$\begin{array}{r} 7{,}004\,\text{g} \\ -6{,}856\,\text{g} \\ \hline \end{array}$$

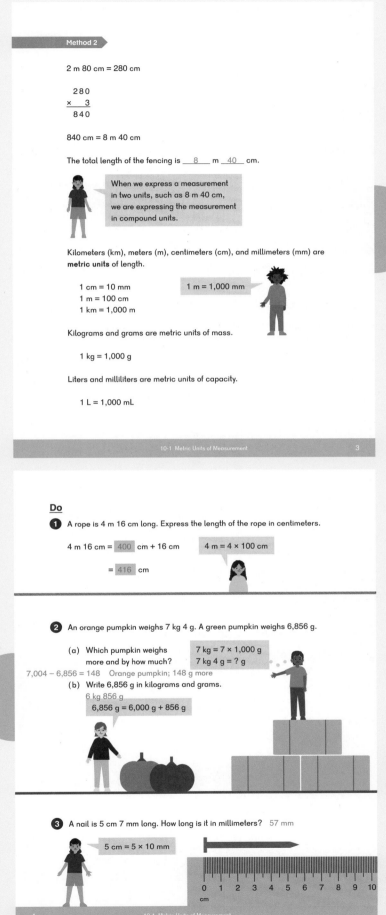

5 — 7 Students should be able to solve these problems independently.

Activity

▲ Convert It!

Materials: Deck of playing cards, face cards removed

Shuffle the cards and place them facedown on the middle of the table. Players take turns being the dealer. On his turn, the dealer chooses a unit: meter, kilogram, or liter, and a corresponding smaller unit of measurement. The dealer then turns over the top card.

The other players convert the number on the card to an equal amount in the smaller measurement.

Example: The dealer calls meters to millimeters, and turns a 7 card faceup.

The first player to say 7,000 millimeters collects the card.

The winner is the player with the most cards at the end of the game.

Possible conversions:

- km to m
- m to cm
- m to mm
- kg to g
- L to mL

Exercise 1 · page 1

---

4 Amelia and Daren are walking from school to the Botanical Garden.

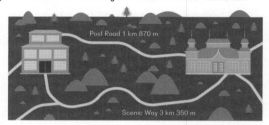

Post Road 1 km 870 m

Scenic Way 3 km 350 m

(a) If they walk to the Botanical Garden on Scenic Way and then walk back to school on Post Road, how far will they walk in kilometers and meters?   1 km 870 m + 3 km 350 m = 5 km 220 m

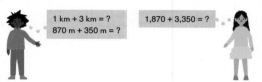

1 km + 3 km = ?
870 m + 350 m = ?

1,870 + 3,350 = ?

(b) How much longer is Scenic Way than Post Road in kilometers and meters?   3 km 350 m − 1 km 870 m = 1 km 480 m

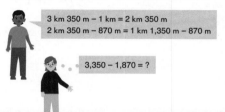

3 km 350 m − 1 km = 2 km 350 m
2 km 350 m − 870 m = 1 km 1,350 m − 870 m

3,350 − 1,870 = ?

---

5 Add or subtract in compound units.

(a) 2 m 45 cm + 4 m 85 cm = 7 m 30 cm

(b) 9 kg 150 g − 5 kg 650 g = 3 kg 500 g

(c) 8 m 7 cm − 4 m 75 cm = 3 m 32 cm

(d) 4 cm 6 mm + 4 cm 6 mm = 9 cm 2 mm

(e) 3 L 856 mL + 6 L 199 mL = 10 L 55 mL

(f) 8 cm 3 mm − 3 cm 8 mm = 4 cm 5 mm

6 Alex filled a barrel with 5 buckets of water. The capacity of the bucket is 2 L 500 mL. Express the total amount of water in the barrel in milliliters and also in liters and milliliters.
5 × 2 L 500 mL = 12 L 500 mL
12,500 mL

7 A yellow ribbon is 2 m 75 cm long. A red ribbon is twice as long as the yellow ribbon. A blue ribbon is twice as long as the red ribbon. How much longer is the blue ribbon than the yellow ribbon in meters and centimeters?

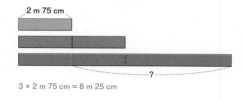

2 m 75 cm

3 × 2 m 75 cm = 8 m 25 cm

Exercise 1 · page 1

Lesson 2 Customary Units of Length

Objective

- Express customary measurements of length (inches, feet, yards, miles) in compound units and single units.

Lesson Materials

- 1-ft rulers
- 10-ft measuring tapes
- Meter sticks
- Rulers with centimeter and inch markings
- Yardsticks

Think

Provide pairs of students with yardsticks and measuring tapes and pose the **Think** questions. Students should be familiar with inches, feet, and yards. Have them work with their partners to measure their own heights.

Discuss student solutions to the **Think** questions. Lead students to see that although the heights are expressed in different units, they can be changed to single units for comparison. Have students compare their height to their partner's height in either compound or single units.

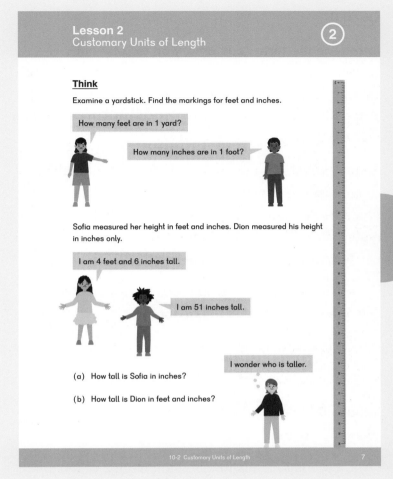

Teacher's Guide 4B Chapter 10

Learn

Introduce the term "customary units" of length. Customary units are units of measurement commonly used in a particular country (such as inches, pounds, and gallons in the U.S.) or enterprise (such as nautical miles in sailing).

Emma provides a comparison between lengths that are measured in metric and customary units. Have students compare the length of a yardstick and a meter stick. Then have students compare the length of a 1-ft ruler and a metric ruler (about 30 cm).

Have students compare their solutions from **Think** with the ones shown in the textbook.

(a) Sofia converts her height into single units—inches.

We can compare Sofia and Dion's heights in inches:

Sofia is 54 in tall.
Dion is 51 in tall.

(b) Dion converts his height into compound units— feet and inches.

We can compare Sofia's and Dion's heights in compound units:

Sofia is 4 ft 6 in tall.
Dion is 4 ft 3 in tall.

Alex introduces the unit of 1 mile as a customary unit and compares that to kilometers, a metric unit.

Have students measure and compare their own heights with the heights of other students in the class in both inches and compound units.

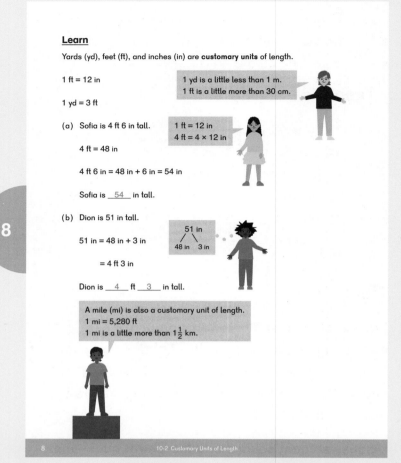

8

Do

1—**7** For each question, discuss the problems and the given examples with students.

3 3 ft $\longrightarrow$ 3 × 12 in = 36 in
36 in + 6 in = 42 in

4 If needed, ask students how many inches are in 1 foot. Then ask how they would find the number of inches in 2 feet, 3 feet, etc.

They should recall:

1 ft $\longrightarrow$ 12 in
2 ft $\longrightarrow$ 2 × 12 in = 24 in
3 ft $\longrightarrow$ 3 × 12 in = 36 in...

5 (a) Alex is splitting 11 oz into 7 oz and 4 oz in order to make 1 lb: 7 oz + 9 oz.

(b) Dion subtracts 2 feet first. He splits the 9 in into 7 in and 2 in. He subtracts the 7 in first and then subtracts: 2 ft − 2 in.

6 Sofia helps students convert from yards to feet.

Do

1 Use a measuring tape.

(a) Measure something that is between 2 and 3 feet long and express the length in feet and inches, and in inches only.

(b) Measure something that is between 5 and 6 feet long and express the length in feet and inches, and in inches only.

(c) Measure something that is between 1 and 3 yards long and express the length in yards, feet, and inches.

2 Copy and complete the table.

ft	1	2	3	4	5
in	12	24	36	48	60

3

Two flagpoles are placed 3 feet 6 inches apart. Express this length in inches.

3 ft 6 in = 36 in + 6 in = 42 in

4 Sofia's cousin is 70 inches tall. How tall is he in feet and inches?

70 in = 60 in + 10 in = 5 ft 10 in

---

5 A green ribbon is 4 ft 7 in long. A red ribbon is 2 ft 9 in long.

(a) What is their total length?

4 ft 7 in $\xrightarrow{\ +2\,\text{ft}\ }$ 6 ft 7 in $\xrightarrow{\ +9\,\text{in}\ }$ 7 ft 4 in

6 ft 7 in + 9 in
 5 in   4 in

(b) What is the difference in lengths?

4 ft 7 in $\xrightarrow{\ -2\,\text{ft}\ }$ 2 ft 7 in $\xrightarrow{\ -9\,\text{in}\ }$ 1 ft 10 in

2 ft 7 in − 9 in
 7 in   2 in

6 The height of the ceiling in a cafeteria is 4 yards 2 feet. Express this height in feet.

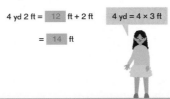

4 yd 2 ft = 12 ft + 2 ft   4 yd = 4 × 3 ft

= 14 ft

---

7 The quotient will be the number of yards, and the remainder will be the number of feet left over. Alex divides 20 ft by 3 to find the number of yards: 6 yd with a remainder of 2 ft. Show students they can check their answers by converting the compound units back to feet.

6 yd ⟶ 6 × 3 ft = 18 ft
18 ft + 2 ft = 20 ft

For students who need additional help, draw or show 20 counters to represent 20 feet. Circle or put counters into groups of 3 feet to convert them to yards. There should be 2 feet remaining.

8 — **9** Students should be able to solve these problems independently.

9 Students can convert to single units:

2 yd 2 ft = 8 ft
2 × 16 ft = 32 ft
32 ft + 8 ft = 40 ft
40 ft = 13 yd 1 ft

Students can also convert to compound units:

2 × 16 ft = 32 ft
32 ft = 10 yd 2 ft
10 yd 2 ft + 2 yd 2 ft = 13 yd 1 ft

Activities

▲ Measurement Practice

Materials: 1-ft rulers, yardsticks, chalk

Provide students with 1-ft rulers and yardsticks. Have them draw a line on the sidewalk or playground with chalk to a given measurement, for example: 2 yards, 1 foot, 2 inches.

▲ Convert It!

Materials: Deck of playing cards, face cards removed

Modify the game from Lesson 1 to include yards to feet, or feet to inches.

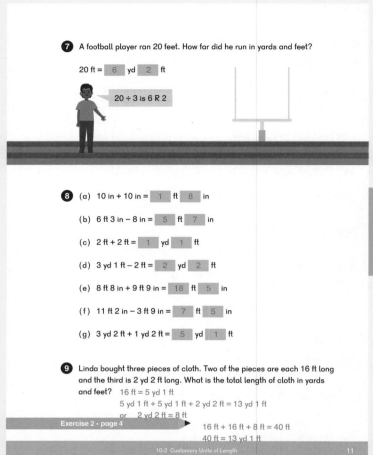

7 A football player ran 20 feet. How far did he run in yards and feet?

20 ft = [6] yd [2] ft

20 ÷ 3 is 6 R 2

8 (a) 10 in + 10 in = [1] ft [8] in

(b) 6 ft 3 in − 8 in = [5] ft [7] in

(c) 2 ft + 2 ft = [1] yd [1] ft

(d) 3 yd 1 ft − 2 ft = [2] yd [2] ft

(e) 8 ft 8 in + 9 ft 9 in = [18] ft [5] in

(f) 11 ft 2 in − 3 ft 9 in = [7] ft [5] in

(g) 3 yd 2 ft + 1 yd 2 ft = [5] yd [1] ft

9 Linda bought three pieces of cloth. Two of the pieces are each 16 ft long and the third is 2 yd 2 ft long. What is the total length of cloth in yards and feet? 16 ft = 5 yd 1 ft
5 yd 1 ft + 5 yd 1 ft + 2 yd 2 ft = 13 yd 1 ft
or   2 yd 2 ft = 8 ft
16 ft + 16 ft + 8 ft = 40 ft
40 ft = 13 yd 1 ft

Exercise 2 • page 4

10-2 Customary Units of Length   11

11

► Exercise 2 • page 4

Lesson 3 Customary Units of Weight

Objective

- Express customary units of weight (ounces, pounds) in compound units and single units.

Lesson Materials

- Items that weigh between 1–5 pounds
- Platform scales measuring customary units

Think

Discuss the **Think** tasks and Emma's comment about pounds and ounces. Just as there are customary units of measurement for length, there are also customary units for weight, such as pounds and ounces.

Provide students with platform scales and discuss the markings on the scales. Hand out items for students to weigh and practice reading the scale.

Have students answer questions (a) and (b). Discuss student solutions to the **Think** questions.

Learn

Have students compare their solutions from **Think** with the ones shown in the textbook.

(a) Dion converts the weight of the cantaloupe into single units—ounces.

To convert from pounds to ounces, Dion and Mei multiply each pound by 16 ounces.

We can compare the weights of the cantaloupe and the honeydew melon in ounces:

The cantaloupe weighs 36 oz.
The honeydew melon weighs 50 oz.

(b) Now that both melons are expressed in the same units, it is simple to subtract.

Sofia provides a comparison between the customary units of weight, pounds and ounces, and the metric units of weight students have learned about.

Think

Examine the platform scale. Find the markings for pounds and ounces.

We abbreviate pounds as **lb** and ounces as **oz**. 1 lb = 16 oz

Dion is weighing melons on the platform scale.

The cantaloupe weights 2 lb 4 oz.   The honeydew melon weighs 3 lb 2 oz.

(a) Express the weight of each melon in ounces.

(b) How many more ounces does the honeydew melon weigh than the cantaloupe?

Learn

(a) 2 lb = 32 oz

2 lb 4 oz = 32 oz + 4 oz = 36 oz

The cantaloupe weighs __36__ oz.

1 lb = 16 oz
2 lb = 2 × 16 oz

3 lb = 48 oz

3 lb = 3 × 16 oz

3 lb 2 oz = 48 oz + 2 oz = 50 oz

The honeydew melon weighs __50__ oz.

(b) 50 oz − 36 oz = 14 oz

The honeydew melon weighs __14__ oz more than the cantaloupe.

Pounds (lb) and ounces (oz) are customary units of weight.

1 lb = 16 oz

1 pound is about $\frac{1}{2}$ kilogram.
1 ounce is about 28 grams.

Teacher's Guide 4B Chapter 10

Do

1—**5** For each question, discuss the problems and the given examples with students.

1 Provide students with platform scales.

5 (a) Alex is splitting 11 oz into 7 oz and 4 oz in order to make 1 lb: 7 oz + 9 oz.

(b) Mei uses a similar strategy to subtract.

14

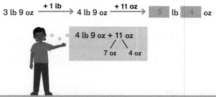

Do

1 Use a platform scale. Find something that weighs between 1 and 2 lb. Express the weight in pounds and ounces, and in ounces only.

2 Copy and complete the table.

lb	1	2	3	4	5
oz	16	32	48	64	80

3 A kitten weighs 3 lb 10 oz. Express the weight of the kitten in ounces.

3 lb 10 oz = 48 oz + 10 oz = 58 oz

4 A squash weighs 34 oz. Express the weight of the squash in pounds and ounces.

34 oz = 32 oz + 2 oz = 2 lb 2 oz

5 One package weighs 3 lb 9 oz and another package weighs 1 lb 11 oz.

(a) What is the total weight of both packages?

3 lb 9 oz $\xrightarrow{+1 \text{ lb}}$ 4 lb 9 oz $\xrightarrow{+11 \text{ oz}}$ 5 lb 4 oz

4 lb 9 oz + 11 oz
7 oz   4 oz

6 — **8** Students should be able to solve these problems independently.

8 Total weight of 1 textbook and 1 workbook:

1 lb 6 oz + 1 lb 3 oz = 2 lb 9 oz

Total weight of 5 textbooks and 5 workbooks:

2 lb 9 oz × 5 = 10 lb 45 oz

$$\diagup \qquad \diagdown$$

2 lb   9 oz

To convert 45 oz to lb, students can think:

1 lb $\longrightarrow$ 16 oz
2 lb $\longrightarrow$ 2 × 16 oz = 32 oz
3 lb $\longrightarrow$ 3 × 16 oz = 48 oz (too much)

45 oz − 32 oz = 13 oz

The combined weight is 12 lb 13 oz.

Activities

▲ Measurement Practice

Materials: Platform scales measuring customary units

Have students find objects in the classroom that can be weighed on the platform scale. Students should first estimate the weight, then find the actual weight of the object.

▲ Convert It!

Materials: Deck of playing cards, face cards removed

Modify the game from Lesson 1 to include pounds to ounces.

Exercise 3 • page 8

(b) What is the difference in weight between the two packages?

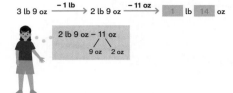

6 Add or subtract in compound units.

(a) 12 oz + 6 oz
    1 lb 2 oz
(b) 1 lb 10 oz + 14 oz
    2 lb 8 oz
(c) 4 lb 5 oz + 1 lb 15 oz
    6 lb 4 oz
(d) 1 lb − 7 oz
    9 oz
(e) 3 lb 4 oz − 10 oz
    2 lb 10 oz
(f) 6 lb 1 oz − 3 lb 8 oz
    2 lb 9 oz

7 A bag of apples weighs 2 lb 8 oz. A bag of plums weighs 1 lb 14 oz.

(a) What is the total weight of the bags of fruit in pounds and ounces?
    4 lb 6 oz
(b) What is the difference in weight between the bags of fruit in ounces?
    10 oz

8 A math textbook weighs 1 lb 6 oz. A math workbook weighs 1 lb 3 oz. What is the combined weight of 5 textbooks and 5 workbooks in pounds and ounces?
    5 × 1 lb 6 oz = 6 lb 14 oz
    5 × 1 lb 3 oz = 5 lb 15 oz
    6 lb 14 oz + 5 lb 15 oz = 12 lb 13 oz

Exercise 3 • page 8

10-3 Customary Units of Weight   15

Lesson 4 Customary Units of Capacity

Objective

- Express the capacity of objects using customary units (gallons, quarts, pints, cups, fluid ounces) in compound units and single units.

Lesson Materials

- 1-cup and 1-quart measuring cups
- Conversions of Measurement (BLM)
- Empty bottles

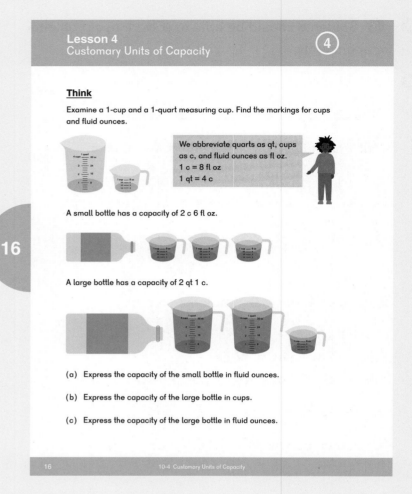

Think

Examine a 1-cup and a 1-quart measuring cup. Find the markings for cups and fluid ounces.

We abbreviate quarts as qt, cups as c, and fluid ounces as fl oz.
1 c = 8 fl oz
1 qt = 4 c

A small bottle has a capacity of 2 c 6 fl oz.

A large bottle has a capacity of 2 qt 1 c.

(a) Express the capacity of the small bottle in fluid ounces.

(b) Express the capacity of the large bottle in cups.

(c) Express the capacity of the large bottle in fluid ounces.

16   10-4 Customary Units of Capacity

Think

Discuss the **Think** questions and Dion's comment about fluid ounces. In the U.S., we customarily measure capacity in fluid ounces, cups, pints, quarts, and gallons. Provide students with measuring cups and discuss the markings on the sides. Students will not be using the fraction markings on the measuring cups for now.

Provide students with empty bottles so they can get a sense for estimating the capacity of a container. Have them partially fill the bottles with water and then estimate how many fluid ounces of water are in the bottle and how many more fluid ounces are needed to fill the container. They can pour the water into the measuring cups to check the accuracy of their estimates.

Remind students that fluid ounces measure capacity and ounces measure weight. The measuring tools for fluid ounces and ounces that measure weight are different.

Have students answer questions (a) through (c). Discuss student solutions to the **Think** questions.

Learn

Have students compare their solutions from **Think** with the ones shown in the textbook.

(a) Sofia converts 2 cups into fluid ounces by multiplying each cup by 8 fluid ounces.

(b) Alex converts 2 quarts into cups by multiplying each quart by 4 cups.

(c) Once we know the number of cups in the large bottle, we can multiply that by 8 to find the number of fluid ounces in the bottle.

Students may also see that if 4 cups = 1 quart, then there are 4 × 8 fluid ounces = 32 fluid ounces in each quart.

Ask students why we use different units of capacity.

For example:

- "Why do we not use fluid ounces to measure large containers of milk?"
- "Why do we not use gallons to measure the amount of juice we drink?"
- "What measurement might a gas station use to measure all of the gas in their tanks?"

Emma provides a comparison between the customary units of capacity that students have just learned and metric units of capacity, which students should recall from earlier levels.

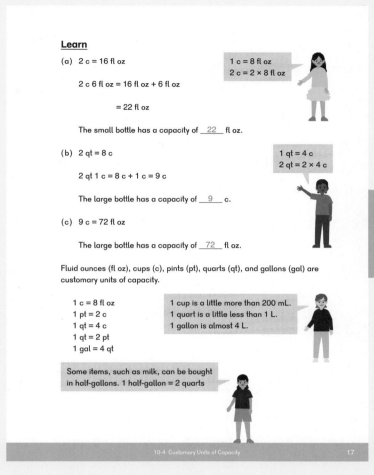

Do

①—⑤ For each question, discuss the problems and the given examples with students. Conversions of Measurement (BLM) is available for students that may need a reference tool.

①—③ Students may refer to Conversions of Measurement (BLM) or the conversions on the previous textbook page.

(a) $1 c \longrightarrow 8$ fl oz

$8 c \longrightarrow 8 \times 8$ fl oz $= 64$ fl oz

(b) $2 c \longrightarrow 1$ pt

$8 c \longrightarrow 8$ pt $\div 2 = 4$ pt

(c) $4 c \longrightarrow 1$ qt

$8 c \longrightarrow 8$ qt $\div 4 = 2$ qt

(d) 1 gal $\longrightarrow 4$ qt

We learned in (c) that 8 cups = 2 quarts, so we need 2 more quarts, or 8 more cups, to fill the jug.

③ Dion suggests dividing 38 quarts by 4 quarts in each gallon to find how many gallons of water are needed to fill the tank. The quotient is the number of gallons, and the remainder is the number of quarts leftover.

1 gal $\longrightarrow 4$ qt
38 qt $\longrightarrow 38$ gal $\div 4 = 9$ gal 2 qt

Do

① 8 cups of water are poured into a 1-gallon jug.

(a) Express the amount of water in fluid ounces.
8×8 fl oz $= 64$ fl oz

(b) Express the amount of water in pints.
8 pt $\div 2 = 4$ pt

(c) Express the amount of water in quarts.
8 qt $\div 4 = 2$ qt

(d) How many more cups of water are needed to fill the jug to 1 gal?
1 gal $= 4$ qt $= 4 \times 4$ c $= 16$ c
16 c $- 8$ c $= 8$ c

② A bottle has a capacity of 4 qt 2 c. Express the capacity of the bottle in cups.

4 qt 2 c $=$ 16 c $+ 2$ c $=$ 18 c

③ Emma used 38 quarts of water to fill a fish tank. How much water is in the tank in gallons and quarts?

38 qt $=$ 9 gal 2 qt    $38 \div 4$ is 9 R ?

④ Teaspoons (tsp) and tablespoons (tbsp) are customary units of measurement used in cooking. How many teaspoons equal 1 cup?
16×3 tsp $= 48$ tsp

1 c = 16 tbsp
1 tbsp = 3 tsp

18   10-4 Customary Units of Capacity

6 — 7 Students should be able to solve these problems independently.

6 First, find how many fluid ounces of water is in the 24-pack:

24 × 20 fl oz = 480 fl oz

Then find how much water is in 5 gallons:

1 gal ⟶ 16 c ⟶ 16 × 8 fl oz = 128 fl oz
5 gal ⟶ 5 × 128 fl oz = 640 fl oz

Finally, subtract to find how much more water is in the large water bottle than in the 24-pack:

640 fl oz − 480 fl oz = 160 fl oz

7 To make 20 jars of salad dressing, Anna needs:

- 20 cups of oil
- 20 cups of vinegar
- 60 tbsp of mustard

To find the amount of oil needed:

1 gal ⟶ 16 c

Anna needs 20 cups so 1 bottle is not enough.
She needs 2 gallon bottles.

To find the amount of vinegar needed:

1 qt ⟶ 4 c

Anna needs 20 cups, which is 5 × 4 cups or 5 quart bottles.

To find the amount of mustard needed:

1 c ⟶ 16 tbsp

Anna needs 20 × 3 tbsp, which is 60 tbsp. If she buys 4 cup-sized bottles, she will have 4 × 16 tbsp, or 64 tbsp of mustard.

Exercise 4 • page 11

---

5 A pitcher has 2 qt 3 c of mango juice and a bottle has 4 qt 2 c of pineapple juice.

(a) How much juice is there altogether?

4 qt 2 c $\xrightarrow{+2\,qt}$ [6] qt [2] c $\xrightarrow{+3\,c}$ [7] qt [1] c

(b) How much more pineapple than mango juice is there?

4 qt 2 c $\xrightarrow{-2\,qt}$ [2] qt [2] c $\xrightarrow{-3\,c}$ [1] qt [3] c

(c) Both juices are poured into a 2 gal punch bowl and mixed together. How much ginger ale must be added to fill the bowl?

2 gal − [7] qt [1] c = [3] c

Methods may vary.

6 There are 24 bottles of water in a pack. Each bottle has 20 fl oz of water. A large bottle for a water dispenser has 5 gal of water. How much more water is in the large bottle than in all the bottles in the 24-pack?
1 gal = 4 qt; 4 qt = 4 × 4 c = 16 c; 16 c = 16 × 8 fl oz = 128 fl oz;
5 gal = 5 × 128 fl oz = 640 fl oz; 24 × 20 fl oz = 480 fl oz

7 640 − 480 = 160; 160 fl oz (or 20 c or 5 qt or 1 gal 1 qt)

Anna is selling jars of salad dressing at the farmers market. Each jar needs 1 cup of oil, 1 cup of vinegar, 3 tbsp of mustard, and other spices. The olive oil comes in gallon bottles and the vinegar in quart bottles. Each bottle of mustard has 1 cup of mustard. How many bottles of oil, vinegar, and mustard does she need to buy to make 20 jars of salad dressing?
1 gal = 16 c; She needs 2 bottles of olive oil to have 20 c. 1 qt = 4 c; She needs 5 bottles of vinegar for 20 c. 1 c = 16 tbsp; 20 × 3 tbsp = 60 tbsp

Exercise 4 • page 11

16, 32, 48, 64; She needs 4 bottles of mustard to have 60 tbsp.

19

Objectives

- Express a measurement of time in compound units and in single units.
- Multiply time expressed in compound units.

Lesson Materials

- Analog clock

Think

Discuss the **Think** problems and Alex's comment about hours, minutes, and seconds. Have students look at an analog clock to observe how the second hand moves.

Discuss student solutions to the **Think** questions.

Learn

Have students compare their solutions from **Think** with the ones shown in the textbook.

(a) Emma converts hours into minutes by multiplying the total number of hours by 60 minutes.

(b) Students then multiply the number of minutes from (a) 139, by 60 seconds in each minute to find the number of seconds it took the runner to complete the marathon.

Ask students what units of time we use to communicate duration of various activities.

Examples:

- "Is it easier to figure out how long you sleep in hours, minutes, or seconds?"
- "What unit would you use to tell someone how long you brushed your teeth — hours, minutes, or seconds?"

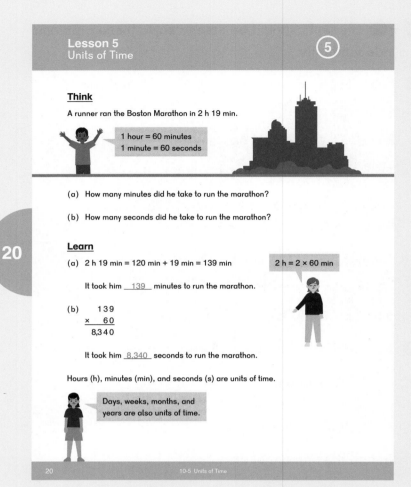

20

Do

①—⑤ For each question, discuss the problems and the given examples with students.

④ Students can convert Saturday's time to compound units:

$$76 \text{ s} = 1 \text{ min } 16 \text{ s}$$
$$\diagdown \quad \diagup$$
$$60 \text{ s} \quad 16 \text{ s}$$

$$1 \text{ min } 23 \text{ s} - 1 \text{ min } 16 \text{ s} = 7 \text{ s}$$

Alternatively, they could convert Sunday's time to seconds:

$$1 \text{ min } 23 \text{ s} = 60 \text{ s} + 23 \text{ s} = 83 \text{ s}$$
$$83 \text{ s} - 76 \text{ s} = 7 \text{ s}$$
On Saturday, he ran 7 seconds faster.

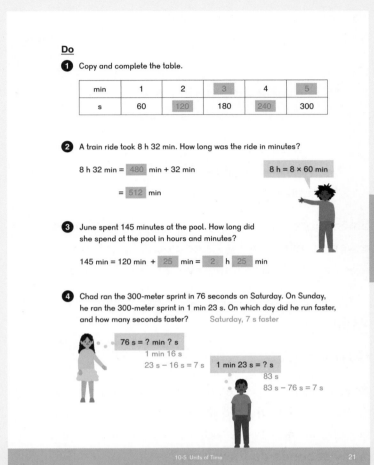

6 — **9** Students should be able to solve these problems independently.

8 (a) 1 h × 7 = 7 h

15 min × 7 = 105 min = 1 h 45 min

7 h + 1 h 45 min = 8 h 45 min

(b) 1 h ⟶ 60 min

8 h ⟶ 8 × 60 min = 480 min

480 min + 45 min = 525 min

9 Since there are 4 weeks in a month and 7 days in a week, multiply 4 by 7 and add 1 to get the next Monday. February in leap years has 29 days.

Activity

▲ How Long?

Have students convert the amount of time they spend doing activities during the day into different units. For example, if they study for 40 minutes a day, how many seconds do they study?

If they ride their bikes 15 minutes each way to school, how many seconds is it to ride round trip?

Exercise 5 • page 14

---

5 Sofia's watch shows the seconds as well as the minutes. When she looked at her watch, it was 10:12:40. The next time she looked at her watch, it was 10:15:32. How many seconds passed?

10:12:40 means 10 h 12 min 40 s

3 min 32 s − 40 s = 2 min 52 s = 172 s; 172 s

6 It is 4:47 p.m.

(a) What time will it be in 130 minutes?
130 min = 2 h 10 min; 4 h 47 min + 2 h 10 min = 6 h 57 min; 6:57 p.m

(b) What time was it 130 minutes ago?
4 h 47 min − 2 h 10 min = 2 h 37 min
2:37 p.m.

7 (a) How many minutes are there in a day?
24 × 60 min = 1,440 min

(b) How many minutes are there in a week?
7 × 1,440 min = 10,080 min

8 Alex spends 1 h 15 min practicing piano each day.

(a) How many hours and minutes does he spend practicing the piano in one week?
7 × 1 h 15 min = 7 h 105 mi = 8 h 45 min

(b) How many minutes does he spend practicing the piano in one week?
8 h 45 min = 480 min + 45 min = 525 min

9 How many days are there in a month that begins and ends on a Monday?

Each month has 28, 29, 30, or 31 days.

A month has at least 4 weeks. Monday to Monday is 4 weeks and 1 day. 29 days (February in a leap year).

Exercise 5 • page 14

Lesson 6 Practice A

Objective

- Practice concepts from the chapter.

After students complete the **Practice** in the textbook, have them continue to practice converting measurements with activities from the chapter.

8 Remind students that perimeter is the distance around a shape. If necessary, help students see that the perimeter is twice the length plus twice the width:

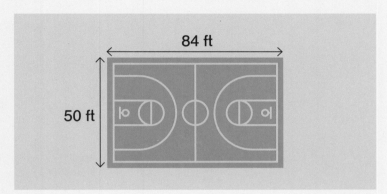

84 ft

50 ft

2 × 84 ft = 168 ft
2 × 50 ft = 100 ft
168 ft + 100 ft = 268 ft
268 ft ÷ 3 ft in each yard = 89 yd 1 ft

or

84 ft + 50 ft = 134 ft
134 ft ÷ 3 ft in each yard = 44 yd 2 ft
44 yd 2 ft × 2 = 88 yd 4 ft = 89 yd 1 ft

11 Since there are three 30 second increments in 1 min 30 s, students can find the answer by multiplying the cost for each 30 second increment by 3: $200 × 3.

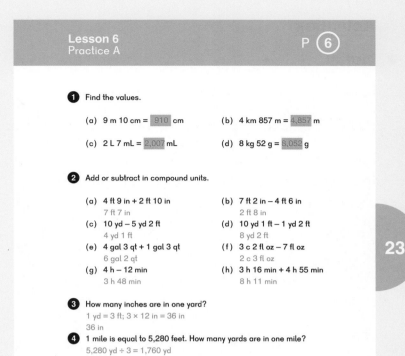

1 Find the values.

(a) 9 m 10 cm = 910 cm
(b) 4 km 857 m = 4,857 m
(c) 2 L 7 mL = 2,007 mL
(d) 8 kg 52 g = 8,052 g

2 Add or subtract in compound units.

(a) 4 ft 9 in + 2 ft 10 in
7 ft 7 in
(b) 7 ft 2 in − 4 ft 6 in
2 ft 8 in
(c) 10 yd − 5 yd 2 ft
4 yd 1 ft
(d) 10 yd 1 ft − 1 yd 2 ft
8 yd 2 ft
(e) 4 gal 3 qt + 1 gal 3 qt
6 gal 2 qt
(f) 3 c 2 fl oz − 7 fl oz
2 c 3 fl oz
(g) 4 h − 12 min
3 h 48 min
(h) 3 h 16 min + 4 h 55 min
8 h 11 min

3 How many inches are in one yard?
1 yd = 3 ft; 3 × 12 in = 36 in
36 in

4 1 mile is equal to 5,280 feet. How many yards are in one mile?
5,280 yd ÷ 3 = 1,760 yd
1,760 yd

5 A snake is 3 ft 9 in long. How long is the snake in inches?
3 ft 9 in = 36 in + 9 in = 45 in
45 in

6 A football player ran 12 yards 2 feet. How many feet did he run?
12 yd 2 ft = 36 ft + 2 ft = 38 ft
38 ft

10-6 Practice A   23

7 A basketball hoop is 10 ft high. How high is it in yards and feet?
3 yd 1 ft

8 A basketball court is 84 feet long and 50 feet wide. What is the perimeter of the basketball court in yards and feet?
84 + 84 + 50 + 50 = 268; 268 ft
268 ÷ 3 is 89 R 1; 89 yd 1 ft

9 An athlete threw a discus 215 ft. How far did he throw the discus in yards and feet?
215 ÷ 3 is 71 R 2
71 yd 2 ft

10 Two packages weigh 5 lb 4 oz each and two other packages weigh 3 lb 12 oz each. How much do the four packages weigh altogether?
2 × 5 lb 4 oz = 10 lb 8 oz; 2 × 3 lb 12 oz = 6 lb 24 oz = 7 lb 8 oz
10 lb 8 oz + 7 lb 8 oz = 18 lb; 18 lb

11 A local television station charges $200 for every 30-second commercial. How much will a commercial that lasts 1 minute 30 seconds cost?
1 min 30 s is three 30-second intervals.
3 × $200 = $600; $600

12 The length of a basketball court is 31 yd 1 ft. The length of a hockey rink is 66 yd 2 ft.

(a) What is the difference between the length of the basketball court and the length of the hockey rink in yards and feet?
66 yd 2 ft − 31 yd 1 ft = 35 yd 1 ft; 35 yd 1 ft
(b) What is the difference between the lengths in feet?
35 yd 1 ft = 105 ft + 1 ft = 106 ft; 106 ft

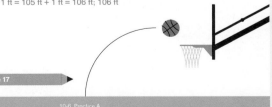

Exercise 6 • page 17

24   10-6 Practice A

Activities

● **Match**

Materials: Measurement Match Cards (BLM)

Use this game as a review of equivalent measurements.

Lay cards in a faceup array. Have students find two Measurement Match Cards (BLM) that show equivalent measurements.

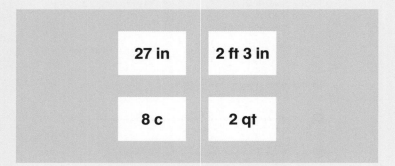

▲ **Memory**

Materials: Measurement Match Cards (BLM)

Play using the same rules as **Match**, but set the cards out facedown in an array.

Exercise 6 • page 17

Objective

- Express a smaller unit of measurement as a fraction of a larger unit of measurement.

Lesson Materials

- 3-ft strips of paper, or ribbon
- 1-ft rulers

Think

Discuss the **Think** problems. Give students strips of paper or ribbon and have them measure and cut them as Mei is doing in **Think**. Students may also draw bar models to solve the problems.

Give students time to solve the problems independently and then discuss student solutions.

Learn

Have students compare their solutions from **Think** with the ones shown in the textbook.

(a) Students should recall multiplying a fraction by a whole number. They may also have drawn a bar model:

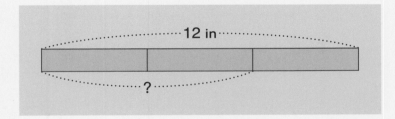

3 units $\longrightarrow$ 12 in
1 unit $\longrightarrow$ 12 in ÷ 3 = 4 in
2 units $\longrightarrow$ 2 × 4 in = 8 in

(b) To express a part as a fraction of the whole, both the part and the whole have to be in the same units.

Sofia reminds students that 1 ft is 12 inches, so 1 inch is $\frac{1}{12}$ of a foot.

1 in $\longrightarrow \frac{1}{12}$ ft
Students should think 10 inches is $\frac{?}{12}$ of a foot.

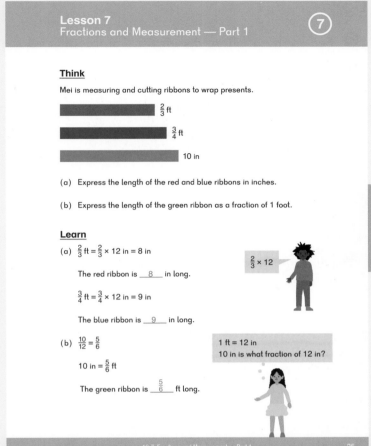

10 in $\longrightarrow$ 10 × $\frac{1}{12}$ ft = $\frac{10}{12}$ ft

Help students see that the green ribbon is 10 out of 12 inches, $\frac{10}{12}$ of a foot, which simplifies to $\frac{5}{6}$ of a foot.

Do

①—③ For each question, discuss the problems and the given examples with students.

① (b) 1 m ⟶ 100 cm
$\frac{4}{5}$ m ⟶ $\frac{4}{5}$ × 100 cm = 80 cm

(c) 1 lb ⟶ 16 oz
$\frac{3}{8}$ lb ⟶ $\frac{3}{8}$ × 16 oz = 6 oz

(d) 1 day ⟶ 24 h
$\frac{2}{3}$ day ⟶ $\frac{2}{3}$ × 24 h = 16 h

④—⑦ Students should be able to solve these problems independently.

⑥ $\frac{3}{4}$ × 1,000 m = 750 m
750 m × 2 = 1,500 m or 1 km 500 m

⑦ Convert compound units to the same units:

2 m 10 cm = 210 cm
300 cm − 210 cm = 90 cm
Students should think of 90 cm as $\frac{?}{300}$ of the pole.

Exercise 7 • page 20

Do

① (a) A string is $\frac{2}{3}$ yd long. Express the length of the string in feet.

$\frac{2}{3}$ yd = $\frac{2}{3}$ × 3 ft ⋯  1 yd = ? ft

= **2** ft

(b) A desk is $\frac{4}{5}$ m wide. Express the width of the desk in centimeters.

$\frac{4}{5}$ m = $\frac{4}{5}$ × **100** cm = **80** cm

(c) A melon weighs $\frac{3}{8}$ lb. Express the weight of the melon in ounces.

$\frac{3}{8}$ lb = $\frac{3}{8}$ × **16** oz = **6** oz

(d) A cat sleeps about $\frac{2}{3}$ of a day. About how many hours a day does a cat sleep?

$\frac{2}{3}$ day = $\frac{2}{3}$ × **24** h = **16** h

② Express 75 cm as a fraction of 1 m. Express the fraction in simplest form.

$\frac{75}{100}$ = $\frac{3}{4}$

1 m = 100 cm
75 out of 100 is ?

75 cm = $\frac{3}{4}$ m

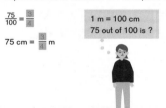

③ Express 20 min as a fraction of 2 hours.

$\frac{20}{120}$ = $\frac{1}{6}$

2 h = 120 min
20 min out of 120 min is ?

20 minutes is $\frac{1}{6}$ of 2 hours.

④ (a) $\frac{5}{6}$ ft = **10** in   (b) $\frac{1}{2}$ qt = **2** c

(c) $\frac{1}{3}$ yd = **1** ft   (d) $\frac{3}{10}$ m = **30** cm

(e) $\frac{3}{4}$ gal = **3** qt   (f) $\frac{4}{5}$ L = **800** mL

⑤ (a) 25 cm = $\frac{1}{4}$ m   (b) 12 oz = $\frac{3}{4}$ lb

(c) 25 min = $\frac{5}{12}$ h   (d) 250 m = $\frac{1}{4}$ km

⑥ Jessie swam $\frac{3}{4}$ km on Saturday and the same distance on Sunday. Express how far he swam altogether in kilometers and meters.
$\frac{3}{4}$ km = 750 m; 750 m + 750 m = 1,500 m = 1 km 500 m

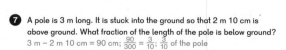

⑦ A pole is 3 m long. It is stuck into the ground so that 2 m 10 cm is above ground. What fraction of the length of the pole is below ground?
3 m − 2 m 10 cm = 90 cm; $\frac{90}{300}$ = $\frac{3}{10}$; $\frac{3}{10}$ of the pole

Exercise 7 • page 20

Objectives

- Convert a measurement given as a mixed number to compound units and single units.
- Express a smaller unit of measurement as a fraction of a larger unit of measurement that is not a whole number.

Think

Pose the **Think** problem. Provide students with time to solve the problems independently.

Discuss student solutions to the **Think** questions.

Learn

Have students compare the methods shown in **Learn** with their solutions from **Think**.

(a) Since the question asks for the answer to be expressed in feet and inches, help students see that only the fraction part of the solution needs to be converted into inches. Alex is converting $\frac{2}{3}$ ft into in.

As in the previous lesson, students may have drawn a bar model to solve for the number of inches in the problem:

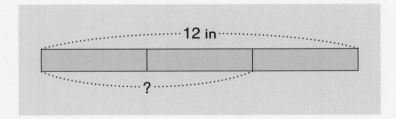

3 units $\longrightarrow$ 12 in
1 unit $\longrightarrow$ 12 in ÷ 3 = 4 in
2 units $\longrightarrow$ 2 × 4 in = 8 in

(b) Since the question asks for the answer to be expressed in inches, even the feet in whole number need to be converted into inches. First convert 3 feet to 36 inches, then add $\frac{2}{3}$ of a foot, which was calculated in (a).

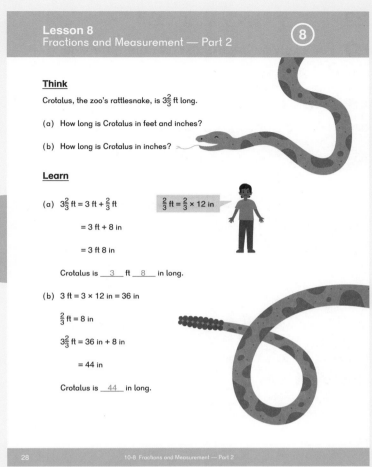

Think

Crotalus, the zoo's rattlesnake, is $3\frac{2}{3}$ ft long.

(a) How long is Crotalus in feet and inches?

(b) How long is Crotalus in inches?

Learn

(a) $3\frac{2}{3}$ ft = 3 ft + $\frac{2}{3}$ ft $\frac{2}{3}$ ft = $\frac{2}{3}$ × 12 in

   = 3 ft + 8 in

   = 3 ft 8 in

Crotalus is ___3___ ft ___8___ in long.

(b) 3 ft = 3 × 12 in = 36 in

$\frac{2}{3}$ ft = 8 in

$3\frac{2}{3}$ ft = 36 in + 8 in

   = 44 in

Crotalus is ___44___ in long.

28   10-8 Fractions and Measurement — Part 2

Do

1 — 4 For each question, discuss the different calculations shown to find the answer.

1 Ask students, "What needs to be converted in (a) and (b), the fraction or the whole number?"

(a) Since we want to know the weight in pounds and ounces, we only need to convert into ounces the part of the weight that is expressed as a fraction of a pound. The whole number of pounds stay as pounds. Dion knows that 1 lb = 16 oz so he can convert $\frac{1}{2}$ pound into 8 ounces.

(b) We want to know the weight in ounces, so we need to convert all the units into ounces.

2 Discuss Sofia's comment. Help students think of it as 4 out of 44 inches.

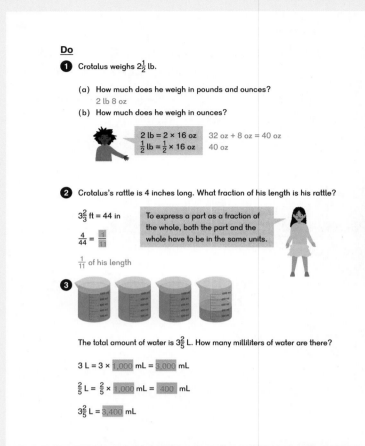

6 — 9 Students should be able to solve these problems independently.

6 1 m ⟶ 100 cm
$\frac{3}{5}$ m ⟶ $\frac{3}{5}$ × 100 cm = 60 cm

7 Students can add the mixed numbers together first, and then express the distance as meters:

$2\frac{1}{2} + 3\frac{3}{4} = 6\frac{1}{4}$ km
6 km ⟶ 6 × 1,000 m = 6,000 m
$\frac{1}{4}$ km ⟶ $\frac{1}{4}$ × 1,000 m = 250 m
6,000 m + 250 m = 6,250 m

Students could also convert to meters first, and then add.

Saturday:

2 km ⟶ 2 × 1,000 m = 2,000 m
$\frac{1}{2}$ km ⟶ $\frac{1}{2}$ × 1,000 m = 500 m
2,000 m + 500 m = 2,500 m

Sunday:

3 km ⟶ 3 × 1,000 m
$\frac{3}{4}$ km ⟶ $\frac{3}{4}$ × 1,000 m = 750 m
3,000 m + 750 m = 3,750 m

Altogether:

2,500 m + 3,750 m = 6,250 m

8 Milk at first:

3 c ⟶ 3 × 8 fl oz = 24 fl oz
$\frac{1}{4}$ c ⟶ $\frac{1}{4}$ × 8 fl oz = 2 fl oz
24 fl oz + 2 fl oz = 26 fl oz

Milk used:

1 c ⟶ 8 fl oz
$\frac{1}{2}$ c ⟶ $\frac{1}{2}$ × 8 fl oz = 4 fl oz

Milk left:

26 fl oz − 12 fl oz = 14 fl oz

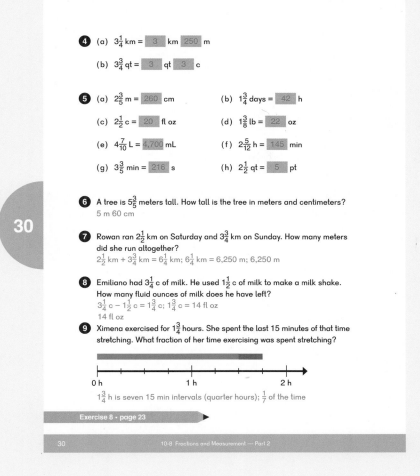

9 Express the part and the whole in the same units:

1 h ⟶ 60 min
$\frac{3}{4}$ h ⟶ $\frac{3}{4}$ × 60 min = 45 min
60 min + 45 min = 105 min
$\frac{15}{105} = \frac{1}{7}$

Exercise 8 • page 23

Objective

- Practice concepts from the chapter.

Activity

▲ Measurement Puzzle

Materials: Measurement Puzzle (BLM)

Have students cut out the triangles and match equivalent measurements. The final figure should be a triangle.

Answer:

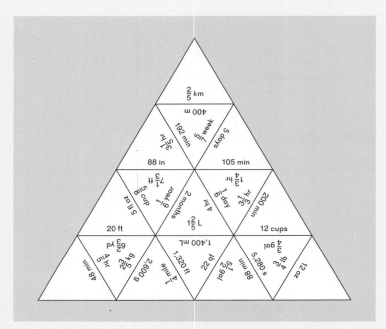

Exercise 9 • page 26

1 (a) $\frac{3}{4}$ ft = 9 in   (b) $\frac{2}{3}$ yd = 2 ft

(c) $\frac{4}{5}$ km = 800 m   (d) $\frac{9}{10}$ m = 90 cm

(e) $\frac{3}{4}$ kg = 750 g   (f) $\frac{3}{10}$ L = 300 mL

(g) $\frac{5}{12}$ h = 25 min   (h) $\frac{4}{5}$ min = 48 s

2 (a) $3\frac{1}{4}$ h = 3 h 15 min

(b) $3\frac{3}{4}$ c = 3 c 6 fl oz

3 (a) $2\frac{3}{4}$ lb = 44 oz   (b) $4\frac{1}{2}$ gal = 18 qt

(c) $2\frac{1}{2}$ h = 150 min   (d) $4\frac{2}{5}$ min = 264 s

(e) $7\frac{1}{3}$ yd = 22 ft   (f) $2\frac{3}{5}$ kg = 2,600 g

4 (a) 10 oz = $\frac{5}{8}$ lb

(b) 4 cm = $\frac{1}{25}$ m

5 (a) Express $\frac{3}{4}$ km in centimeters. $\frac{3}{4}$ km = 750 m = 75,000 cm

(b) Express $\frac{3}{4}$ day in minutes. $\frac{3}{4}$ day = 18 h = 1,080 min

6 Samantha's arm span measures $5\frac{2}{3}$ ft. How long is her arm span in inches?
$5\frac{2}{3}$ ft = 60 in + 8 in = 68 in; 68 in

7 There is $\frac{3}{4}$ gal of milk left in a gallon jug. How many quarts of milk have been used already?
1 qt

8 Aaron was asleep for 10 hours. What fraction of the day was he awake?
$\frac{14}{24} = \frac{7}{12}$; $\frac{7}{12}$ of the day

9 A bag of red grapes weighs $\frac{5}{8}$ lb. A bag of green grapes weighs $\frac{3}{4}$ lb. How much do the grapes weigh altogether in ounces?
$\frac{5}{8}$ lb + $\frac{3}{4}$ lb = $1\frac{3}{8}$ lb; $1\frac{3}{8}$ lb = 16 oz + 6 oz = 22 oz; 22 oz

10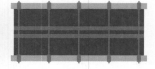

Hailey spent $\frac{3}{4}$ hour practicing programming and $1\frac{1}{2}$ hours practicing drums. How many more minutes did she spend practicing drums than practicing coding?
$1\frac{1}{2}$ h − $\frac{3}{4}$ h = $\frac{3}{4}$ h; $\frac{3}{4}$ h = 45 min; 45 more min

11 Last week, Jasmine did her homework for $\frac{3}{4}$ hour a day for 5 days. How much time did she spend doing her homework last week in hours and minutes?
$5 \times \frac{3}{4}$ h = $3\frac{3}{4}$ h; $3\frac{3}{4}$ h = 3 h 45 min

12 There are 4 bottles that each contains $\frac{2}{5}$ L of juice. How much juice is in all of the bottles in liters and milliliters?
$4 \times \frac{2}{5}$ L = $1\frac{3}{5}$ L; $1\frac{3}{5}$ L = 1 L 600 mL

Exercise 9 • page 26

Brain Works

★ Measurement Puzzlers

1 You have two buckets, one holds 3 liters and the other holds 5 liters.

How can you measure out just 1 liter of water using the two buckets?

Answer:

Fill the 3-liter bucket and pour it into the 5-liter bucket. There are now 3 liters in the 5-liter bucket.

Fill the 3-liter bucket again, and fill the rest of the 5-liter bucket. You should have 1 liter of water left in the 3-liter bucket.

2 A batch of cookies needs to bake for 15 minutes. You have a 7 minute hourglass timer and an 11 minute hourglass timer.

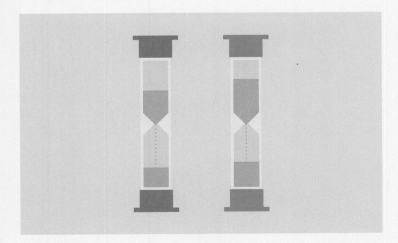

How can you measure 15 minutes using just these two timers?

Answer:

(a) Turn both timers over at the same time.

When the 7 minute timer is empty, turn it over again. The 11 minute timer is still running.

When the 11 minute timer is empty, 11 minutes have passed. At this time, 4 minutes have passed through the 7 minute timer.

Turn the 7 minute timer over again. It will take 4 minutes for it to empty. 11 min + 4 min = 15 min and the cookies are done!

(b) Before baking the cookies, turn both timers over to start.

When the 7 minute timer is empty, start baking the cookies. The 11 minute timer has 4 minutes to go.

When the 11 minute timer also runs out, 4 minutes have passed. Flip it back over to measure out 11 more minutes.

Chapter 10 Measurement

Exercise 1

Basics

1 (a) 6 m = 6 × 100 cm = ☐600☐ cm

   (b) 6 m 52 cm = ☐600☐ cm + 52 cm

   = ☐652☐ cm

1 cm = 10 mm
1 m = 100 cm
1 km = 1,000 m
1 kg = 1,000 g
1 L = 1,000 mL

2 (a) 5,000 mL = ☐5☐ L

   (b) 5,450 mL = ☐5☐ L ☐450☐ mL

3 5,450 cm = ☐54☐ m ☐50☐ cm

4 4 L 450 mL —+ 3 L→ ☐7☐ L 450 mL —+ 800 mL→ ☐8☐ L ☐250☐ mL

   4 L 450 mL + 3 L 800 mL = ☐8☐ L ☐250☐ mL

5 9 kg 600 g —− 5 kg→ ☐4☐ kg 600 g —− 450 g→ ☐4☐ kg ☐150☐ g

   9 kg 600 g − 5 kg 450 g = ☐4☐ kg ☐150☐ g

6 (a) 3 × 8 m = ☐24☐ m

   (b) 3 × 42 cm = ☐126☐ cm = ☐1☐ m ☐26☐ cm

   (c) 3 × 8 m 42 cm = ☐25☐ m ☐26☐ cm

Practice

7 (a) 1 km − 300 m = ☐700☐ m   (b) 1 km − 30 m = ☐970☐ m

   (c) 1 m − 3 cm = ☐97☐ cm   (d) 1 cm − 3 mm = ☐7☐ mm

8 A bar of soap weighs 235 g. How much do 8 bars of soap weigh?
Express the answer in compound units.
8 × 235 g = 1,880 g
1 kg 880 g

9 2 blocks of concrete weigh 45 kg altogether. One of the blocks weighs
35 kg 230 g. How much does the other block weigh? Express the answer in
compound units.
45 kg − 35 kg 230 g = 9 kg 770 g
9 kg 770 g

10 A rope is 12 m 40 cm long. 3 pieces that are each 2 m 85 cm long are cut
from it. How long is the remaining piece of rope? Express the answer in
compound units.
3 × 2 m 85 cm = 8 m 55 cm
12 m 40 cm − 8 m 55 cm = 3 m 85 cm
3 m 85 cm

11 Amy bought 5 bottles of juice. Each bottle contains 650 mL of juice.
How much juice does she have in all? Express the answer in compound units.
5 × 650 mL = 3,250 mL
3 L 250 mL

Exercise 2

Basics

1 The diagram below shows the relative lengths of some customary units of length. Use the diagram to find the missing numbers.

1 inch

1 foot

1 yard

(a) 1 ft = ☐12 in

(b) 1 yd = ☐3 ft

(c) 1 yd = ☐36 in

2 (a) 4 ft = 4 × 12 in = ☐48 in

(b) 4 ft 8 in = ☐48 in + 8 in = ☐56 in

3 (a) 5 ft = ☐60 in

(b) 64 in = ☐60 in + 4 in = ☐5 ft ☐4 in

4 (a) 47 ÷ 3 is ☐15 with a remainder of ☐2 .

(b) 47 ft = ☐15 yd ☐2 ft

5 (a) 7 in + ☐5 in = 1 ft

(b) 7 in + 8 in = ☐1 ft ☐3 in

(c) 1 ft − 2 in = ☐10 in

(d) 2 ft − 2 in = ☐1 ft ☐10 in

(e) 2 ft 3 in − 5 in = ☐1 ft ☐10 in

6 4 ft 7 in $\xrightarrow{+\,6\,ft}$ ☐10 ft 7 in $\xrightarrow{+\,8\,in}$ ☐11 ft ☐3 in

4 ft 7 in + 6 ft 8 in = ☐11 ft ☐3 in

7 9 ft 3 in $\xrightarrow{-\,7\,ft}$ ☐2 ft 3 in $\xrightarrow{-\,5\,in}$ ☐1 ft ☐10 in

9 ft 3 in − 7 ft 5 in = ☐1 ft ☐10 in

Practice

8 (a) Fill in the missing numbers.

Object	Measurement	
length of a couch	6 ft 2 in	☐74 in
height of a couch	☐3 ft ☐4 in	40 in
length of a bookshelf	2 yd 5 in	☐77 in
height of a bookshelf	☐2 ft ☐3 in	27 in

(b) Find the sum of the lengths of the bookshelf and the couch. Express the answer in feet and inches.
Bookshelf: 2 yd 5 in = 6 ft 5 in
6 ft 2 in + 6 ft 5 in = 12 ft 7 in

(c) Find the difference in height of the bookshelf and the couch. Express the answer in feet and inches.
40 in − 27 in = 13 in
1 ft 1 in

9 A bolt (roll) of fabric has 40 yards of fabric. 2 yd 2 ft were cut from it to make a dress and 1 yd 2 ft to make a skirt.

(a) What is the length of fabric that was used? Express the answer in yards and feet.
2 yd 2 ft + 1 yd 2 ft = 4 yd 1 ft
4 yd 1 ft

(b) What is the length of fabric that was left on the bolt? Express the answer in yards and feet.
40 yd − 4 yd 1 ft = 35 yd 2 ft
35 yd 2 ft

Challenge

10 1 mile is equal to 5,280 feet. 4 laps around a track is 1 mile.

(a) What is the length in feet of one lap around this track?
5,280 ft ÷ 4 = 1,320 ft
1,320 ft

(b) What is the length in yards of one lap around this track?
1,320 yd ÷ 3 = 440 yd
440 yd

Exercise 3

Basics

1 The picture shows a scale marked in pounds. The interval between each tick mark is 1 ounce. You can use it to answer the following questions.

(a) 1 lb = $\boxed{16}$ oz

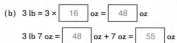

(b) 3 lb = 3 × $\boxed{16}$ oz = $\boxed{48}$ oz

3 lb 7 oz = $\boxed{48}$ oz + 7 oz = $\boxed{55}$ oz

The block weighs $\boxed{55}$ oz.

(c) 2 lb = $\boxed{32}$ oz

36 oz = $\boxed{32}$ oz + 4 oz = $\boxed{2}$ lb $\boxed{4}$ oz

(d) 1 lb − 9 oz = $\boxed{7}$ oz

4 lb − 9 oz = $\boxed{3}$ lb $\boxed{7}$ oz

2 3 lb 7 oz $\xrightarrow{+\ 2\ lb}$ $\boxed{5}$ lb 7 oz $\xrightarrow{+\ 9\ oz}$ $\boxed{6}$ lb $\boxed{0}$ oz

3 lb 7 oz + 2 lb 9 oz = $\boxed{6}$ lb $\boxed{0}$ oz

3 6 lb 2 oz $\xrightarrow{-\ 4\ lb}$ $\boxed{2}$ lb 2 oz $\xrightarrow{-\ 9\ oz}$ $\boxed{1}$ lb $\boxed{9}$ oz

6 lb 2 oz − 4 lb 9 oz = $\boxed{1}$ lb $\boxed{9}$ oz

Practice

4 (a) Fill in the missing numbers.

Object	Weight		
a boot	$\boxed{1}$ lb $\boxed{7}$ oz		23 oz
a bottle of ketchup	3 lb 14 oz		$\boxed{62}$ oz
a pumpkin	4 lb 2 oz		$\boxed{66}$ oz
a book	$\boxed{2}$ lb $\boxed{1}$ oz		33 oz

(b) Find the sum of the weights of the lightest and heaviest objects. Express the answer in compound units.
1 lb 7 oz + 4 lb 2 oz = 5 lb 9 oz
5 lb 9 oz

(c) Find the difference in the weights of the lightest and heaviest objects. Express the answer in compound units.
4 lb 2 oz − 1 lb 7 oz = 2 lb 11 oz
2 lb 11 oz

5 Alex weighed 6 lb 4 oz at birth. Emma weighed 120 oz. Who weighed more and by how much? Express the answer in compound units.
6 lb 4 oz = 100 oz
120 oz − 100 oz = 20 oz
Emma weighed 1 lb 4 oz more.

6 A brick weighs 5 lb 10 oz. How much do 3 bricks weigh? Express the answer in compound units.
3 × 5 lb 10 oz = 16 lb 14 oz
16 lb 14 oz

Challenge

7 Dion found that 100 pennies weigh 9 ounces and 100 dimes weigh 8 ounces. How much do 500 pennies and 500 dimes weigh altogether? Express the answer in compound units.
The weight of 100 coins is 5 times the weight of 100 coins.
Pennies: 5 × 9 oz = 45 oz
Dimes: 5 × 8 oz = 40 oz
45 oz + 40 oz = 85 oz
5 lb 5 oz

Exercise 4

Basics

1. The diagram below shows the relative sizes of some customary units of capacity. Use the diagram to find the missing numbers.

1 fluid ounce   1 cup   1 pint   1 quart   1 gallon

(a) 1 c = [8] fl oz

(b) 1 pt = [2] c | 1 pt = [16] fl oz

(c) 1 qt = [2] pt | 1 qt = [4] c

(d) 1 gal = [4] qt | 1 gal = [8] pt

(e) 1 gal = [16] c | 1 gal = [128] fl oz

2. (a) 3 gal = 3 × [4] qt = [12] qt

   (b) 3 gal 3 qt = [12] qt + 3 qt = [15] qt

3. (a) 62 ÷ 4 is [15] with a remainder of [2].

   (b) 62 qt = [15] gal [2] qt

Practice

4. (a) 5 gal = [20] qt   (b) 5 qt = [20] c

   (c) 5 pt = [10] c   (d) 5 c = [40] fl oz

5. (a) 32 fl oz = [4] c   (b) 32 c = [16] pt

   (c) 32 pt = [16] qt   (d) 32 qt = [8] gal

6. (a) 7 c = [3] pt [1] c

   (b) 7 c = [1] qt [3] c

   (c) 15 qt = [3] gal [3] qt

   (d) 30 fl oz = [3] c [6] fl oz

7. A recipe calls for 3 tablespoons of soy sauce. Yara only has a teaspoon. She knows there are 3 teaspoons in a tablespoon. She is doubling the recipe. How many teaspoons of soy sauce does she need?
   3 tbsp = 3 × 3 tsp = 9 tsp
   2 × 9 tsp = 18 tsp
   18 tsp

8. A coffee shop sells coffee in 3 sizes: redwood, cedar, and fir. A redwood is 16 fl oz. A cedar is 14 fl oz. A fir is 10 fl oz.

   (a) Which sizes are more than 1 cup?
        All 3 sizes.

   (b) What is the total capacity of 2 cedars? Express the answer in cups and fluid ounces.
        2 × 14 fl oz = 28 fl oz
        3 c 4 fl oz

   (c) A family orders 2 redwoods, 1 cedar, and 3 firs. What is the total amount of coffee they got? Express the answer in cups and fluid ounces.
        2 × 16 fl oz = 32 fl oz
        3 × 10 fl oz = 30 fl oz
        32 fl oz + 30 fl oz + 14 fl oz = 76 fl oz
        9 c 4 fl oz

Teacher's Guide 4B Chapter 10

Exercise 5

Basics

1 (a) 4 min = 4 × ☐60☐ s = ☐240☐ s

1 min = 60 s
1 h = 60 min
1 day = 24 h
1 week = 7 days

(b) 4 min 18 s = ☐240☐ s + 18 s = ☐258☐ s

2 (a) 3 h = ☐180☐ min

(b) 190 min = ☐180☐ min + 10 min = ☐3☐ h ☐10☐ min

3 (a) 5 × 3 h = ☐15☐ h

(b) 5 × 35 min = ☐2☐ h ☐55☐ min

(c) 5 × 3 h 35 min = ☐17☐ h ☐55☐ min

4 (a) 1 h − 34 min = ☐26☐ min

(b) 5 h − 34 min = ☐4☐ h ☐26☐ min

5 3 min 35 s —+ 8 min→ ☐11☐ min 35 s —+ 48 s→ ☐12☐ min ☐23☐ s

3 min 35 s + 8 min 48 s = ☐12☐ min ☐23☐ s

6 7 h 20 min —− 2 h→ ☐5☐ h 20 min —− 34 min→ ☐4☐ h ☐46☐ min

7 h 20 min − 2 h 34 min = ☐4☐ h ☐46☐ min

Practice

7 (a) 95 min = ☐1☐ h ☐35☐ min

(b) What time is it 95 min after 11:35 a.m.?
1:10 p.m.

(c) What time is it 95 min before 11:35 a.m.?
10:00 a.m.

8 How many hours is it from Monday at 9:00 a.m. to Friday at 5:00 p.m. of the same week?
9:00 a.m. Monday to 9:00 a.m. Friday: 4 × 24 h = 96 h
9:00 a.m Friday to 5:00 p.m Friday: 8 h
96 h + 8 h = 104 h
104 h

9 Jacob used a stopwatch to time two races. After the first race, the stopwatch said 00:03:42. After the second race, it said 00:07:27. Jacob realized that he forgot to reset the stopwatch back to 0 after the first race. How long was the second race in minutes and seconds?
7 min 27 s − 3 min 42 s = 3 min 45 s
3 min 45 s

10 Laila went on a bus ride that lasted 3 h 14 min. Gavin went on a train ride that lasted exactly half as long as Laila's bus ride. How long was Gavin's train ride in hours and minutes?
3 h 14 min ÷ 2 = 194 min ÷ 2 = 97 min
1 h 37 min

Challenge

11 There are 365 days in a year, and 366 days in a leap year. A leap year occurs every 4 years. There are 10 years in a decade. What is the least possible number of days in a decade?
A decade could have 2 or 3 leap years. It would have to have 2 leap years to have the least possible number of days.
365 days × 8 = 2,920 days
366 days × 2 = 732 days
2,920 days + 732 days = 3,652 days
3,652 days

Exercise 6

Check

1 (a) 5 cm 2 mm = [52] mm

(b) 5 min 5 s = [305] s

(c) 5 lb 2 oz = [82] oz

(d) 5 kg 2 g = [5,002] g

(e) 26 in = [2] ft [2] in

(f) 35 qt = [8] gal [3] qt

(g) 6 km 735 m + 2 km 825 m = [9] km [560] m

(h) 6 lb 4 oz − 2 lb 9 oz = [3] lb [11] oz

(i) 10 ft 7 in − 4 ft 9 in = [5] ft [10] in

10-6 Practice A   17

2 A soaker hose is 200 ft long. Brandon needs it to reach a distance of 58 yd. How many extra yards and feet of hose will he have?
58 yd = 174 ft
200 ft − 174 ft = 26 ft
8 yd 2 ft

3 Brandon has an automatic timer for his soaker hose. He wants to run the water for 200 minutes and have it shut off at 7:30 a.m. What time should he set the timer to start?
200 min = 3 h 20 min
4:10 a.m.

4 2 L 658 mL of Solution A and 1 L 162 mL of Solution B are mixed together, and then 500 mL is poured out. How much of the mixture is left? Express the answer in liters and milliliters.
2 L 658 mL + 1 L 162 mL = 3 L 820 mL
3 L 820 mL − 500 mL = 3 L 320 mL
3 L 320 mL

18   10-6 Practice A

Challenge

5 3 c of orange juice, 1 pt of peach juice, and 1 c 6 fl oz of mango juice are mixed together and poured equally into 6 cups. How many fluid ounces of juice are in each cup?
3 c = 24 fl oz
1 pt = 16 fl oz
1 c 6 fl oz = 14 fl oz
24 fl oz + 16 fl oz + 14 fl oz = 54 fl oz
54 fl oz ÷ 6 = 9 fl oz
9 fl oz

6 A slime mold moves 120 mm every minute.

(a) How far will it move in 15 seconds?
120 mm in 60 s = 2 mm in 1 s
15 × 2 mm = 30 mm
30 mm or 3 cm

(b) How many centimeters will it move in 5 minutes?
120 mm × 5 = 600 mm
60 cm

7 A "hand" is used to measure the height of horses. 1 hand equals 4 inches. If a horse is 14 hands tall, how tall is it in feet and inches?
14 × 4 in = 56 in
4 ft 8 in

10-6 Practice A   19

Exercise 7

Basics

1 (a) 1 ft = [12] in

   (b) $\frac{1}{4}$ ft = $\frac{1}{4}$ × [12] in = [3] in

   (c) $\frac{3}{4}$ ft = $\frac{3}{4}$ × [12] in = [9] in

2 (a) 1 min = [60] s

   (b) $\frac{1}{3}$ min = $\frac{1}{3}$ × [60] s = [20] s

   (c) $\frac{1}{10}$ min = $\frac{1}{10}$ × [60] s = [6] s

   (d) $\frac{5}{6}$ min = $\frac{5}{6}$ × [60] s = [50] s

3 Express 8 ounces as a fraction of a pound.

   [16] oz = 1 lb

   8 oz = [$\frac{8}{16}$] lb = [$\frac{1}{2}$] lb

4 Express 40 cm as a fraction of 1 m.

   [100] cm = 1 m

   40 cm = [$\frac{40}{100}$] m = [$\frac{2}{5}$] m

Practice

5 (a) $\frac{3}{4}$ lb = [12] oz   (b) $\frac{3}{4}$ qt = [3] c

   (c) $\frac{5}{12}$ h = [25] min   (d) $\frac{5}{12}$ day = [10] h

   (e) $\frac{3}{5}$ m = [60] cm   (f) $\frac{3}{5}$ L = [600] mL

6 Give the answers in simplest form.

   (a) 40 min = [$\frac{2}{3}$] h

   (b) 8 in = [$\frac{2}{3}$] ft

   (c) 450 m = [$\frac{9}{20}$] km

   (d) 16 cm = [$\frac{4}{25}$] m

7 Two identical cans weigh $\frac{7}{8}$ lb together.

   (a) How many ounces do both cans weigh together?
      $\frac{7}{8}$ × 16 oz = 14 oz
      14 oz

   (b) How many ounces does one can weigh?
      14 oz ÷ 2 = 7 oz
      7 oz

8 John took $\frac{7}{12}$ of an hour to wash his car. He spent $\frac{2}{5}$ of the time it took him to wash the car cleaning the interior.

   (a) How many minutes did it take him to wash the car?
      $\frac{7}{12}$ × 60 min = 35 min
      35 min

   (b) How many minutes did it take him to clean the interior?
      $\frac{2}{5}$ × 35 min = 14 min
      14 min

9 A block of cheese weighed 4 lb. $\frac{5}{8}$ of it was used to make macaroni and cheese. How much does the block of cheese weigh now? Express the answer in compound units.
   4 lb = 64 oz
   $\frac{3}{8}$ × 64 oz = 24 oz
   1 lb 8 oz

Exercise 8

Basics

1 (a) $\frac{3}{4}$ ft = $\frac{3}{4}$ × 12 in = $\boxed{9}$ in

(b) $1\frac{3}{4}$ ft = 1 ft $\boxed{9}$ in

(c) $1\frac{3}{4}$ ft = 12 in + $\boxed{9}$ in = $\boxed{21}$ in

2 (a) 3 h = $\boxed{180}$ min

(b) $\frac{2}{3}$ h = $\boxed{40}$ min

(c) $3\frac{2}{3}$ h = $\boxed{220}$ min

3 Express 25 cm as a fraction of $1\frac{1}{2}$ m.

$1\frac{1}{2}$ m = $\boxed{150}$ cm

$\frac{25}{150}$ = $\boxed{\frac{1}{6}}$

25 cm is $\boxed{\frac{1}{6}}$ of $1\frac{1}{2}$ m.

4 Express 24 h as a fraction of $1\frac{1}{2}$ days.

$1\frac{1}{2}$ days = $\boxed{36}$ h

$\frac{24}{36}$ = $\boxed{\frac{2}{3}}$

24 h is $\boxed{\frac{2}{3}}$ of $1\frac{1}{2}$ days.

Practice

5 (a) $2\frac{7}{10}$ km = $\boxed{2}$ km $\boxed{700}$ m

(b) $3\frac{3}{4}$ lb = $\boxed{3}$ lb $\boxed{12}$ oz

6 (a) $4\frac{3}{4}$ ft = $\boxed{57}$ in   (b) $3\frac{3}{5}$ min = $\boxed{216}$ s

(c) $6\frac{2}{5}$ cm = $\boxed{64}$ mm   (d) $5\frac{5}{20}$ m = $\boxed{525}$ cm

(e) $2\frac{1}{2}$ c = $\boxed{20}$ fl oz   (f) $3\frac{2}{3}$ yd = $\boxed{11}$ ft

7 Carlos ran $1\frac{3}{5}$ km each day three days in a row. How far did he run altogether? Express the answer in kilometers and meters.

$1\frac{3}{5}$ km = 1,600 m

3 × 1,600 m = 4,800 m

4 km 800 m

8 Two boards laid end-to-end measure $2\frac{1}{3}$ ft. How long are 5 such boards laid end-to-end? Express the answer in feet and inches.

$2\frac{1}{3}$ ft = 28 in

1 board: 28 in ÷ 2 = 14 in

5 × 14 in = 70 in

5 ft 10 in

9 A bag of beans weighed $2\frac{1}{2}$ lb. 12 ounces of beans were used for soup.

(a) What fraction of the bag of beans was used?

$2\frac{1}{2}$ lb = 40 oz

$\frac{12}{40}$ = $\frac{3}{10}$

$\frac{3}{10}$ of the bag

(b) Another $1\frac{1}{8}$ lb of beans was used to make chili. How many ounces does the bag of beans now weigh?

$1\frac{1}{8}$ lb = 18 oz

40 oz − 12 oz − 18 oz = 10 oz

10 oz

BEANS

Exercise 9

Check

1 1 inch is about $2\frac{1}{2}$ cm. Using this approximation, about how many centimeters is 1 foot?

$12 \times 2\frac{1}{2}$ cm = 30 cm

About 30 cm

2 Laura swam a mile in $20\frac{2}{3}$ min. Express this time in minutes and seconds.

20 min 40 s

3 Dennis is 75 inches tall. Express his height in feet using a mixed number in simplest form.

$6\frac{1}{4}$ ft

4 Aliyah has $2. She spent 80¢ on a snack. What fraction of her money did she spend?

$\frac{80}{200} = \frac{2}{5}$

$\frac{2}{5}$ of her money

5 6 hours is what fraction of $2\frac{1}{2}$ days? Give the answer in simplest form.

$2\frac{1}{2}$ days = 60 h

$\frac{6}{60} = \frac{1}{10}$

$\frac{1}{10}$ of $2\frac{1}{2}$ days

6 Irene had 5 lb of flour. She used $1\frac{1}{2}$ lb of flour on Monday, $\frac{3}{4}$ lb of flour on Tuesday, and $2\frac{1}{8}$ lb of flour on Wednesday.

(a) How much flour did she use all three days? Give the answer in pounds and ounces.

$1\frac{1}{2}$ lb $+ \frac{3}{4}$ lb $+ 2\frac{1}{8}$ lb $= 4\frac{3}{8}$ lb

4 lb 6 oz

(b) How many ounces of flour does she have left?

5 lb − 4 lb 6 oz = 10 oz

10 oz

7 Dexter had two pieces of fabric. One was $2\frac{2}{3}$ yd long and the other was $3\frac{2}{3}$ yd long. He used $5\frac{1}{3}$ yd of fabric for a project. How many inches of fabric does he have left over?

$2\frac{2}{3}$ yd $+ 3\frac{2}{3}$ yd $- 5\frac{1}{3}$ yd = 1 yd

36 in

8 A stack of 200 quarters is 35 cm tall. How many millimeters thick is one quarter? Give the answer as a mixed number in simplest form.

200 quarters $\longrightarrow$ 35 cm

1 quarter $\longrightarrow \frac{35}{200}$ cm $= \frac{7}{40}$ cm

$\frac{7}{40} \times 10$ mm $= \frac{7}{4}$ mm $= 1\frac{3}{4}$ mm

$1\frac{3}{4}$ mm

Challenge

9 In the U.S., temperature is measured in degrees Fahrenheit (°F). In most other countries, temperature is measured in degrees Celsius (°C). To convert °C to °F, multiply the numbers of degrees Celsius by $\frac{9}{5}$ and then add 32.

(a) Water freezes at 0°C. What temperature is that in °F?

$\frac{9}{5} \times 0 = 0$

0 + 32

32 °F

(b) Water boils at 100°C. What temperature is that in °F?

$\frac{9}{5} \times 100 = 180$

180 + 32 = 212

212 °F

(c) What is 20°C in °F?

$\frac{9}{5} \times 20 = 36$

36 + 32 = 68

68 °F

(d) Normal body temperature is 37°C. What is this in °F? Express the answer as a mixed number in simplest form.

$\frac{9}{5} \times 37 = 66\frac{3}{5}$

$66\frac{3}{5} + 32 = 98\frac{3}{5}$

$98\frac{3}{5}$ °F

(e) On Thursday, a weather station said it was 25°C in Vancouver, Canada. The next day, a U.S. weather station said it was 62°F there. On which day was it cooler and by how many degrees Fahrenheit?

$\frac{9}{5} \times 25 = 45$

45 + 32 = 77

77 − 62 = 15

Friday by 15 °F.

Suggested number of class periods: 6–7

	Lesson	Page	Resources		Objectives
	Chapter Opener	p. 45	TB:	p. 33	Investigate area and perimeter.
1	Area of Rectangles — Part 1	p. 46	TB: WB:	p. 34 p. 29	Find the area of a figure given the side lengths by converting units.
2	Area of Rectangles — Part 2	p. 49	TB: WB:	p. 38 p. 32	Find the unknown side length of a rectangle given the area and one side length.
3	Area of Composite Figures	p. 51	TB: WB:	p. 41 p. 35	Find the area of rectangular paths.
4	Perimeter — Part 1	p. 55	TB: WB:	p. 46 p. 39	Find the perimeter of rectangles. Find the length of the unknown side of a rectangle given the length of one side and the perimeter.
5	Perimeter — Part 2	p. 58	TB: WB:	p. 51 p. 42	Find the perimeter of composite figures.
6	Practice	p. 62	TB: WB:	p. 56 p. 45	Practice finding area and perimeter.
	Workbook Solutions	p. 64			

In Dimensions Math 3B, students learned:

- the definitions of area and perimeter.
- how to find the area and perimeter of composite shapes made up of rectangles.

In this chapter, the concepts on area and perimeter covered in Dimensions Math 3B are extended to more complex rectilinear figures. Students will also learn how to find an unknown side length of a rectangle, given total area or perimeter and the length of one side.

Students should recall the units of area are square units. The area of a figure is equal to the number of square units that completely cover the interior of the figure.

They should also recall that the area of a rectangle can be found by multiplying the length of the two adjacent sides.

In this chapter, students will use the skills learned in Chapter 10 and convert one or both of the side lengths into different units to find the perimeter or area.

For example, students may be given the figure below and asked to find the area in square feet. They will convert the side lengths to feet first.

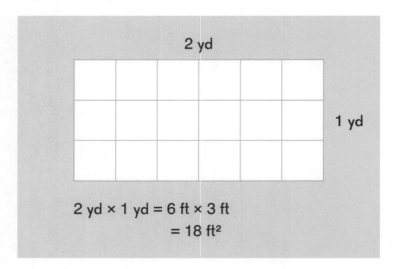

$$2 \text{ yd} \times 1 \text{ yd} = 6 \text{ ft} \times 3 \text{ ft}$$
$$= 18 \text{ ft}^2$$

Students will then be given side lengths in compound or fractional units and have to convert to smaller units of measurement to find the area or perimeter of a figure.

Composite Figures

Students will extend their practice with finding the area of composite rectilinear figures. Problems will include finding the area of a rectilinear path around a rectangle, and finding the area of compound rectilinear figures where some or all of the side lengths first need to be converted to single units.

For example, students will be asked to find the area of the red border shown below:

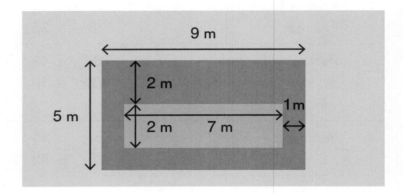

Two methods, outlined below, are taught.

Method 1

Find the total area of the large rectangle and subtract the area of the yellow rectangle.

Area of large rectangle $\longrightarrow 9 \times 5 = 45 \text{ m}^2$
Area of small rectangle $\longrightarrow 2 \times 7 = 14 \text{ m}^2$
Area of red border $\longrightarrow 45 - 14 = 31 \text{ m}^2$
The area of the red border is 31 m².

This method works well for figures with borders.

Method 2

Partition the rectangles into smaller rectangles:

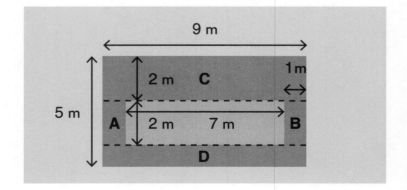

Area of Rectangle A ⟶ 2 × 1 = 2 m²
Area of Rectangle B ⟶ 2 × 1 = 2 m²
Area of Rectangle C ⟶ 2 × 9 = 18 m²
Area of Rectangle D ⟶ 1 × 9 = 9 m²
Total area ⟶ 2 + 2 + 18 + 9 = 31 m²

Note that students may partition a figure in different ways as long as they are covering all the area.

Students should understand that the underlying idea in both methods is to see rectangles in the figure and apply the area formula.

Areas can be added or subtracted as long as they are all expressed in the same unit. This is similar to calculations with other measurements such as length, liquid volume, weight, time, money, etc.

Perimeter

Lessons 4 and 5 develop perimeter concepts and formulas.

In Dimensions Math 3B, students learned two methods for finding the perimeter of a rectangle:

*   l + w + l + w = perimeter of four sides
*   l + w = two sides
    Sum of two sides × 2 = perimeter of all four sides

Students are not given a formula involving combined operations for finding perimeter — for example, 2 × L + 2 × W or 2 × (L + W) — because they have not yet formally learned the order of operations, which they will learn in Dimensions Math 5A.

Building on this understanding, students will find unknown side lengths, given the perimeter and length of one side.

Example:

The perimeter of a rectangular volleyball court is 54 m. What is the length of the unknown side?

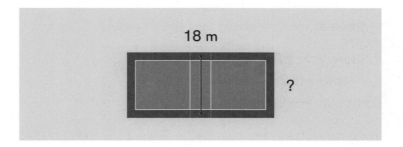

Method 1

2 × length ⟶ 2 × 18 = 36 m
2 × width ⟶ 54 − 36 = 18 m
Length of unknown side ⟶ 18 ÷ 2 = 9 m

Method 2

Length + width ⟶ 54 ÷ 2 = 27 m
Width ⟶ 27 − 18 = 9 m

The unknown side is 9 m long.

Finally, in Lesson 5, students will find perimeters of composite figures, and will discover that composite shapes with different areas can have the same perimeter.

The **Learn** Method 2 in Lesson 5 introduces a method for finding perimeter that involves "moving" or pushing out some of the sides.

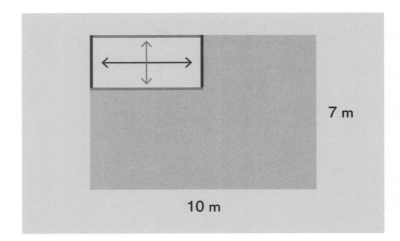

Removing square units from a corner does not change the perimeter. Removing square units from the middle (not along any corners) changes the perimeter.

If we push out the lengths of the sides to form a rectangle, we can easily find the perimeter:

$2 \times$ length $\longrightarrow 2 \times 10 = 20$ m
$2 \times$ width $\longrightarrow 2 \times 7 = 14$ m
Perimeter $\longrightarrow 20 + 14 = 34$ m

Imagine walking the perimeter. If we walk around the original figure or outer rectangle, we have walked the same distance up and down, and the same distance left and right, as we would have along a rectangle.

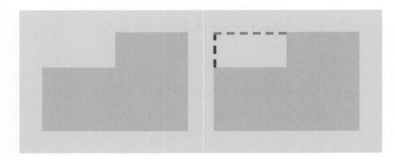

This is easy to show with toothpicks.

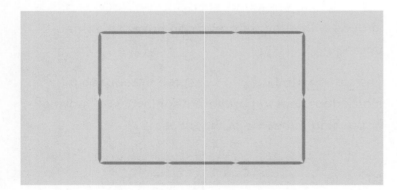

Students can make a rectangle and find the perimeter, then make other rectilinear figures using the same number of toothpicks. The perimeter is always the same:

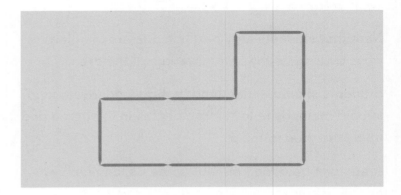

Perimeter of rectangle $\longrightarrow 3 + 2 + 3 + 2 = 10$ toothpicks
Perimeter of composite figure $\longrightarrow$
$3 + 2 + 1 + 1 + 2 + 1 = 10$ toothpicks

Materials

- 1-ft ruler
- 1-ft square papers
- Dry erase markers, 2 colors
- Dry erase sleeve
- Toothpicks
- Whiteboards
- Yardsticks

Blackline Masters

- Centimeter Graph Paper (BLM)
- Grid Paper (BLM)
- Number Cards (BLM)
- Pool and Patio (BLM)

Activities

Fewer games and activities are included in this chapter. The included activities can be used after students complete the **Do** questions, or anytime additional practice is needed.

Chapter Opener

Objective

- Investigate area and perimeter.

Lesson Materials

- 1-ft rulers

Discuss the different questions that the friends are asking. Students can answer Emma's question and find the area and the perimeter of the whiteboard.

Measure some objects in the classroom that have whole number measurements. If necessary, create some objects. For example, cut $\frac{1}{2}$ inch off the width of a sheet of paper so that it measures 8 in by 11 in. Make a list of the objects you find. Then have students measure some of the listed objects in the classroom and express the length and width in the same units. Continue to Lesson 1.

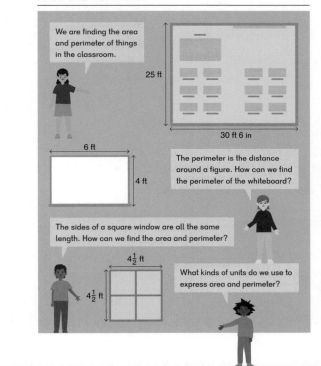

Lesson 1 Area of Rectangles — Part 1

Objective

- Find the area of a figure given the side lengths by converting units.

Lesson Materials

- 1-ft square papers, 11 per group of students
- Yardsticks, 8 per group of students

Think

Provide students with yardsticks and square papers and discuss the **Think** problem.

Discuss Sofia's comment. If needed, ask students:

- "In what units are the sheets of plywood given?" (yards)
- "In what units are the square tiles given?" (feet)
- "What do we need to do to express the plywood and the tiles in the same units?" (Convert yards to feet.)
- "What do we need to do to express the lengths of the plywood and the tiles in the same units?" (Convert yards to feet.)

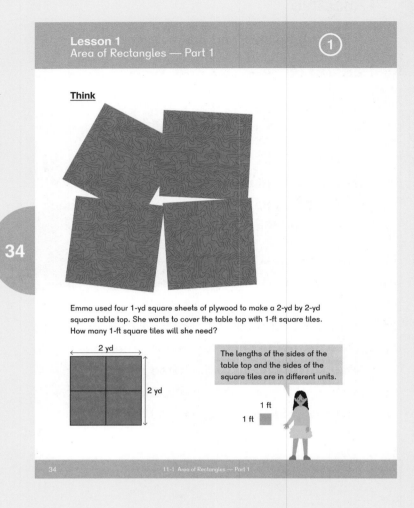

Think

34

Emma used four 1-yd square sheets of plywood to make a 2-yd by 2-yd square table top. She wants to cover the table top with 1-ft square tiles. How many 1-ft square tiles will she need?

2 yd

2 yd

The lengths of the sides of the table top and the sides of the square tiles are in different units.

1 ft

1 ft

Learn

Have students compare their solutions from **Think** with the ones shown in the textbook. Discuss the two methods shown.

Here the side lengths are given in yards and the final answer is to be expressed in feet. To help students understand this concept, have them lay out 8 yardsticks to make a square (2 yardsticks for each side). They can then lay the 1-ft square papers inside to see how many square feet are in each square yard.

Method 1

Ask students why Mei converts 2 yards to 6 feet first. She knows 1 yard is 3 feet, so 2 yards is 6 feet on each side. The area is 6 feet × 6 feet, or 36 square feet.

Method 2

Ask students how Dion's method is different from Mei's method. He finds the number of square feet in 1 square yard: 9. He multiplies that by the number of square yards in the square.

Do

1—**7** Discuss the problems and given examples with students.

1 If needed, have students imagine the square filled with 12 rows and 12 columns of 1-in tiles.

2 There are 100 centimeters in 1 meter, so the area of a square meter is equal to 100 cm × 100 cm, or 10,000 cm². Emma helps students think about 100 hundreds as 100,000.

3 Ask students why Alex suggests converting the compound units of length to feet. Converting measurements to the smaller unit is usually a more efficient problem solving strategy than converting to the larger unit. Students should see that converting to larger units will often result in fractional or mixed number measurements.

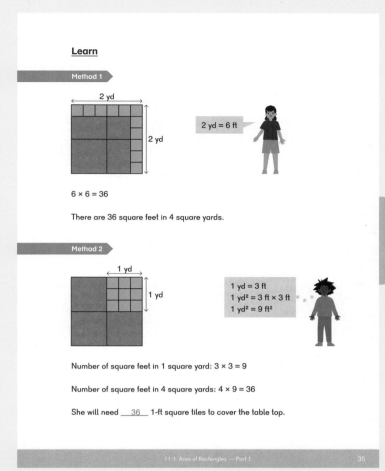

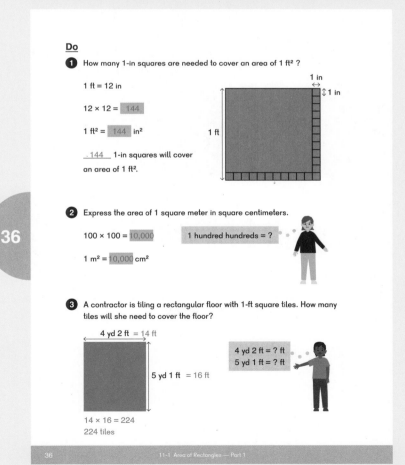

④—⑤ Ask students why we would want to express the side lengths in the same units. (Area is always in **square** units. So units have to be the same on both sides.)

Sofia and Dion remind students how to convert measurements so that the lengths of the sides are expressed in the same units.

⑥ Mei reminds students how to convert the measurement when it is expressed as a fraction.

⑦ Students may solve in a similar way as Method 2 in **Learn** by finding the area of one foot first:

$1 \text{ ft} \times 1 \text{ ft} = 12 \text{ in} \times 12 \text{ in} = 144 \text{ in}^2$

There are 4 feet per side, and that means 16 squares equal to 1 square foot.

$16 \times 144 = 2,304 \text{ in}^2$

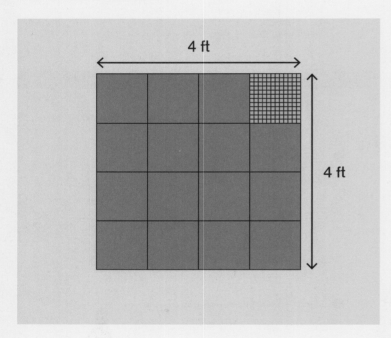

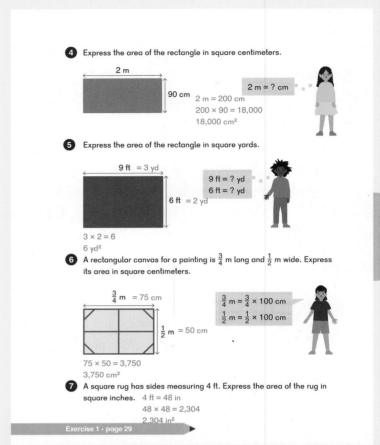

④ Express the area of the rectangle in square centimeters.

2 m
90 cm
2 m = ? cm
2 m = 200 cm
$200 \times 90 = 18,000$
$18,000 \text{ cm}^2$

⑤ Express the area of the rectangle in square yards.

9 ft = 3 yd
6 ft = 2 yd
9 ft = ? yd
6 ft = ? yd
$3 \times 2 = 6$
6 yd^2

⑥ A rectangular canvas for a painting is $\frac{3}{4}$ m long and $\frac{1}{2}$ m wide. Express its area in square centimeters.

$\frac{3}{4}$ m = 75 cm
$\frac{1}{2}$ m = 50 cm
$\frac{3}{4}$ m = $\frac{3}{4} \times 100$ cm
$\frac{1}{2}$ m = $\frac{1}{2} \times 100$ cm
$75 \times 50 = 3,750$
$3,750 \text{ cm}^2$

⑦ A square rug has sides measuring 4 ft. Express the area of the rug in square inches.
4 ft = 48 in
$48 \times 48 = 2,304$
$2,304 \text{ in}^2$

Exercise 1 • page 29

Exercise 1 • page 29

Objective

- Find the unknown side length of a rectangle given the area and one side length.

Lesson Materials

- Grid Paper (BLM)

Think

Pose the **Think** problem. If necessary, provide students with Grid Paper (BLM) and have them draw the floor of the rectangular room to help them see the unknown side length (each square on Grid Paper (BLM) represents 1 foot). To do this, students would add rows of 8 squares until they reached a total of 96, then count the number of rows.

Learn

Discuss Emma's comments. Help students see that they are solving a missing factor problem similar to their introduction to division: What multiplied by 4 equals 12? What length multiplied by 8 ft makes 96 ft²? This concept can be illustrated by giving students fewer square tiles than called for in the problem (for example, 24) and telling them to make a rectangle using all of the tiles, where the length of one side is 8. Next, show them that when you divide 24 by 8 you get the length of the other side. They can then think about the problem with 96 tiles.

Alex knows that area can be found by multiplying length by width.

Students have learned that the number in each group multiplied by the number of groups equals the total. Here, students are given a group, 8, and are asked to find how many groups of 8 make 96.

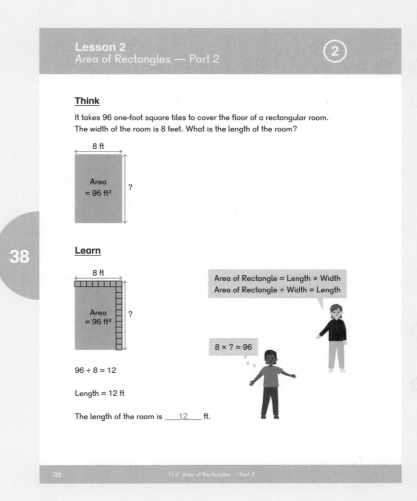

Do

1 — 3 Discuss the problems with students.

3 Ask students, "Are the square units given for the area the same as the units given for the length?"

(a) The area is given in square feet, but the side length is expressed in yards. Convert the length in yards to feet, and then find the unknown length.

(b) The area is given in square feet, and the length of the side is expressed in compound units. Convert the length from compound units to feet, and then find the unknown length.

4 — 7 Students should be able to work the problems independently.

6 Ask students, "How can we express the side lengths in the same unit?"

Since the square and the rectangle have the same area, we can first find the area of the square, then use that area to find the unknown side of the rectangle.

Since the rectangle and square have the same area, divide 64 in² by 4 in to find the length of the unknown side of the rectangle.

7 The area is given in square feet and the length in compound units. Before finding the width, convert the length of the garden from compound units to feet.

Exercise 2 • page 32

Do

1 Find the length of the rectangle.

144 cm²   6 cm

144 ÷ 6 = 24

Length = 24 cm

2 Find the unknown length.

(a) ?
180 ft²   6 ft
180 ÷ 6 = 30; 30 ft

(b) 7 m
105 m²   ?
105 ÷ 7 = 15; 15 m

(c) 9 cm
81 cm²   ?
81 ÷ 9 = 9; 9 cm

3 Find the unknown length in feet.

(a) 135 ft²   3 yd
?
3 yd = 9 ft
135 ÷ 9 = 15
15 ft

(b) 45 ft²   1 yd 2 ft
?
1 yd 2 ft = 5 ft
45 ÷ 5 = 9
9 ft

11-2 Area of Rectangles — Part 2   39

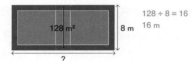

4 The area of a volleyball court is 128 m². The width of the court is 8 m. What is the length of the court?

128 m²   8 m
?
128 ÷ 8 = 16
16 m

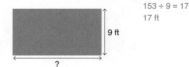

5 Emma's backyard is in the shape of a rectangle. It has an area of 153 ft² and a width of 9 ft. What is the length of her backyard?

9 ft
?
153 ÷ 9 = 17
17 ft

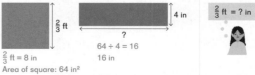

6 The square and the rectangle have the same area. Express the unknown length of the rectangle in inches.

$\frac{2}{3}$ ft   4 in
?
$\frac{2}{3}$ ft = ? in

64 ÷ 4 = 16
16 in
$\frac{2}{3}$ ft = 8 in
Area of square: 64 in²

7 The area of a rectangular garden is 72 ft². One side of the garden is 2 yd 2 ft. What is the length of the other side of the garden in feet?

2 yd 2 ft = 8 ft
72 ÷ 8 = 9
9 ft

Exercise 2 • page 32

40   11-2 Area of Rectangles — Part 2

Lesson 3 Area of Composite Figures

Objective

- Find the area of rectangular paths.

Lesson Materials

- Pool and Patio (BLM)

Think

Provide students with the Pool and Patio (BLM) and have them cut out the pool and patio. Pose the **Think** problem and have students use the cutouts to solve the problem.

Discuss student methods for finding the area of the patio.

Learn

Have students compare their solutions from **Think** with the ones shown in the textbook.

Discuss the two methods shown.

Method 1

Ask students why Dion's method will work.

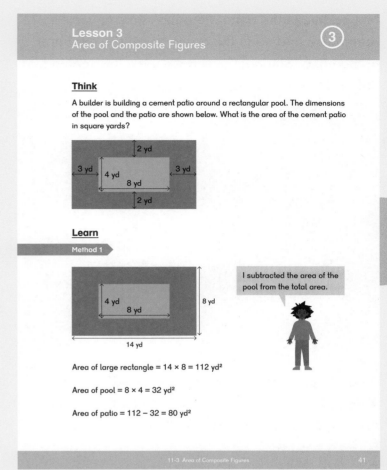

Mei partitions the concrete patio into smaller rectangles and adds the areas to get the total area of the patio. Students may have used this method, but partitioned the shape differently:

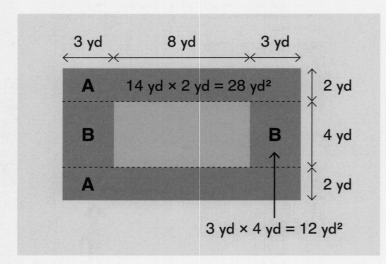

Area of Rectangle A $\longrightarrow$ 28 × 2 = 56 yd²
Area of Rectangle B $\longrightarrow$ 12 × 2 = 24 yd²
Area of Rectangle A + Rectangle B $\longrightarrow$
56 + 24 = 80 yd²
The area of the patio is 80 yd².

Ask students which method they found most efficient. Ensure students understand Method 1 as it will be applied in later grades with area of a triangle and other figures.

Emma prompts students to recall that to convert square yards to square feet we multiply by 9, not 3.

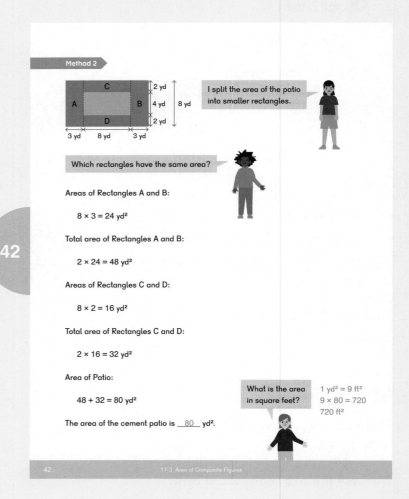

Do

❶—**❷** Discuss the problems and given examples with students.

❶ Ask students to recall Methods 1 and 2 in **Learn**. Sofia is thinking about both methods. Students may use either method to solve.

❷ The answer key shows one method to solve question (a). Students may find the area of the countertop using Method 2 in **Learn**. They can partition the countertop into two rectangles:

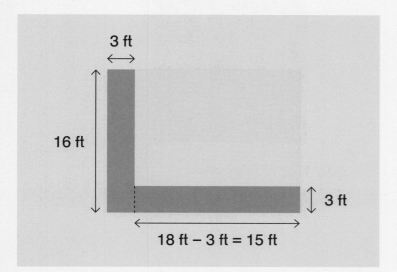

Area of left rectangle ⟶ 16 × 3 = 48 ft²

Area of bottom rectangle ⟶ 15 × 3 = 45 ft²

Total countertop area ⟶ 48 + 45 = 93 ft²

❸—**❻** Students should be able to solve the problems independently. They may use either method from **Learn** to solve the problems.

❸ Mei reminds students to convert each side measurement to inches before solving the problem.

❹ If students need additional help, ask them, "Are the lengths given in the same units?"

Do

❶ Some workers are replacing the grass around the school basketball court. How many square meters of sod will they need?

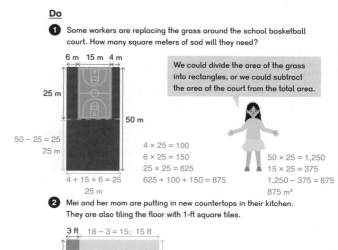

We could divide the area of the grass into rectangles, or we could subtract the area of the court from the total area.

50 − 25 = 25

4 + 15 + 6 = 25

4 × 25 = 100	50 × 25 = 1,250
6 × 25 = 150	15 × 25 = 375
25 × 25 = 625	1,250 − 375 = 875
625 + 100 + 150 = 875	875 m²

❷ Mei and her mom are putting in new countertops in their kitchen. They are also tiling the floor with 1-ft square tiles.

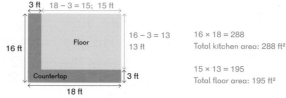

18 − 3 = 15; 15 ft

16 − 3 = 13
13 ft

16 × 18 = 288
Total kitchen area: 288 ft²

15 × 13 = 195
Total floor area: 195 ft²

(a) How many square feet of countertop do they need?
288 − 195 = 93; 93 ft²

(b) How many 1-ft square tiles do they need for the floor?
195 tiles

11-3 Area of Composite Figures   43

Methods may vary.

❸ The shape below is made of rectangles. Find the area of the shape in square inches.

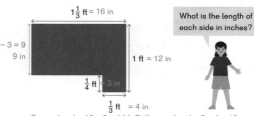

$1\frac{1}{3}$ ft = 16 in

What is the length of each side in inches?

12 − 3 = 9
9 in

1 ft = 12 in

$\frac{1}{4}$ ft = 3 in

$\frac{1}{3}$ ft = 4 in

Top rectangle: 16 × 9 = 144; Bottom rectangle: 3 × 4 = 12
144 + 12 = 156; 156 in²

❹ Dion's backyard has a rectangular patio with a lawn around it.

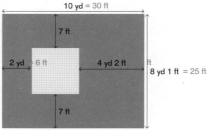

10 yd = 30 ft

7 ft

2 yd = 6 ft   4 yd 2 ft

8 yd 1 ft = 25 ft

7 ft

(a) What is the area of the patio in square feet?
25 − 7 − 7 = 11; 30 − 6 − 14 = 10; 11 × 10 = 110; 110 ft²

(b) What is the area of the lawn in square feet?
25 × 30 = 750
750 − 110 = 640
640 ft²

44   11-3 Area of Composite Figures

Teacher's Guide 4B Chapter 11

5 Ask students how this problem is different from the **Think** problem and prior **Do** questions. To find the total area of the wall, first find the unknown side length of the window by thinking, what number, multiplied by itself is equal to 9?

3 × 3 = 9, so the side of the window is 3 ft.

Then find the height of the wall: 2 ft + 3 ft + 3 ft = 8 ft.

The area of the whole wall including the window and the door is: 16 ft × 8 ft = 128 ft².

Ask students to think of another strategy to find the height of the room. If necessary, give them the hint that they can use the information given about the door. Then they could divide the area of the door, 21 ft², by its width, 3 ft, to find the height of the door, 7 ft. The 1 ft difference between the top of the door and the ceiling is given.

Subtract the areas of the window and door from the area of the whole wall to find the area of the wall to be painted: 128 ft² − 21 ft² − 9 ft² = 98 ft².

6 If necessary, help students by asking how many squares would fit into the green space in the picture. They should be able to visualize the area of one square as 64 cm² and the green paper as made up of 6 such squares. Then, to find the area of the green colored paper: 64 cm² × 6 = 384 cm².

Exercise 3 · page 35

---

5 A wall in a room has a square window and a door. Alex wants to paint the wall blue. How many square feet of the wall will he paint?

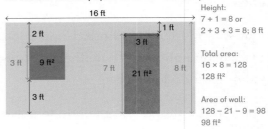

Height:
7 + 1 = 8 or
2 + 3 + 3 = 8; 8 ft

Total area:
16 × 8 = 128
128 ft²

Area of wall:
128 − 21 − 9 = 98
98 ft²

6 Mei glued 3 square pieces of red paper, each with an area of 64 cm², on a large sheet of paper and colored the rest of the paper green. What is the area of the paper that is colored green?

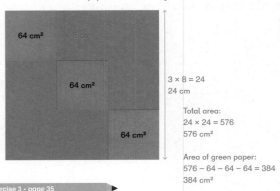

3 × 8 = 24
24 cm

Total area:
24 × 24 = 576
576 cm²

Area of green paper:
576 − 64 − 64 − 64 = 384
384 cm²

Exercise 3 · page 35

11-3 Area of Composite Figures   45

45

Lesson 4 Perimeter — Part 1

Objectives

- Find the perimeter of rectangles.
- Find the length of the unknown side of a rectangle given the length of one side and the perimeter.

Lesson Materials

- Toothpicks, 20 per student

Think

Pose the **Think** problem and have students try to solve the problem independently. Provide students with toothpicks to make a model of the garden, as needed. They should experiment until they find a way to use the 20 toothpicks to fully enclose a rectangular garden.

Learn

Have students compare their solutions from **Think** with the ones shown in the textbook. Discuss the two methods shown.

Method 1

Alex knows that the two lengths require 2 × 6 m = 12 m of fencing. That leaves 8 meters for the widths of the garden.

8 ÷ 2 = 4, so each width of the garden will require 4 meters of fencing.

Method 2

Sofia finds half of the perimeter of the garden.

If the sum of the width and the length is 10 m, and the length is 6 m, then the width must be 10 m − 6 m = 4 m. The garden will be 4 meters wide.

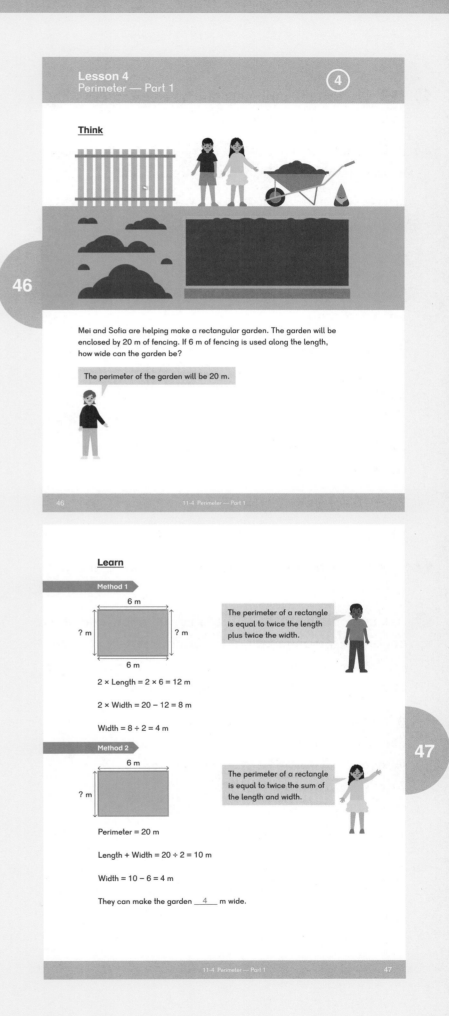

Do

①—**②** Discuss the problems and given examples with students as necessary.

② Ask students to look at (a) and (b) and determine which method from **Learn** each one is using.

Here students know the perimeter is 26 cm. They can divide that by 2 to find the combined length and width:

$26 \div 2 = 13$ cm

They can then subtract the given side to find the unknown side:

$13 - 5 = 8$ cm

Twice the width:

$2 \times 5 = 10$ cm

Subtract twice the width from the perimeter to find twice the length:

$26 - 10 = 16$ cm

Divide 16 cm by 2 to find the length.

③—**⑧** Students should be able to solve the problems independently.

⑤ Ask students how to find the length of each side of the square. If the perimeter of the square is 40 cm, then each side must be 40 cm $\div$ 4 = 10 cm long. The area of the square is 10 cm $\times$ 10 cm = 100 cm².

If the area of the two figures is the same, 100 cm², then the unknown side of the rectangle is 4 cm $\times$? = 100 cm² or 100 cm² $\div$ 4 cm = 25 cm.

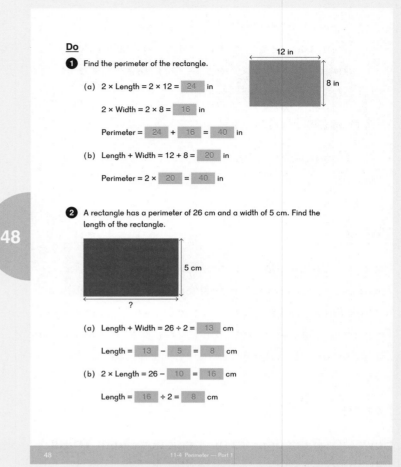

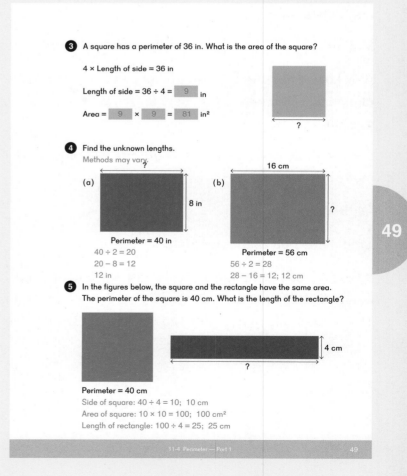

Teacher's Guide 4B Chapter 11

⑦ Ask students what they know about the lengths of opposite sides of a rectangle (they are the same). Ask them how they can figure out the length of two of the sides ($4\frac{1}{2}$ ft + $4\frac{1}{2}$ ft = 9 ft).

To find the two horizontal sides (or top and bottom) lengths, students can subtract 9 ft from the perimeter, 18 ft.

18 ft − 9 ft = 9 ft

Since the two horizontal sides also equal 9 ft, the painting must be a square. Students can see without calculating that all four sides must be $4\frac{1}{2}$ ft long.

(b) Convert the side of the painting to inches:

4 ft $\longrightarrow$ 4 × 12 in = 48 in
$\frac{1}{2}$ ft $\longrightarrow$ $\frac{1}{2}$ × 12 in = 6 in

⑧ Students should convert the length to inches to calculate, then convert the final length back to feet and inches.

Activity

★ Toothpick Puzzler

Materials: Toothpicks, 12 per student

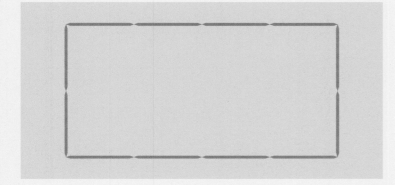

If each toothpick is 1 unit, the perimeter of this rectangle is 12 units and the area is 8 square units.

Make different polygons with the 12 toothpicks. What is the smallest area you can make with a perimeter of 12 units? What is the largest area?

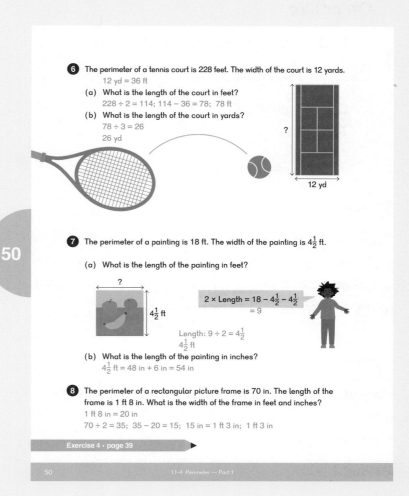

⑥ The perimeter of a tennis court is 228 feet. The width of the court is 12 yards.
12 yd = 36 ft
(a) What is the length of the court in feet?
228 ÷ 2 = 114; 114 − 36 = 78; 78 ft
(b) What is the length of the court in yards?
78 ÷ 3 = 26
26 yd

⑦ The perimeter of a painting is 18 ft. The width of the painting is $4\frac{1}{2}$ ft.
(a) What is the length of the painting in feet?
2 × Length = 18 − $4\frac{1}{2}$ − $4\frac{1}{2}$
= 9
Length: 9 ÷ 2 = $4\frac{1}{2}$
$4\frac{1}{2}$ ft
(b) What is the length of the painting in inches?
$4\frac{1}{2}$ ft = 48 in + 6 in = 54 in

⑧ The perimeter of a rectangular picture frame is 70 in. The length of the frame is 1 ft 8 in. What is the width of the frame in feet and inches?
1 ft 8 in = 20 in
70 ÷ 2 = 35; 35 − 20 = 15; 15 in = 1 ft 3 in; 1 ft 3 in

Exercise 4 · page 39

50   11-4 Perimeter — Part 1

50

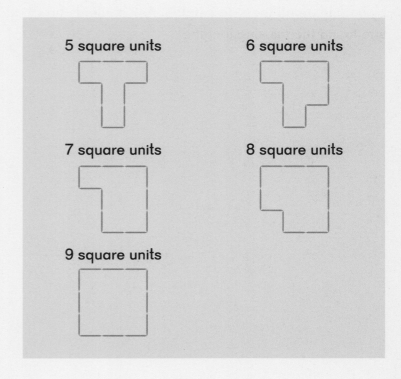

5 square units   6 square units

7 square units   8 square units

9 square units

Exercise 4 · page 39

Lesson 5 Perimeter — Part 2

Objective

- Find the perimeter of composite figures.

Lesson Materials

- Grid Paper (BLM)
- Toothpicks

Think

Pose the **Think** problem and have students try to solve the problem independently. Provide students with toothpicks to make the puppy pen, or Grid Paper (BLM) to draw it.

Learn

Have students compare their solutions from **Think** with the ones shown in the textbook. Discuss the two methods shown.

Method 1

Mei knows that she can find the perimeter of a figure by adding up all the side lengths. Ask students how she found the missing lengths.

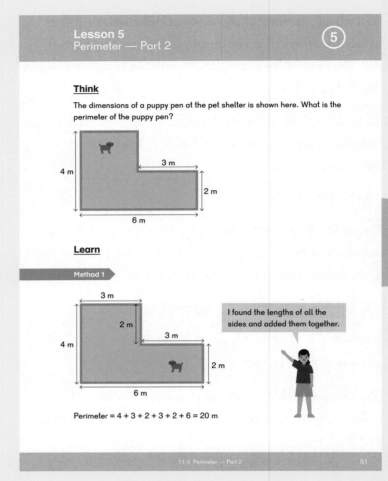

Think

The dimensions of a puppy pen at the pet shelter is shown here. What is the perimeter of the puppy pen?

4 m

3 m

2 m

6 m

Learn

Method 1

3 m

2 m

4 m

3 m

2 m

6 m

I found the lengths of all the sides and added them together.

Perimeter = 4 + 3 + 2 + 3 + 2 + 6 = 20 m

51

Method 2

Emma moves the two sides out. This allows her to find the perimeter using fewer calculations, since the perimeter is the same as the perimeter of a rectangle with side lengths of 4 m and 6 m.

To help students understand this, have them make the figure with toothpicks. Each toothpick represents 1 m. Have them move the toothpicks as shown in the textbook. Ask students, "What do you notice? Do you notice you have the same length on the top and the bottom?"

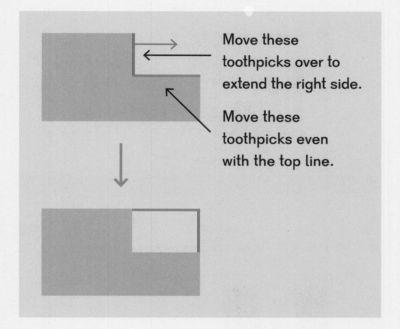

Move these toothpicks over to extend the right side.

Move these toothpicks even with the top line.

Using this method, students should see that the area changes, but the perimeter remains the same.

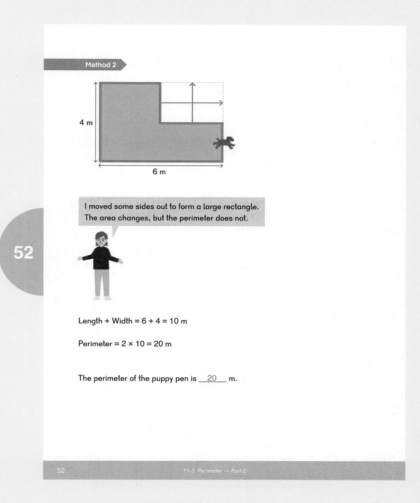

52

Do

1 — **4** Discuss the problems and given examples with students as necessary.

2 The answer key uses Method 2 from **Learn**. If students use Method 1 from **Learn**, the measurement of the left side would be:

$$5 - 2\frac{1}{2} = 2\frac{1}{2} \text{ ft}$$

The bottom side would be:

$$9 - 2\frac{1}{4} = 6\frac{3}{4} \text{ ft}$$

The measurement of the perimeter would be:

$$9 + 5 + 6\frac{3}{4} + 2\frac{1}{2} + 2\frac{1}{4} + 2\frac{1}{2} = 28 \text{ ft}$$

Alex asks students which method's calculations are easier. They should see that Method 2 results in fewer calculations.

3 Method 2 from **Learn** is further developed in this problem. Students are not able to determine the measurement of the right side of the figure, and will need to consider moving the sides out. Sofia's thought bubble gives the hint to do that.

4 Discuss the two methods that Dion and Emma use to solve the problem.

Ask students how Dion can find the measurement of the missing side length $(36 - 12 - 12 = 12)$. The missing pink length is 12 feet.

Ask students which two 12 ft sides Emma needs to add. They should see that the two pink sides are not included in her calculation of the perimeter of the large rectangle. She will need to add them to the perimeter.

5 Mei thinks of the entire figure as a rectangle and adds in two sides that have the length of 13 cm. If students struggle, allow them to draw the figure on graph paper to scale, and count the units of the perimeter.

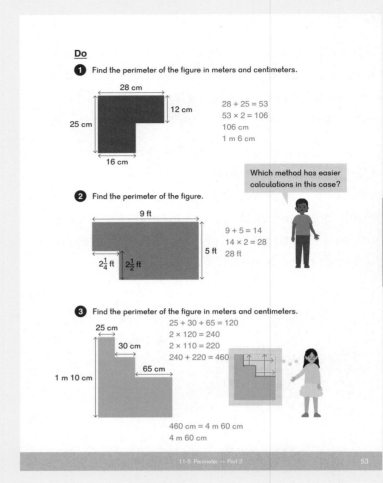

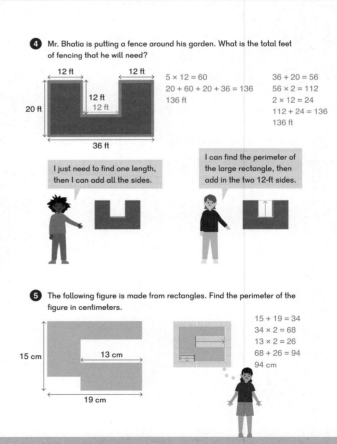

5 Encourage students to redraw and label the given lengths in the figure. Students should see that the strip of paper forming the back of the "E" overlaps with the three strips forming the horizontal parts.

If students think of the outline of the E as a rectangle, each side length is 15 in. The perimeter of the whole square is 15 in × 4 = 60 in. There are also the 4 lengths of 11 inches each (shown in red below), which must be added to find the perimeter of the figure.

Exercise 5 • page 42

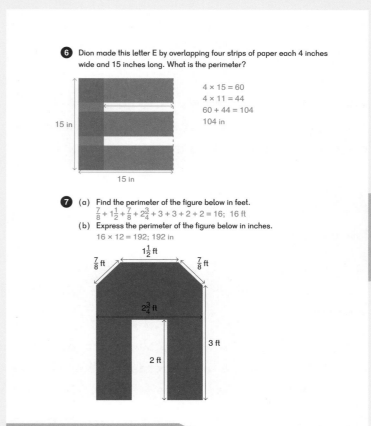

6 Dion made this letter E by overlapping four strips of paper each 4 inches wide and 15 inches long. What is the perimeter?

15 in

15 in

4 × 15 = 60
4 × 11 = 44
60 + 44 = 104
104 in

7 (a) Find the perimeter of the figure below in feet.
$\frac{7}{8} + 1\frac{1}{2} + \frac{7}{8} + 2\frac{3}{4} + 3 + 3 + 2 + 2 = 16$; 16 ft

(b) Express the perimeter of the figure below in inches.
16 × 12 = 192; 192 in

$1\frac{1}{2}$ ft

$\frac{7}{8}$ ft

$\frac{7}{8}$ ft

$2\frac{3}{4}$ ft

3 ft

2 ft

Exercise 5 • page 42

11-5 Perimeter — Part 2   55

Objective

- Practice finding area and perimeter.

After students complete the **Practice** in the textbook, have them continue to practice finding area and perimeter with activities from the chapter.

Activity

▲ Blockout

Materials: Centimeter Graph Paper (BLM) in a dry erase sleeve, Number Cards (BLM) 1–9, two colors of dry erase markers

Players take turns drawing two cards. On each turn, they add the numbers on the cards and then shade any equivalent area on the Centimeter Graph Paper (BLM).

In the example shown, Player 1 (blue) drew a 5 and a 1, and fenced an area of 6 square units.

He found the perimeter of his figure, 12 cm, and wrote it on his figure.

Player 2 (green) rolled a 6 and a 4, and fenced in 10 square units.

She found and recorded the perimeter of her figure.

When the graph paper is filled and players cannot add any more shaded areas, they add up the perimeters of their shaded areas. The winner is the player with the greatest total perimeter.

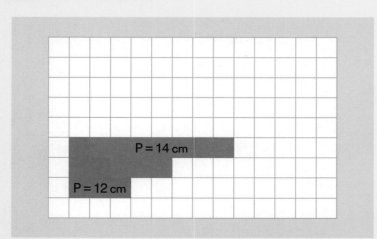

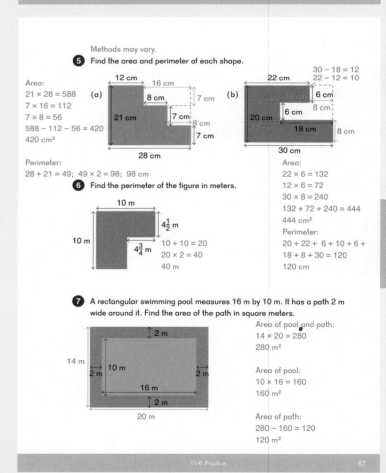

Lesson 6
Practice   P ⑥

① How many square feet are in a 2-yard square?

2 yd = 6 ft
$6 \times 6 = 36$
36 ft²

② Express the area of the rectangle in square feet.

5 yd 1 ft = 16 ft
3 yd 2 ft = 11 ft
$16 \times 11 = 176$
176 ft²

③ The rectangle has a perimeter of 40 in. Find the area of the rectangle.

6 in
$40 \div 2 = 20$
$20 - 6 = 14$
Length: 14 in
$6 \times 14 = 84$
Area: 84 in²

④ Find the perimeter of each rectangle.

(a) 9 cm, Area = 63 cm²
$63 \div 9 = 7$
$7 + 9 = 16$
$2 \times 16 = 32; \ 32$ cm

(b) 2 yd 1 ft = 7 ft, Area = 42 ft²
$42 \div 7 = 6$
$6 + 7 = 13$
$2 \times 13 = 26; \ 26$ ft

56

Methods may vary.

⑤ Find the area and perimeter of each shape.

(a) 12 cm, 16 cm, 8 cm, 7 cm, 21 cm, 7 cm, 8 cm, 7 cm, 28 cm

Area:
$21 \times 28 = 588$
$7 \times 16 = 112$
$7 \times 8 = 56$
$588 - 112 - 56 = 420$
420 cm²

Perimeter:
$28 + 21 = 49; \ 49 \times 2 = 98; \ 98$ cm

(b) 22 cm, $30 - 18 = 12$, $22 - 12 = 10$, 10 cm, 6 cm, 20 cm, 6 cm, 8 cm, 12 cm, 18 cm, 8 cm, 30 cm

Area:
$22 \times 6 = 132$
$12 \times 6 = 72$
$30 \times 8 = 240$
$132 + 72 + 240 = 444$
444 cm²

Perimeter:
$20 + 22 + 6 + 10 + 6 +$
$18 + 8 + 30 = 120$
120 cm

⑥ Find the perimeter of the figure in meters.

10 m, $4\frac{1}{2}$ m, 10 m, $4\frac{3}{4}$ m
$10 + 10 = 20$
$20 \times 2 = 40$
40 m

⑦ A rectangular swimming pool measures 16 m by 10 m. It has a path 2 m wide around it. Find the area of the path in square meters.

2 m, 14 m, 2 m, 10 m, 2 m, 16 m, 2 m, 20 m

Area of pool and path:
$14 \times 20 = 280$
280 m²

Area of pool:
$10 \times 16 = 160$
160 m²

Area of path:
$280 - 160 = 120$
120 m²

57

Brain Works

★ Greatest and Least Perimeter

Find the least and greatest possible perimeters of a rectangle with an area of 96 square units.

Hint: Students can think of the factor pairs of 96 (shown below).

1×96

2×48

3×32

4×24

6×16

8×12

Which of these will result in the least and greatest perimeters?

Students can find twice the length + width:

$1 \times 96 \longrightarrow 2 \times 97 = 194$ Greatest perimeter

$2 \times 48 \longrightarrow 2 \times 50 = 100$

$3 \times 32 \longrightarrow 2 \times 35 = 70$

$4 \times 24 \longrightarrow 2 \times 28 = 56$

$6 \times 16 \longrightarrow 2 \times 22 = 44$

$8 \times 12 \longrightarrow 2 \times 20 = 40$ Least perimeter

Exercise 6 • page 45

---

8 This garden shown below has a rock garden in the center and a flower garden around the rock garden. What is the area of the flower garden in square feet?

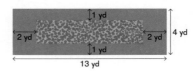

$13 \times 4 = 52$
$9 \times 2 = 18$
$52 - 18 = 34$
34 yd^2

$1 \text{ yd}^2 = 9 \text{ ft}^2$
$34 \times 9 = 306$
306 ft^2

9 Find the perimeter of the figure in centimeters.

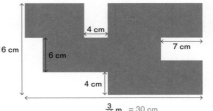

$16 + 30 = 46$
$46 \times 2 = 92$
$92 + 6 + 6 + 7 + 7 = 118$
118 cm

10 Alex made a cardboard stop sign for a game. Each side of the octagon is $1\frac{1}{2}$ ft long. The length of the handle is $2\frac{1}{2}$ ft and the width is $\frac{1}{2}$ ft. What is the perimeter of the whole sign, including the handle, in inches?

Perimeter of sign: $18 \times 8 = 144$

Perimeter of handle: $30 + 6 = 36$; $36 \times 2 = 72$

Overlapping perimeter: $6 \times 2 = 12$

Total perimeter: $144 + 72 - 12 = 204$

204 in

$1\frac{1}{2}$ ft = 18 in

$2\frac{1}{2}$ ft = 30 in

$\frac{1}{2}$ ft = 6 in

Exercise 6 • page 45

58   11-6 Practice

Chapter 11 Area and Perimeter

Exercise 1

Basics

1 Express the area of the rectangle in square inches.

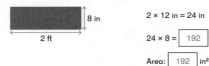

2×12 in $= 24$ in

$24 \times 8 =$ 192

Area: 192 in²

2 Express the area of the rectangle in square centimeters.

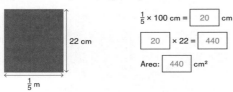

$\frac{1}{5} \times 100$ cm $=$ 20 cm

20 $\times 22 =$ 440

Area: 440 cm²

3 Express the area of the square in square feet.

1 yd 1 ft = 4 ft

$4 \times 4 =$ 16

Area: 16 ft²

Practice

4 Express the area of each rectangle in square centimeters.

(a)

$\frac{1}{10}$ m $= 10$ cm

$\frac{1}{4}$ m $= 25$ cm

$25 \times 10 = 250$

250 cm²

(b)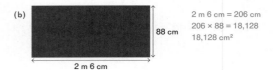

2 m 6 cm = 206 cm

$206 \times 88 = 18{,}128$

18,128 cm²

5 A rectangular piece of cardboard is $1\frac{1}{3}$ ft long. It is half as wide as it is long.

(a) Express the length in inches.

$1\frac{1}{3}$ ft = 16 in

(b) Express the area in square inches.

$\frac{1}{2} \times 16 = 8$

$16 \times 8 = 128$

128 in²

6 A room is 3 yards long and $2\frac{2}{3}$ yd wide. How many 1-ft square tiles are needed to cover the floor?

3 yd = 9 ft

$2\frac{2}{3}$ yd = 8 ft

$9 \times 8 = 72$

72 ft²

72 tiles

Challenge

7 A rectangular piece of cardboard is 3 ft 11 in long and 2 ft 4 in wide. What is the maximum number of 5 in by 8 in rectangles that can be cut from it?

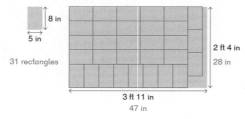

31 rectangles

2 ft 4 in
28 in

3 ft 11 in
47 in

Exercise 2

Basics

1 The area of a rectangle is 126 cm². One side is 9 cm long. How long is the other side?

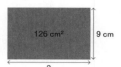

$9 \times \boxed{14} = 126$

$? = \boxed{14}$ cm

2 The area of a rectangle is 104 in². One side is $\frac{2}{3}$ ft long. How long is the other side in inches?

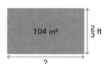

$\frac{2}{3} \times 12 \text{ in} = \boxed{8}$ in

$104 \div \boxed{8} = \boxed{13}$

$? = \boxed{13}$ in

3 The area of a square is 25 cm². What is the length of one side?

$? \times ? = 25$

$? = \boxed{5}$ cm

Practice

4 The area of a rectangle is 112 m². One side is 8 m long. How long is the other side?

$112 \div 8 = 14$
14 m

5 Both rectangles below have the same area. What is the unknown length? Express the answer in inches.

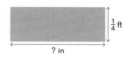

$\frac{1}{3}$ ft = 4 in
$\frac{1}{2}$ ft = 6 in
$4 \times 6 = 24$
Area: 24 in²

$\frac{1}{4}$ ft = 3 in
$24 \div 3 = 8$
8 in

6 It costs $8 per square foot to carpet a room. The total cost to carpet the room is $336. If one side of the room is 6 ft long, what is the length of the other side of the room?
$336 \div 8 = 42$
$42 \div 6 = 7$
7 ft

Challenge

7 This figure is made up of 8 squares. The total area of this figure is 288 cm². What is the length of the side of one square?

$288 \div 8 = 36$
Area of each square is 36 cm², so one side of the square is 6 cm.

8 Both rectangles below have the same area. What is the unknown length? Express the answer in centimeters and millimeters.

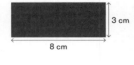

$3 \times 8 = 24$
Area: 24 cm²

$24 \div 5 = \frac{24}{5} = 4\frac{4}{5}$
$\frac{4}{5} \times 10 \text{ mm} = 8 \text{ mm}$
$4\frac{4}{5}$ cm = 4 cm 8 mm
4 cm 8 mm

Exercise 3

Basics

1 There are 3 identical pieces of paper. A square corner is cut from the first piece of paper.

(a) Complete the table.

Rectangle	Area
A	110 cm²
B	24 cm²
C	16 cm²

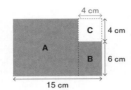

(b) Find the area of the remaining piece of paper by adding areas A and B.
110 + 24 = 134
134 cm²

(c) Find the area of the paper before it was cut.
15 × 10 = 150
150 cm²

(d) Find the area of the remaining piece of paper by subtracting area C from the area of the paper before it was cut.
150 − 16 = 134
134 cm²

(e) A 4-cm square is cut from the other two pieces of paper as shown. What is the area of each remaining piece of paper?

134 cm²

2 Find the unknown lengths. Then find the area of the shaded part of the rectangle.

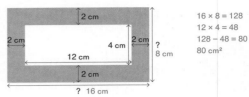

16 × 8 = 128
12 × 4 = 48
128 − 48 = 80
80 cm²

Practice

3 Find the area of each figure.   Methods may vary.

(a)
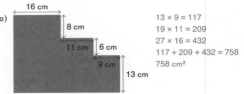

13 × 9 = 117
19 × 11 = 209
27 × 16 = 432
117 + 209 + 432 = 758
758 cm²

(b)
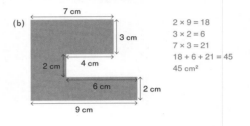

2 × 9 = 18
3 × 2 = 6
7 × 3 = 21
18 + 6 + 21 = 45
45 cm²

4 What is the area of the shaded part of the figure in square inches?

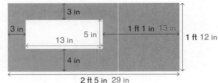

29 × 12 = 348
13 × 5 = 65
348 − 65 = 283
283 in²

5 A rectangular field is 13 m long and 10 m wide. It has a cement path 3½ m wide around it. What is the area of the cement path in square meters?

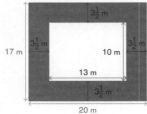

17 × 20 = 340
13 × 10 = 130
340 − 130 = 210
210 m²

Challenge

6 The figure is made up of five overlapping squares, each with an area of 80 cm². The total area of the shaded parts is 360 cm². Find the area of each of the smaller, unshaded squares.

Area of 5 squares:
80 × 5 = 400
400 cm²

Area of each smaller, unshaded square:
400 − 360 = 40
40 ÷ 4 = 10
10 cm²

Exercise 4

Basics

1 The perimeter of a rectangle is 40 cm. One side is 7 cm long. What is the length of the other side?

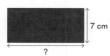
7 cm
?

2 × Width = 2 × 7 = $\boxed{14}$ cm

2 × Length = 40 − $\boxed{14}$ = $\boxed{26}$ cm

Length = $\boxed{26}$ ÷ 2 = $\boxed{13}$ cm

2 The perimeter of a rectangle is 160 cm. One side is 45 cm long. How long is the other side?

?
45 cm

Length + Width = 160 ÷ 2 = $\boxed{80}$ cm

Width = $\boxed{80}$ − 45 = $\boxed{35}$ cm

3 A square has a perimeter of 136 cm. What is the length of one side of the square?

?

Side = 136 ÷ 4 = $\boxed{34}$ cm

Practice

4 Complete the table.

Rectangle	Area	Length	Width	Perimeter
A	180 cm²	15 cm	12 cm	54 cm
B	120 cm²	12 cm	10 cm	44 cm
C	500 cm²	10 cm	50 cm	120 cm
D	198 cm²	22 cm	9 cm	62 cm
E	2,430 cm²	54 cm	45 cm	198 cm

5 The perimeter of a rectangle is 8 ft 8 in. Its width is 1 ft 9 in. Express its length in feet and inches.

1 ft 9 in
21 in
?

8 ft 8 in = 104 in
2 × 21 = 42
104 − 42 = 62
62 ÷ 2 = 31
31 in = 2 ft 7 in
2 ft 7 in

6 Evan ran around a rectangular field twice. He ran a total distance of 1 km 620 m. The width of the field is 195 m. What is the length of the field?
1 km 620 m = 1,620 m
1,620 ÷ 2 = 810
195 × 2 = 390
810 − 390 = 420
420 ÷ 2 = 210
210 m

7 A square 1 ft long and a rectangle 8 in wide have the same perimeter. What is the length of the rectangle?
Perimeter: 4 × 1 ft = 4 ft = 48 in
8 × 2 = 16
48 − 16 = 32
32 ÷ 2 = 16
16 in or 1 ft 4 in

Challenge

8 The figure is made up of 3 identical rectangles. The area of the whole figure is 216 cm². What is the perimeter of the whole figure?

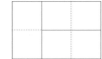

The figure can be divided into 6 squares.
216 ÷ 6 = 36
The side of each square is 6 cm.

Perimeter:
10 × 6 = 60
60 cm

Teacher's Guide 4B Chapter 11

Exercise 5

Basics

1 (a) Find the perimeter of each figure by adding all the side lengths.

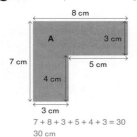

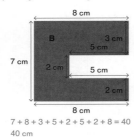

7 + 8 + 3 + 5 + 4 + 3 = 30
30 cm

7 + 8 + 3 + 5 + 2 + 5 + 2 + 8 = 40
40 cm

(b) Compare the perimeters of Figures A and B to Rectangle C. What do you notice? Use this knowledge to find the perimeter of Figure D.

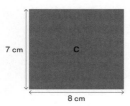

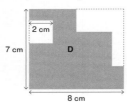

7 + 8 + 7 + 8 = 30
Figure A has the same perimeter as Rectangle C.
Figure B's perimeter is 10 cm more, which is the sum of the lengths of the two sides of the cut out part.

30 + 2 + 2 = 34

Perimeter of Figure D: 34 cm

Practice

2 The sides of the figures are marked in units. Find all the sets of figures that have equal perimeters.   A, D, and G; B and H; E and F

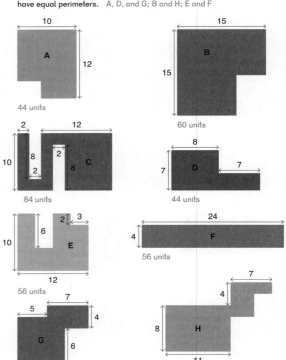

3 Each step of this staircase has the same length and height as the first step. What is the perimeter of the figure?

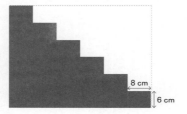

6 × 8 = 48
6 × 6 = 36
48 + 36 = 84
84 × 2 = 168
168 cm

Challenge

4 Each rectangle is 4 in long and has an area of 8 in². What is the perimeter of the figure?

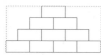

Height of each rectangle:
8 ÷ 4 = 2
2 in

Perimeter:
16 + 16 + 8 + 8 = 48
48 in

Exercise 6

Check

1 It costs $12 per square foot to carpet a room. The perimeter of the room is 54 ft and one side of the room is 15 ft. How much will it cost to carpet the room?

$54 - 15 - 15 = 24$

$24 \div 2 = 12$

Width:
12 ft

Area:
$12 \times 15 = 180$
180 ft²

$180 \times 12 = 2,160$
$2,160

2 A rectangular beach towel is 1 m 10 cm long and 90 cm wide. It has a border that is 3 cm wide around it. What is the area of the border?

1 m 10 cm
110 cm

90 cm

$110 \times 90 = 9,900$
$104 \times 84 = 8,736$
$9,900 - 8,736 = 1,164$
1,164 cm²

3 Amanda has a poster board that is 3 ft long by 2 ft wide. She cuts out 4 identical squares from each corner with sides measuring $\frac{1}{2}$ ft. Find the area of the remaining piece of poster board in square inches and the perimeter in inches.

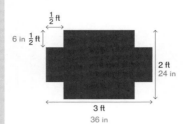

$\frac{1}{2}$ ft

6 in $\frac{1}{2}$ ft

2 ft
24 in

3 ft
36 in

$36 \times 24 = 864$
$6 \times 6 = 36$
$36 \times 4 = 144$
$864 - 144 = 720$
Area: 720 in²

$36 + 36 + 24 + 24 = 120$
Perimeter: 120 in

4 Jamal has a poster board that is 36 cm by 20 cm. He cuts out 3 squares from one side. The largest square is 8 cm long. Find the area and perimeter of the remaining piece of poster board.

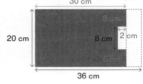

30 cm

20 cm

8 cm 2 cm

36 cm

$36 \times 20 = 720$
$6 \times 6 = 36$
$36 \times 2 = 72$
$8 \times 8 = 64$
$720 - 72 - 64 = 584$
Area: 584 cm²

$30 + 30 + 20 + 20 + 2 + 2 = 104$
Perimeter: 104 cm

5 Ivy has a poster board 3 ft long and 2 ft wide. She glues a rectangular picture in the middle that is 3 inches from each width and 4 inches from each length. What is the area of the picture?

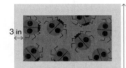

3 in

2 ft

2 ft = 24 in
Width:
$24 - 8 = 16$
16 in

3 ft = 36 in
Length:
$36 - 6 = 30$
30 in

Area: $16 \times 30 = 480$
480 in²

6 This figure is made of triangles with all three sides of equal length. The perimeter of each triangle is 2 ft. What is the perimeter of the figure? Express the answer in feet and inches.

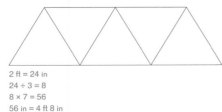

2 ft = 24 in
$24 \div 3 = 8$
$8 \times 7 = 56$
56 in = 4 ft 8 in

Challenge

7 Aaron glued 4 identical strips of paper to form a square. The perimeter of each rectangular strip of paper is 20 cm. What is the area of the larger square formed?

length + width of rectangle = side of larger square
$20 \div 2 = 10$
$10 \times 10 = 100$
100 cm²

8 A 40 cm by 50 cm rectangular flag is painted with 3 stripes, each 5 cm wide. What is the area of the parts that are not painted?

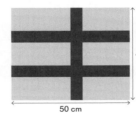

40 cm

50 cm

If the shaded parts are removed and the remaining parts pushed together, the figure will be a rectangle.

$40 - 5 - 5 = 30$
$50 - 5 = 45$
$30 \times 45 = 1,350$
1,350 cm²

Notes

Suggested number of class periods: 10–11

	Lesson	Page	Resources		Objectives
	Chapter Opener	p. 75	TB:	p. 59	Investigate decimals.
1	Tenths — Part 1	p. 76	TB: WB:	p. 60 p. 49	Understand the meaning of decimals to tenths. Express fractions in tenths as a decimal. Express one-place decimals as fractions.
2	Tenths — Part 2	p. 81	TB: WB:	p. 66 p. 52	Express mixed numbers in tenths as one-place decimals. Express one-place decimals greater than 1 as mixed numbers in tenths. Represent decimals on a number line.
3	Hundredths — Part 1	p. 84	TB: WB:	p. 72 p. 56	Interpret two-place decimals less than 1. Express hundredths less than 1 as a decimal. Express two-place decimals less than 1 as a fraction in hundredths.
4	Hundredths — Part 2	p. 88	TB: WB:	p. 77 p. 59	Express mixed numbers in hundredths as two-place decimals. Express two-place decimals greater than 1 as mixed numbers in hundredths. Express a decimal number to hundredths as the sum of place values in expanded form.
5	Expressing Decimals as Fractions in Simplest Form	p. 92	TB: WB:	p. 83 p. 63	Express decimals as fractions in simplest form.
6	Expressing Fractions as Decimals	p. 94	TB: WB:	p. 86 p. 66	Express common fractions and mixed numbers with a denominator that is a factor of 10 or 100 as a decimal.
7	Practice A	p. 96	TB: WB:	p. 89 p. 68	Practice concepts from the chapter.
8	Comparing and Ordering Decimals	p. 97	TB: WB:	p. 91 p. 70	Compare and order decimals to hundredths.
9	Rounding Decimals	p. 100	TB: WB:	p. 96 p. 73	Round decimals given in tenths to the nearest whole number.
10	Practice B	p. 104	TB: WB:	p. 102 p. 76	Practice concepts from the chapter.
	Workbook Solutions	p. 106			

In Dimensions Math 2B and 3B, students were introduced to two-place decimal representations informally through calculations with money. In this chapter, decimals are formally introduced.

Students will begin by learning that the decimal system can be extended to values less than 1 by seeing that the digit to the right of the decimal point is one tenth of the value of the same digit if it were in the ones place.

Just as there are places to the left of ones in a place-value chart, there are places to the right. We separate numbers to the right of the ones place with a decimal point. Numbers with digits following a decimal point are called decimals.

On a place-value chart, the value of the digit in each place is 10 times the value of the digit if it were one place to the right and one tenth the value of the digit if it were one place to the left.

Hundreds	Tens	Ones	Tenths	Hundredths
			× 10	× 10
	× 10	× 10		
× 10	× 10			

Hundreds	Tens	Ones	Tenths	Hundredths
÷ 10	÷ 10			
	÷ 10	÷ 10		
		÷ 10	÷ 10	

In Dimensions Math 4B, students will work with numbers to the hundredths place. Decimals less than 1 will always have the zero in the ones place for clarity.

Two forms of reading decimals are used in the chapter.

Example: 0.3

When we read 0.3 as "three-tenths," we see that decimals are also another notation for fractions. Students can initially read a decimal number, at least to hundredths, as a fraction to emphasize the place-value system. Eventually, they will learn that this way of reading a decimal will become cumbersome as decimal places extend to 4 places and beyond.

Example: Round 23.65 to the nearest tenth.

Saying aloud, "the number twenty-three and sixty-five hundredths is between twenty-three and six tenths and twenty-three and seven tenths" is difficult. Instead, it is easier to simply list digits. "Twenty-three point six five is between twenty-three point six and twenty-three point seven." Ensure that students have a clear understanding of place value before having them read decimals this second way.

Representing Decimals

Decimals will be visually represented in a variety of ways. This chapter will represent decimals using hundred grids, place-value charts, and number lines.

Example: 1.34

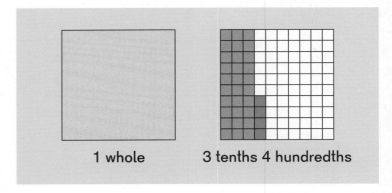

1 whole   3 tenths 4 hundredths

Using hundredths grids, students can easily see that:

$$1.34 = 1 + \frac{3}{10} + \frac{4}{100}$$

Place value representations will also be used. This representation is more abstract and emphasizes that decimals are simply an extension of the decimal system. This emphasis connects students' understanding of calculating with whole numbers to calculating with decimals.

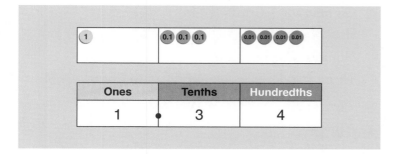

Finally, students will represent a decimal as a point on a number line, as demonstrated below.

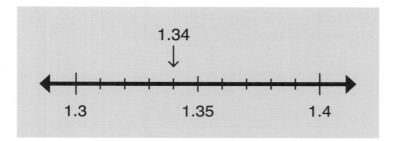

Understanding Decimals as Fractions with Denominators of 10 or 100

Lessons 1 and 2 introduce tenths. Students will express decimals as equivalent fractions with denominators of 10 and fractions with a denominator of 10 as equivalent decimals.

They will also express improper fractions and mixed numbers with denominators of 10 as decimals.

Lessons 3 and 4 follow a similar sequence with hundredths. Students will write numbers in expanded form and show the place values of each digit:

$$3 + \frac{7}{10} + \frac{8}{100} = 3 + \frac{70}{100} + \frac{8}{100} = 3\frac{78}{100} = 3.78$$

Students will use their knowledge of equivalent fractions to rewrite common fractions as fractions with denominators of 10 or 100, and then rewrite them as decimals.

Students will also learn how to express decimals as fractions in tenths or hundredths and then simplify. All denominators at this level will be factors of 100: 1, 2, 4, 5, 10, 20, 25, 50, 100. Students will practice finding equivalent fractions with a denominator of 10 or 100.

Examples:

$$0.8 = \frac{8}{10} \xrightarrow{\div 2} = \frac{4}{5} \xleftarrow{\div 2}$$

$$\frac{4}{25} \xrightarrow{\times 4} = \frac{16}{100} \xleftarrow{\times 4} = 0.16$$

We can always find an equivalent fraction by multiplying the numerator and denominator by another ten: $0.3 = \frac{3}{10} = \frac{30}{100} = 0.30$. We can think of 0.30 as appending this "extra" zero after the decimal digit 0.3. We are not "adding" a zero.

Comparing and Rounding

In Lesson 8, students will formally compare decimals by looking at the digits in each place.

In Dimensions Math 3A and 4A, students learned to round whole numbers to a specific place by looking at the digit one place to the right. They also learned by convention that if that digit is less than 5, they round down, and if it is 5 or greater, they round up. Similarly, students will learn that to round a decimal to a whole number, they look at the value of the digit in the tenths place, and to round a decimal to the nearest tenth, they look at the value of the digit in the hundredths place.

First, students will locate the decimal on a number line and see which whole number it is closest to.

To round to the nearest whole number, students look at the digit in the tenths place:

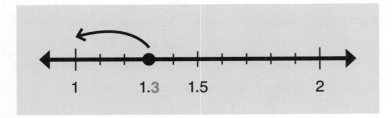

To round to the nearest tenth, students will look at the digit in the hundredths place:

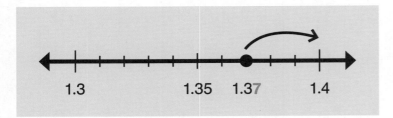

Materials

- 1-ft paper strips
- Brown paper bag
- Counters
- Deck of cards
- Dry erase markers, 2 colors
- Dry erase sleeve
- Meter sticks
- Newspaper Advertising Circulars
- Place-value cards
- Place-value discs
- Whiteboards

Blackline Masters

- Blank Hundredths Grid (BLM)
- Decimal and Fraction Number Line (BLM)
- Decimal Battle Mat (BLM)
- Decimal Match Cards (BLM)
- Fraction Match Cards (BLM)
- Go Fish for 1 Cards (BLM)
- Hex Board (BLM)
- Number Cards (BLM)
- Three in a Row — Round It Game Board (BLM)

Activities

Games and activities included in this chapter are designed to provide practice with understanding and comparing decimals. The included activities can be used after students complete the **Do** questions, or anytime additional practice is needed.

Chapter Opener

Objective

- Investigate decimals

Discuss Emma's question.

Activity

▲ Decimal Hunt

Materials: Newspaper Advertising Circulars

Provide students with different newspaper advertising circulars and have them look for numbers that have a dot in them. These are called decimals. Challenge them to find decimals other than prices for items. Examples might include stock prices and sports averages.

Objectives

- Understand the meaning of decimals to tenths.
- Express fractions in tenths as a decimal.
- Express one-place decimals as fractions.

Lesson Materials

- Decimal and Fraction Number Line (BLM)
- Place-value discs: ones and tenths
- Place-value cards: ones and tenths

Think

Have students answer the **Think** problems. They should write the answers for (a)–(c) as fractions.

Learn

Ask students the following questions while recording the equivalences on the board:

- "How many tens are in 1 hundred?" (10 tens)
- "How many ones are in 1 ten?" (10 ones)

Explain to students that just as 10 tens make 1 hundred, and 10 ones make 1 ten, 10 somethings make 1 one. Students should be able to solve this by recalling what they learned about fractions: $\frac{1}{10}$ (one tenth).

Suggest to students that we need a new place. On the board, draw a place-value chart with places from the ones to the hundreds. Add a decimal point and then the tenths place to the right.

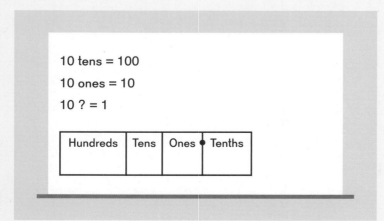

10 tens = 100

10 ones = 10

10 ? = 1

Hundreds	Tens	Ones	Tenths

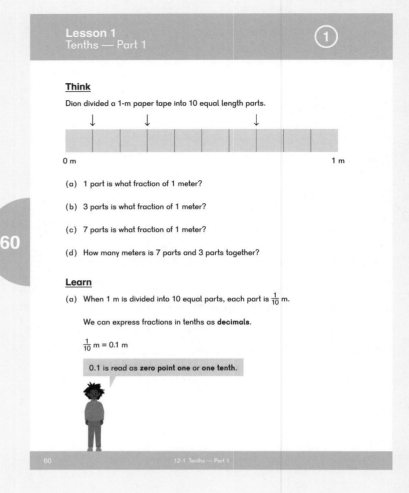

Lesson 1
Tenths — Part 1

1

Think

Dion divided a 1-m paper tape into 10 equal length parts.

0 m   1 m

(a) 1 part is what fraction of 1 meter?

(b) 3 parts is what fraction of 1 meter?

(c) 7 parts is what fraction of 1 meter?

(d) How many meters is 7 parts and 3 parts together?

Learn

(a) When 1 m is divided into 10 equal parts, each part is $\frac{1}{10}$ m.

We can express fractions in tenths as **decimals**.

$\frac{1}{10}$ m = 0.1 m

0.1 is read as **zero point one** or **one tenth**.

60   12-1 Tenths — Part 1

Explain that just as there are places to the left of ones to represent numbers greater than one, there are places to the right of one that represent numbers less than one. We separate numbers to the right of the ones place with a decimal point.

Introduce the term "decimal" and "decimal point" and discuss how decimals are written.

Dion suggests two ways to read 0.1. Pass out place-value discs and place-value cards and discuss tenths as a new place value. Ask students, "How many tenths discs will have the same value as 1 one disc?" (10)

Have students work with a partner to represent the different numbers with the cards and discs for **Think** (a)–(d).

Discuss Mei's comment.

Students already know 1 m = 100 cm, so some of them might wonder why we need to express one tenth of 1 m as 0.1 m instead of 10 cm.

The notation 0.1 m is a way to express the fractional part of 1 m by looking at 1 m as one whole.

The notation 10 cm is a way to look at the fractional part of 1 m with a smaller unit, by looking at 1 cm as one whole.

The unit centimeter is one-hundredth of 1 m and the unit decimeter (dm) is one-tenth of 1 m. Decimeter is not as commonly used in the metric measurement system as other units of measurement.

Students can compare the bar model, place-value, decimal, and fraction forms for 0.1 and 0.3. The zero in the ones place is included to make it clear that we are reading and writing a decimal number that is less than 1.

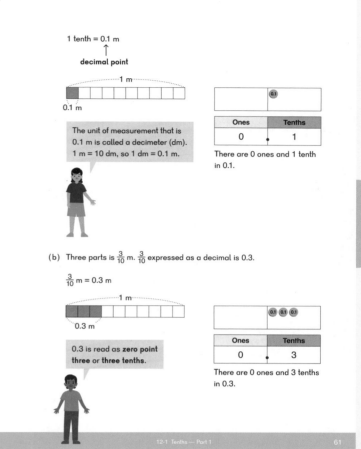

(d) Students can also relate addition of decimals to fractions: $\frac{7}{10} + \frac{3}{10} = \frac{10}{10} = 1$

There are 10 one-tenths in one.

Discuss the comments below Sofia delineating the difference between whole, fractional, and decimal numbers.

Students may be curious if there is a place for $\frac{1}{10}$ of 0.1, like there is a place for, $\frac{1}{10}$ of 1,000, $\frac{1}{10}$ of 100, $\frac{1}{10}$ of 10, and $\frac{1}{10}$ of 1.

Students will work with hundredths in Lesson 3 and thousandths in Dimensions Math 5A. They can reason that the place-value chart continues to the right of the ones place just as it continues to the left of the ones place and that the value of each digit would be one-tenth the value of the same digit one place to the left.

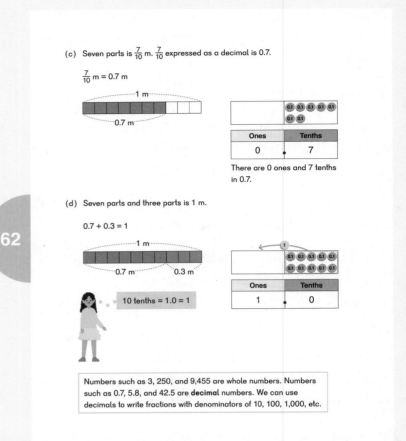

(c) Seven parts is $\frac{7}{10}$ m. $\frac{7}{10}$ expressed as a decimal is 0.7.

$\frac{7}{10}$ m = 0.7 m

Ones	Tenths
0	7

There are 0 ones and 7 tenths in 0.7.

(d) Seven parts and three parts is 1 m.

0.7 + 0.3 = 1

10 tenths = 1.0 = 1

Ones	Tenths
1	0

Numbers such as 3, 250, and 9,455 are whole numbers. Numbers such as 0.7, 5.8, and 42.5 are **decimal** numbers. We can use decimals to write fractions with denominators of 10, 100, 1,000, etc.

62   12-1 Tenths — Part 1

Do

1 — 4 For each question, discuss the problems and given models with students.

2 Ask students questions such as:

- "When the square is divided into (ten parts), what is the value of each of the divisions?" (one-tenth of the whole)
- "How many parts are shaded?"

Here the square is 1 whole and it is divided into 10 parts. Each part represents 1 tenth of the whole. The partitioned square is to help students relate decimals to fractions. The place-value discs are to understand decimals based on place value (base ten number system).

3 This problem is included as a Blackline Master: Decimal and Fraction Number Line (BLM).

Students could also copy the problem into a notebook to help them see the pattern in the decimals.

4 Alex thinks about part-whole bar models for adding fractions to help him solve the problem.

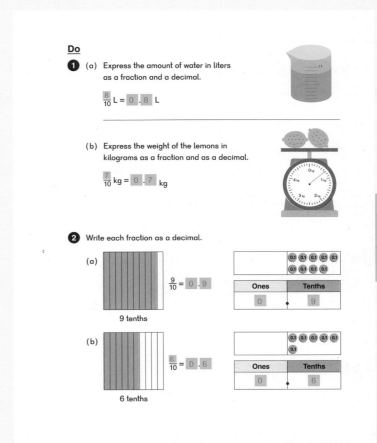

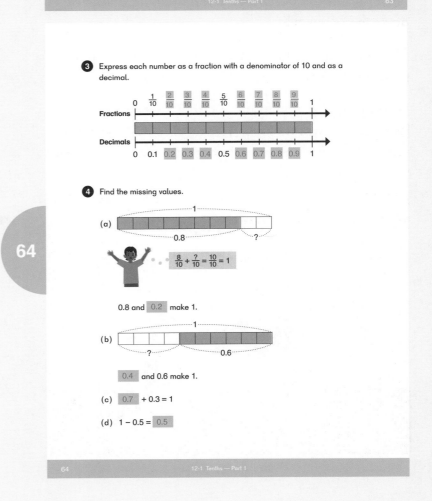

⑤ – ⑧ Students should be able to complete these problems independently.

⑥ (b) Reading decimals as fractions may be helpful in ordering the numbers:

"One-tenth, nine-tenths, one," may be easier to understand than "zero point one, zero point nine, one," because you can tell the place value clearly.

Have students reference Decimal and Fraction Number Line (BLM) from ③ if needed.

⑧ Students should see that each tick mark denotes 0.1 of a kilometer.

Activity

▲ Go Fish for 1

Materials: Go Fish for 1 Cards (BLM)

The game works best with 3 or 4 players. Deal each player six cards and place the remaining cards face down in a draw pile.

Players take turns asking for a number that, when paired with a card they are holding, makes 1.

When Player 1 has a pair of cards that make 1, he lays them down. If Player 1 asks for a card and the opponent asked does not have it, the opponent says, "go fish" and Player 1 draws a card from the draw pile. Play continues clockwise. The first player to pair all of their cards is the winner.

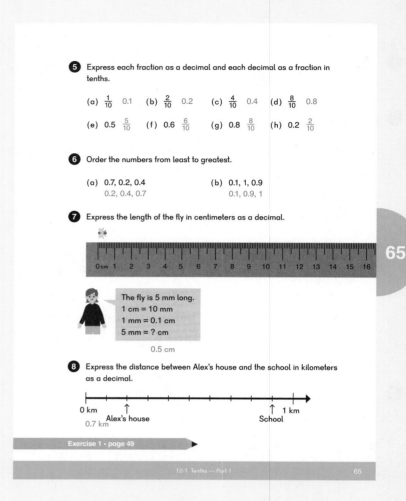

⑤ Express each fraction as a decimal and each decimal as a fraction in tenths.

(a) $\frac{1}{10}$ 0.1   (b) $\frac{2}{10}$ 0.2   (c) $\frac{4}{10}$ 0.4   (d) $\frac{8}{10}$ 0.8

(e) 0.5 $\frac{5}{10}$ (f) 0.6 $\frac{6}{10}$ (g) 0.8 $\frac{8}{10}$ (h) 0.2 $\frac{2}{10}$

⑥ Order the numbers from least to greatest.

(a) 0.7, 0.2, 0.4
0.2, 0.4, 0.7

(b) 0.1, 1, 0.9
0.1, 0.9, 1

⑦ Express the length of the fly in centimeters as a decimal.

The fly is 5 mm long.
1 cm = 10 mm
1 mm = 0.1 cm
5 mm = ? cm

0.5 cm

⑧ Express the distance between Alex's house and the school in kilometers as a decimal.

0 km   ↑ Alex's house   ↑ School   1 km
        0.7 km

Exercise 1 · page 49

65

◀ **Exercise 1 · page 49**

Lesson 2 Tenths — Part 2

Objectives

- Express mixed numbers in tenths as one-place decimals.
- Express one-place decimals greater than 1 as mixed numbers in tenths.
- Represent decimals on a number line.

Lesson Materials

- Place-value discs: ones and tenths
- Place-value cards: ones and tenths

Think

Provide students with place-value discs and cards and pose the **Think** problem. Have students find the heights of the animals and show them with the place-value discs and cards.

Learn

Have students compare their solutions from **Think** with the ones shown in the textbook. Discuss the examples shown.

Discuss Dion's comment. Students should see that the zebra is 3 tenths of a meter taller than 1 meter. The height of the zebra is 0.3 m more than 1 m (1 m + 0.3 m), written as 1.3 m.

Students should realize that $1\frac{3}{10}$ can also be expressed as $\frac{13}{10}$.

The elephant is 5 tenths of a meter taller than 2 meters. The height of the elephant is 0.5 m more than 2 m (2 m + 0.5 m), written as 2.5 m.

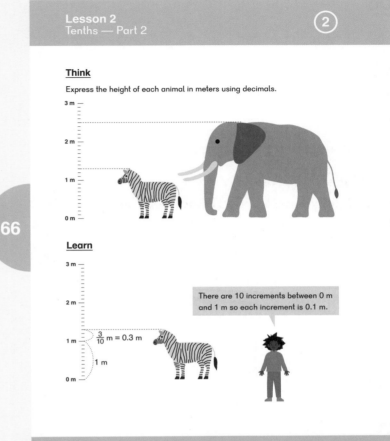

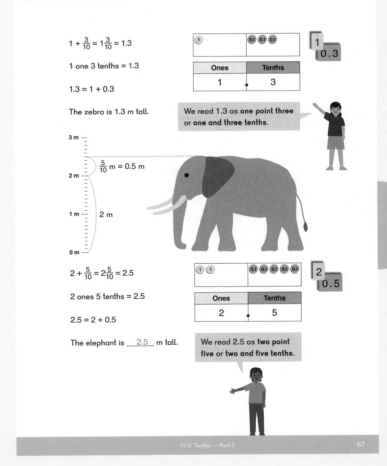

Do

❶ — ❸ For each question, discuss the problems and given models with students.

❶ The 1 L beakers are divided into 10 equal parts so 1 part is 0.1 L.

The fifth measuring cup holds 7 tenths of a liter.

❷ (a) Students are relating regrouping with decimals to what they have learned about fractions. Since 10 tenths equals 1 whole, ten 0.1s make 1.

(b) and (c) Students should connect their knowledge of fractions to check their work with decimals.

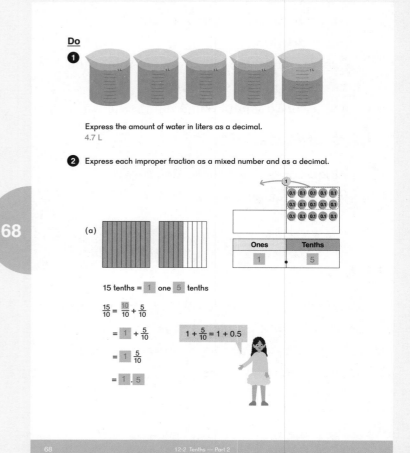

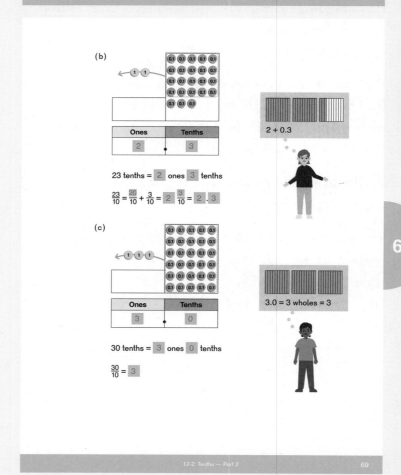

4 Students first express the numbers as decimals, then convert the decimals to fractions or mixed numbers.

In the previous problems, students expressed improper fractions as mixed numbers and then as decimals. Here they are expressing decimals as mixed numbers. The place-value discs show decimal amounts.

6 — 8 Students should be able to complete these problems independently.

7 Students may want to write the number as a fraction first.

(a) $\frac{4}{10} = 0.4$

(b) $\frac{50}{10} = 5.0$

(c) $\frac{52}{10} = 5.2$

(d) 10 and $\frac{32}{10}$ = 10 and 3.2 = 13.2

Activity

▲ Greatest

Materials: Number Cards (BLM) 0—9

Have students draw a personal game board as shown below on paper or a dry erase board:

Players take turns drawing a card. On each turn, they place the number drawn in one of the two empty boxes.

They may discard one of the cards on any turn. After each player has drawn three cards and placed two of them on the game board, the player with the greatest number gets 1 point.

The first player to collect 7 points is the winner.

Exercise 2 • page 52

3 Write the number represented by each letter as a decimal and as a fraction or mixed number with a denominator of 10.

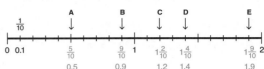

4 Write the numbers as decimals and as mixed numbers.

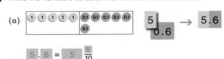

(a) → 5.6

5 . 6 = 5 $\frac{6}{10}$

(b)

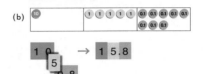

1 0 → 1 5.8
5
0.8

1 5 . 8 = 15 $\frac{8}{10}$

(c)

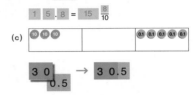

3 0 → 3 0.5
0.5

3 0 . 5 = 30 $\frac{5}{10}$

5 (a) 9 + 0.5 = 9.5   (b) 10 + 6 + 0.5 = 16.5

(c) 50 + 0.8 = 50.8   (d) 500 + 70 + 0.4 = 570.4

(e) 0.1 + 2 = 2.1   (f) 0.6 + 40 + 8 = 48.6

6 (a) 4.8 = 4 + 0.8   (b) 9.2 = 9 + 0.2

(c) 35.7 = 30 + 5 + 0.7   (d) 60.5 = 60 + 0.5

(e) 29.2 = 0.2 + 29   (f) 0.7 + 200 = 200.7

7 Write the numbers as decimals.

(a) 4 tenths   0.4   (b) 50 tenths   5

(c) 52 tenths   5.2   (d) 10 ones 32 tenths   13.2

8 Billy ran 2 km in the morning and 0.6 km in the afternoon. He wants to run a total of 3 km that day. How much farther does he need to run?

(a) How many kilometers has he run so far?
2.6 km

(b) How many more kilometers does he still need to run?
0.4 km

Exercise 2 • page 52

Objectives

- Interpret two-place decimals less than 1.
- Express hundredths less than 1 as a decimal.
- Express two-place decimals less than 1 as a fraction in hundredths.

Lesson Materials

- Blank Hundredths Grid (BLM)
- Meter sticks
- Place-value discs: ones, tenths, and hundredths
- Place-value cards: ones, tenths, and hundredths

Think

Discuss the **Think** problems and Dion's thought. Students may see that there is a pattern and that they can express $\frac{1}{10}$ of 0.1 as 0.01.

Sofia asks students to think about the smaller lengths as $\frac{1}{10}$ of a centimeter.

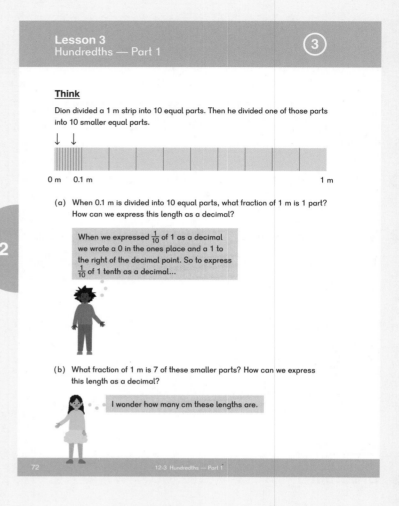

Lesson 3
Hundredths — Part 1   ③

Think

Dion divided a 1 m strip into 10 equal parts. Then he divided one of those parts into 10 smaller equal parts.

0 m   0.1 m   1 m

(a) When 0.1 m is divided into 10 equal parts, what fraction of 1 m is 1 part? How can we express this length as a decimal?

When we expressed $\frac{1}{10}$ of 1 as a decimal we wrote a 0 in the ones place and a 1 to the right of the decimal point. So to express $\frac{1}{10}$ of 1 tenth as a decimal…

(b) What fraction of 1 m is 7 of these smaller parts? How can we express this length as a decimal?

I wonder how many cm these lengths are.

72   12-3 Hundredths — Part 1

Learn

Have students look at meter sticks and discuss Mei's comment.

Students should see that earlier they divided 1 meter into tenths and expressed that number as a one-place decimal.

Now they are dividing each tenth further into tenths, and expressing that number as a two-place decimal. The second place is a tenth of a tenth of 1. Another way to think of this is that the value of the digit in this new place is one tenth of the value of the digit if it were in the tenths place, thus extending the decimal system.

Since $\frac{1}{10}$ of $\frac{1}{10}$ is $\frac{1}{100}$, we call this new place the hundredths place.

(b) Extend the place-value chart from Lesson 1 to the hundredths place and pass out place-value discs and cards to students to represent the numbers in **Think**.

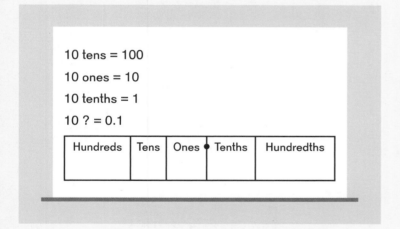

10 tens = 100

10 ones = 10

10 tenths = 1

10 ? = 0.1

Hundreds	Tens	Ones •	Tenths	Hundredths

Learn

(a) When 0.1 m is divided into 10 equal parts, each part is $\frac{1}{100}$ m.

Since there are 100 cm in 1 m, 1 cm is $\frac{1}{100}$ m.

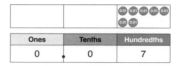

$$\div 10 \begin{cases} 100 \text{ cm} = 1 \text{ m} \\ 10 \text{ cm} = \frac{1}{10} \text{ m} \\ 1 \text{ cm} = \frac{1}{100} \text{ m} \end{cases} \div 10$$

We can write fractions expressed in hundredths as decimals.

$\frac{1}{100}$ m = 0.01 m

We read 0.01 as **zero point zero one** or **one hundredth**.

1 cm = 0.01 m

(b) 7 parts is $\frac{7}{100}$ of 1 m.

$\frac{7}{100}$ m = 0.07 m

Ones	Tenths	Hundredths
0 •	0	7

There are 0 ones, 0 tenths, and 7 hundredths in 0.07.

The hundredths place is also called the **second decimal place**. The tenths place is called the **first decimal place**.

73

Do

1 – 3 For each question, discuss the problems and given models with students.

1 (b) Students can also relate the addition to fractions:

$$\frac{7}{100} + \frac{3}{100} = \frac{10}{100} = \frac{1}{10}$$

2 Ask students questions such as:

- "What value does each box show?"
- "What happens when we regroup decimals?"

The different representations help students relate decimals to both fractions and place value.

Here the square is 1 whole and it is divided into 100 smaller parts. Each part represents 1 hundredth of the whole. Each column represents 1 tenth of the whole.

Blank Hundredths Grid (BLM) can be used by students who need additional help. Placed in a dry erase sleeve, students can shade in the columns for each tenth and the smaller squares for each hundredth.

(b) $\frac{1}{10} + \frac{7}{100}$ is the same as 0.1 + 0.07.

(c) Students should see that $\frac{20}{100}$ can be simplified to $\frac{2}{10}$. Alex points out that since $\frac{20}{100} = \frac{2}{10}$, 20 hundredths can be regrouped as 2 tenths.

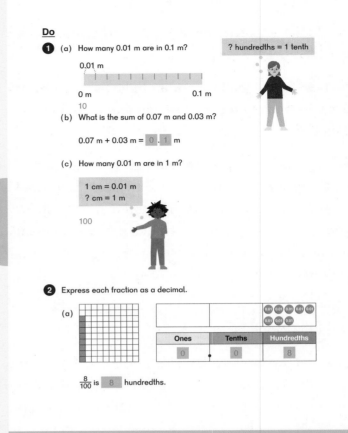

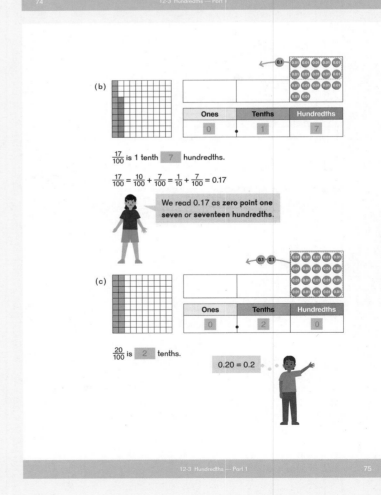

④—⑦ Students should be able to work these problems independently.

Activities

● **Match**

Materials: Decimal Match Cards (BLM), multiple sets

Lay cards in a faceup array. Have students find two Decimal Match Cards (BLM) that, when added together, make 1.

▲ **Memory**

Materials: Decimal Match Cards (BLM), multiple sets

Play using the same rules as **Match**, but arrange the cards facedown in an array.

▲ **Decimal Battle**

Materials: Decimals Match Cards (BLM)

Playing in a group of 2 to 3 students, evenly deal out all Decimal Match Cards (BLM) facedown.

Players each flip over a card at the same time. The greatest decimal (or least, depending on version of game) wins.

0.2	0.8

Exercise 3 · page 56

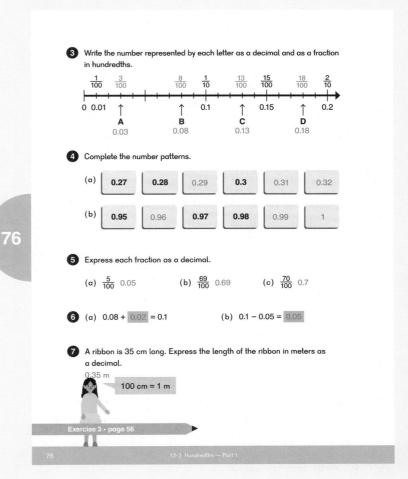

③ Write the number represented by each letter as a decimal and as a fraction in hundredths.

④ Complete the number patterns.

(a) **0.27** | **0.28** | 0.29 | **0.3** | 0.31 | 0.32

(b) **0.95** | 0.96 | **0.97** | **0.98** | 0.99 | 1

⑤ Express each fraction as a decimal.

(a) $\frac{5}{100}$ 0.05   (b) $\frac{69}{100}$ 0.69   (c) $\frac{70}{100}$ 0.7

⑥ (a) 0.08 + 0.02 = 0.1   (b) 0.1 − 0.05 = 0.05

⑦ A ribbon is 35 cm long. Express the length of the ribbon in meters as a decimal.

0.35 m

100 cm = 1 m

Exercise 3 · page 56

76   12-3 Hundredths — Part 1

76

Objectives

- Express mixed numbers in hundredths as two-place decimals.
- Express two-place decimals greater than 1 as mixed numbers in hundredths.
- Express a decimal number to hundredths as the sum of place values in expanded form.

Lesson Materials

- Blank Hundredths Grid (BLM)
- Place-value discs: ones, tenths, and hundredths
- Place-value cards: ones, tenths, and hundredths

Think

Allow students to choose between place-value cards, discs, or the Blank Hundredths Grids (BLM) to represent the amounts of water the pets require and then answer the question.

Record strategies on the board and discuss the methods students used.

Learn

Have students compare their solutions from **Think** with the ones shown in the textbook. Discuss the two methods shown.

Method 1

Students may also have drawn the sum of 3 tenths and 5 hundredths on one grid:

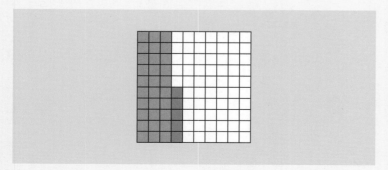

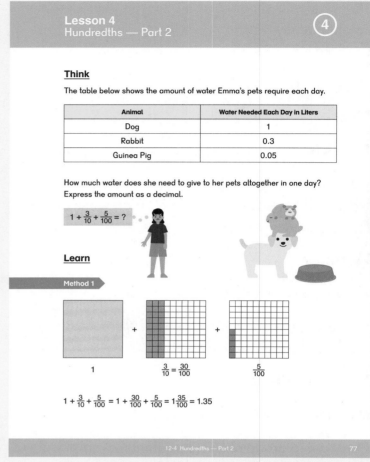

Think

The table below shows the amount of water Emma's pets require each day.

Animal	Water Needed Each Day in Liters
Dog	1
Rabbit	0.3
Guinea Pig	0.05

How much water does she need to give to her pets altogether in one day? Express the amount as a decimal.

$$1 + \frac{3}{10} + \frac{5}{100} = ?$$

Learn

Method 1

$$1 \qquad \frac{3}{10} = \frac{30}{100} \qquad \frac{5}{100}$$

$$1 + \frac{3}{10} + \frac{5}{100} = 1 + \frac{30}{100} + \frac{5}{100} = 1\frac{35}{100} = 1.35$$

12-4 Hundredths — Part 2   77

77

This method allows students to see how the decimals relate to fractions.

Method 2

This method emphasizes the place value of each digit in the decimal.

Use the questions about digits and their values from the textbook as examples when working with the **Do** problems.

Dion reminds students of the term "expanded form." Students should relate decimals to their knowledge of place values in whole numbers. Just as we wrote whole numbers in expanded form, we can do the same with decimals.

Note the way to write a decimal as fraction in expanded form is not $1.35 = 1 + \frac{35}{100}$ but $1.35 = 1 + \frac{3}{10} + \frac{5}{100}$. The emphasis is on place value.

Do

❶—❸ Students should be able to work these problems independently.

❶ This problem presents multiple ways to understand the same decimal. Students who can easily convert between these methods have mastered the place value of decimals and their connection to fractions.

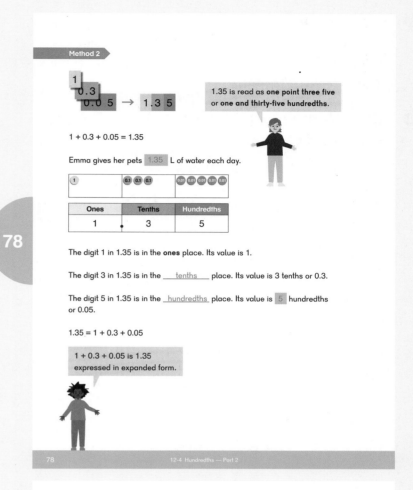

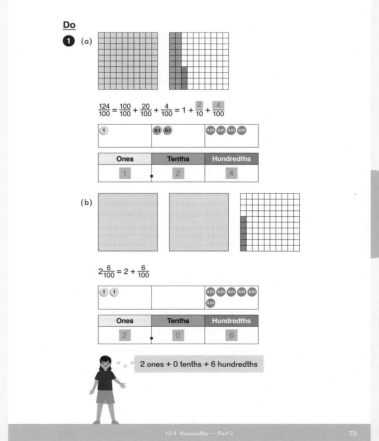

③ (c) Ensure students understand that a place without a digit will need a zero to show its place value when written in standard form, but not in expanded form: 90 + 6 + 0.07 = 96.07.

④—⑧ Students should be able to work these problems independently.

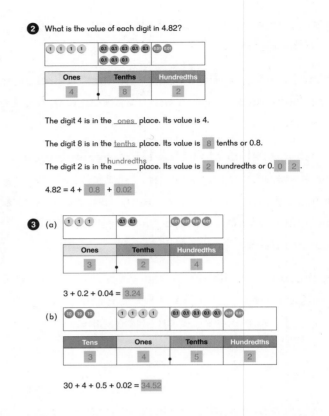

② What is the value of each digit in 4.82?

Ones	Tenths	Hundredths
4	8	2

The digit 4 is in the <u>ones</u> place. Its value is 4.

The digit 8 is in the <u>tenths</u> place. Its value is 8 tenths or 0.8.

The digit 2 is in the <u>hundredths</u> place. Its value is 2 hundredths or 0.02.

4.82 = 4 + 0.8 + 0.02

③ (a)

Ones	Tenths	Hundredths
3	2	4

3 + 0.2 + 0.04 = 3.24

(b)

Tens	Ones	Tenths	Hundredths
3	4	5	2

30 + 4 + 0.5 + 0.02 = 34.52

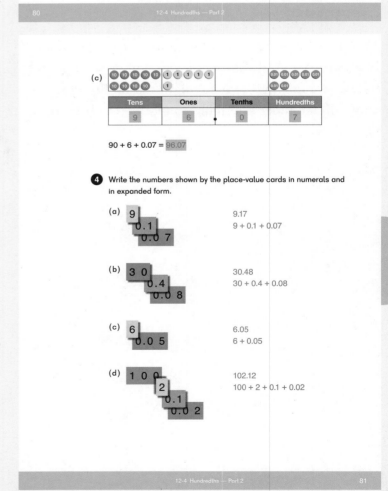

(c)

Tens	Ones	Tenths	Hundredths
9	6	0	7

90 + 6 + 0.07 = 96.07

④ Write the numbers shown by the place-value cards in numerals and in expanded form.

(a) 9.17
   9 + 0.1 + 0.07

(b) 30.48
   30 + 0.4 + 0.08

(c) 6.05
   6 + 0.05

(d) 102.12
   100 + 2 + 0.1 + 0.02

Activity

▲ Grab Bag

Materials: Place-value discs: hundredths to hundreds, brown paper bag

Students can grab a handful of discs from the bag and organize them into a number. They should regroup ten of any place to the next greater place value. Once they have created their numbers, have them record them in standard form, expanded form, and word form.

For example:

135.67
100 + 30 + 5 + 0.6 + 0.07
One hundred thirty-five and sixty-seven hundredths

Exercise 4 • page 59

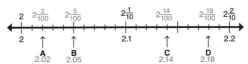

5 Write the number represented by each letter as a mixed number in hundredths and as a decimal.

6 Express each mixed number as a decimal.

(a) $2\frac{9}{100}$ 2.09   (b) $4\frac{25}{100}$ 4.25   (c) $30\frac{40}{100}$ 30.4

7 (a) 50 + 0.07 = 50.07

(b) 4.68 = 4 + 0.6 + 0.08

(c) 29.05 = 20 + 9 + 0.05

(d) 4.73 − 0.7 = 4.03

(e) 39.75 − 0.75 = 39

(f) 892.05 − 90 = 802.05

8

Sofia had 2.75 m of ribbon. She used 0.7 m of ribbon to wrap a present. How much ribbon does she have left?
2.75 − 0.7 = 2.05
2.05 m

Exercise 4 • page 59

Objective

- Express decimals as fractions in simplest form.

Lesson Materials

- 1-ft paper strips

Think

Provide students with 1-ft paper strips and have them mark off $\frac{1}{4}$, $\frac{1}{2}$, and $\frac{3}{4}$ of the paper. Discuss the **Think** questions with students. They should think about how to mark the 1-ft paper strip with decimals and then with fractions.

Discuss student solutions to the questions.

Learn

Have students compare their solutions from **Think** with the ones shown in the textbook. Discuss the ruler and number line in the textbook.

(a) Students should first express 0.75 as $\frac{75}{100}$. They have learned how to simplify the fraction $\frac{75}{100}$.

(b) Students may multiply $\frac{75}{100}$ by 12 (1 foot = 12 inches) to find the length of the football. This strategy, though correct, is not the most efficient.

Once $\frac{75}{100}$ is simplified to $\frac{3}{4}$, the product is much easier to find.

1 foot $\longrightarrow$ 12 in
$\frac{3}{4}$ ft $\longrightarrow \frac{3}{4} \times$ 12 in = 9 in

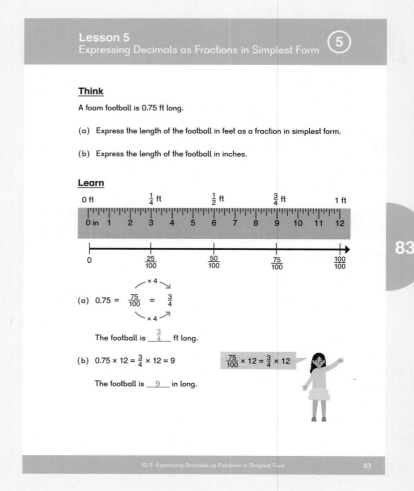

Lesson 5
Expressing Decimals as Fractions in Simplest Form ⑤

Think

A foam football is 0.75 ft long.

(a) Express the length of the football in feet as a fraction in simplest form.

(b) Express the length of the football in inches.

Learn

(a) $0.75 = \frac{75}{100} = \frac{3}{4}$ (×4)

The football is $\frac{3}{4}$ ft long.

(b) $0.75 \times 12 = \frac{3}{4} \times 12 = 9$ $\frac{75}{100} \times 12 = \frac{3}{4} \times 12$

The football is _9_ in long.

83

12-5 Expressing Decimals as Fractions in Simplest Form   83

Do

①—③ For each question, discuss the problems and given models with students.

① Emma reminds students that they can cross off the numerator and denominator after they divide them by a common factor and write the quotient. This is a shorthand method of finding the simplest form of a fraction.

② (a) The yellow marked area is one-twentieth of 1 (the whole).

④—⑤ Students should be able to solve the problems independently.

④ Students should realize that most of the problems are in the hundredths and will first be expressed as a fraction with a denominator of 100. Encourage students to think about the factors of 100.

Using prior knowledge of equivalent fractions, they will see that problems (b), (d), and (e) can be expressed as a fraction with a denominator of 10.

In (h)–(j), the whole number is given and the decimal part needs to be expressed as a fraction with a denominator of 100 (for example, $4\frac{5}{100}$, not $\frac{405}{100}$), and then simplified.

Exercise 5 • page 63

Do

① (a) Express 0.6 as a fraction in simplest form.

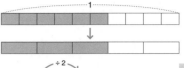

$$0.6 = \frac{6}{10} = \frac{3}{5}$$
(÷2)

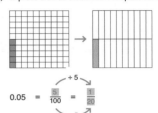

(b) Express 3.6 as a mixed number in simplest form.

$$3.6 = 3\frac{6}{10} = 3\frac{3}{5}$$

② (a) Express 0.05 as a fraction in simplest form.

$$0.05 = \frac{5}{100} = \frac{1}{20}$$
(÷5)

(b) Express 4.05 as a mixed number in simplest form.

$$4.05 = 4\frac{5}{100} = 4\frac{1}{20}$$

③ (a) Express 0.84 as a fraction in simplest form.

$$0.84 = \frac{84}{100} = \frac{21}{25}$$
(÷4)

(b) Express 8.84 as a mixed number in simplest form.

$$8.84 = 8\frac{84}{100} = 8\frac{21}{25}$$

④ Express each decimal as a fraction or as a mixed number in simplest form.

(a) 0.25 $\frac{1}{4}$ (b) 0.5 $\frac{1}{2}$

(c) 0.75 $\frac{3}{4}$ (d) 0.2 $\frac{1}{5}$

(e) 0.8 $\frac{4}{5}$ (f) 0.08 $\frac{2}{25}$

(g) 0.64 $\frac{16}{25}$ (h) 5.04 $5\frac{1}{25}$

(i) 11.36 $11\frac{9}{25}$ (j) 50.02 $50\frac{1}{50}$

⑤

A book weighs 0.25 lb.

(a) Express the weight of the book in pounds as a fraction in simplest form.
$\frac{1}{4}$ lb

(b) Express the weight of the book in ounces.
$\frac{1}{4} \times 16$ oz = 4 oz

Exercise 5 • page 63

Objective

- Express common fractions and mixed numbers with a denominator that is a factor of 10 or 100 as a decimal.

Think

Pose the **Think** problem. Students know that one-place decimals can be expressed as a fraction with a denominator of 10, and two-place decimals can be expressed as a fraction with a denominator of 100.

Ask students to think about how to create an equivalent fraction for $\frac{3}{5}$ with a denominator of 10 or 100.

Discuss student solutions to the questions.

Learn

Ask students why Dion needs to make an equivalent fraction with a denominator of 10. (He needs to express the fraction as a decimal.)

Discuss the textbook page and have students compare their solutions from **Think** with the one shown in the textbook.

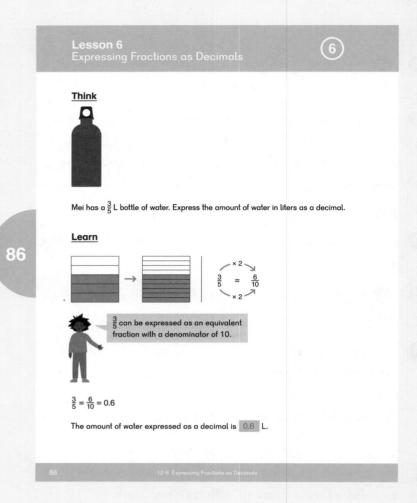

86

Lesson 6
Expressing Fractions as Decimals ⑥

Think

Mei has a $\frac{3}{5}$ L bottle of water. Express the amount of water in liters as a decimal.

Learn

$$\frac{3}{5} \xrightarrow{\times 2} = \frac{6}{10} \xleftarrow{\times 2}$$

$\frac{3}{5}$ can be expressed as an equivalent fraction with a denominator of 10.

$\frac{3}{5} = \frac{6}{10} = 0.6$

The amount of water expressed as a decimal is 0.6 L.

Do

1 — 4 For each question, discuss the problems and given models with students.

1 $\frac{7}{20}$ cannot be expressed as a fraction with a denominator of 10, so we need to find an equivalent fraction with a denominator of 100. Since $20 \times 5 = 100$, we can multiply both the numerator and denominator by 5 to get a fraction with a denominator of 100.

2 $\frac{3}{4}$ cannot be expressed as a fraction with a denominator of 10, so we need a denominator of 100. Students may also recall that $\frac{3}{4} = \frac{75}{100}$.

3 When given a mixed number, students should see that it is not necessary to first find an improper fraction before finding a decimal number. The whole number, in this case, 1, is already given. Students only need to express the fraction part, in this case, $\frac{1}{2}$, as a decimal by first finding an equivalent fraction with a denominator of 10.

4 — 5 Students should be able to solve the problems independently.

5 — 6 Students have worked with factors since Dimensions Math 4A Chapter 3. By the end of this chapter, students should recognize that all the denominators in this lesson are factors of 10 or 100.

7 $\frac{4}{5} + \frac{4}{5} = \frac{8}{5} = 1\frac{3}{5}$

Convert $\frac{3}{5}$ to a decimal with a denominator of 10: $\frac{6}{10}$.

$1 + \frac{6}{10} = 1.6$

Exercise 6 • page 66

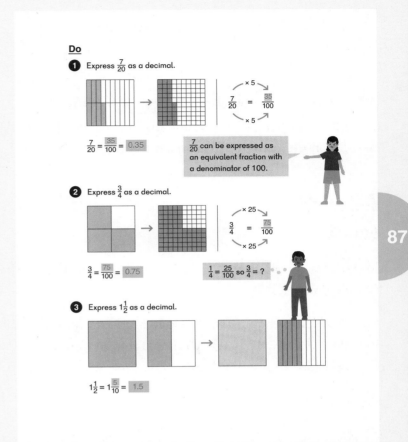

Do

1 Express $\frac{7}{20}$ as a decimal.

$\frac{7}{20} = \frac{35}{100} = \boxed{0.35}$

$\frac{7}{20}$ can be expressed as an equivalent fraction with a denominator of 100.

2 Express $\frac{3}{4}$ as a decimal.

$\frac{3}{4} = \frac{75}{100} = \boxed{0.75}$

$\frac{1}{4} = \frac{25}{100}$ so $\frac{3}{4} = ?$

3 Express $1\frac{1}{2}$ as a decimal.

$1\frac{1}{2} = 1\frac{5}{10} = \boxed{1.5}$

4 Express $\frac{7}{5}$ as a decimal.

$\frac{7}{5} = 1\frac{2}{5} = 1\frac{4}{10} = \boxed{1.4}$

5 Express each fraction as a decimal.

(a) $\frac{1}{2}$ 0.5   (b) $\frac{1}{4}$ 0.25   (c) $\frac{1}{5}$ 0.2

(d) $\frac{1}{20}$ 0.05   (e) $\frac{1}{25}$ 0.04   (f) $\frac{1}{50}$ 0.02

6 Express each fraction or mixed number as a decimal.

(a) $\frac{9}{25}$ 0.36   (b) $\frac{13}{20}$ 0.65   (c) $\frac{4}{5}$ 0.8

(d) $\frac{28}{50}$ 0.56   (e) $\frac{7}{4}$ 1.75   (f) $\frac{3}{2}$ 1.5

(g) $1\frac{3}{4}$ 1.75   (h) $2\frac{4}{5}$ 2.8   (i) $5\frac{17}{20}$ 5.85

7 Two packages each weigh $\frac{4}{5}$ lb. Express the total weight of the packages in pounds as a decimal.

$\frac{4}{5} + \frac{4}{5} = \frac{8}{5} = 1\frac{3}{5} = 1\frac{6}{10} = 1.6$

1.6 lb

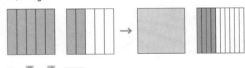

Lesson 7 Practice A

Objective

- Practice concepts from the chapter.

After students complete the **Practice** in the textbook, have them continue to practice converting fractions and decimals with activities from the chapter.

Activities

● **Match**

Materials: Decimal Match Cards (BLM), Fraction Match Cards (BLM)

Lay cards in a faceup array. Have students find two Fraction Match Cards (BLM) and Decimal Match Cards (BLM) that have the same value.

For example:

$\frac{3}{50}$	**0.06**

▲ **Memory**

Materials: Decimal Match Cards (BLM), Fraction Match Cards (BLM)

Play using the same rules as **Match**, but arrange the cards facedown in an array.

Exercise 7 • page 68

---

1 Express each decimal as a fraction or as a mixed number.

(a) 4.7 $\quad 4\frac{7}{10}$ (b) 3.9 $\quad 3\frac{9}{10}$ (c) 0.03 $\quad \frac{3}{100}$

(d) 3.23 $\quad 3\frac{23}{100}$ (e) 40.19 $\quad 40\frac{19}{100}$ (f) 100.01 $\quad 100\frac{1}{100}$

2 Express each fraction or mixed number as a decimal.

(a) $\frac{3}{10}$ $\quad 0.3$ (b) $\frac{17}{100}$ $\quad 0.17$ (c) $15\frac{8}{10}$ $\quad 15.8$

(d) $2\frac{5}{100}$ $\quad 2.05$ (e) $9\frac{12}{100}$ $\quad 9.12$ (f) $\frac{12}{10}$ $\quad 1.2$

3 (a) 9 + 0.5 + 0.03 = 9.53 (b) 3 + 0.02 = 3.02

(c) 60 + 0.15 = 60.15 (d) 2.8 = 2 + 0.8

(e) 3.24 = 3 + 0.2 + 0.04 (f) 45.76 = 45.7 + 0.06

(g) 2.8 + 3 + 0.07 = 5.87 (h) 43 + 6.04 + 0.5 = 49.54

4 What is the value of the digit 3 in each number?

(a) 3.06 (b) 4.13
3 ones 3 hundredths

(c) 30.01 (d) 0.35
3 tens 3 tenths

12-7 Practice A   89

---

5 (a) 0.2 and 0.8 make 1. (b) 0.4 and 0.6 make 1.

6 Express each value as a whole number or as a decimal.

(a) 32 tenths $\quad 3.2$ (b) 56 hundredths $\quad 0.56$

(c) 200 hundredths $\quad 2$ (d) 10 tenths 4 hundredths $\quad 1.04$

7 Express each decimal as a mixed number in simplest form.

(a) 1.6 $\quad 1\frac{3}{5}$ (b) 4.5 $\quad 4\frac{1}{2}$ (c) 9.08 $\quad 9\frac{2}{25}$

(d) 6.25 $\quad 6\frac{1}{4}$ (e) 24.14 $\quad 24\frac{7}{50}$ (f) 50.05 $\quad 50\frac{1}{20}$

8 Express each fraction or mixed number as a whole number or as a decimal.

(a) $\frac{12}{50}$ $\quad 0.24$ (b) $3\frac{1}{2}$ $\quad 3.5$ (c) $7\frac{2}{5}$ $\quad 7.4$

(d) $\frac{7}{20}$ $\quad 0.35$ (e) $\frac{7}{4}$ $\quad 1.75$ (f) $\frac{75}{25}$ $\quad 3$

9 Jason ran in the morning and in the afternoon. He ran a total distance of 1 mile. If he ran $\frac{2}{5}$ miles in the morning, how far did he run in the afternoon? Express the answer as a decimal.
$\frac{2}{5} = 0.4$; $1 - 0.4 = 0.6$; 0.6 mi

10 A melon weighs 2 lb, an apple weighs 0.3 lb, and a grape weighs 0.02 lb. How much do the three fruits weigh altogether? Express the answer as a mixed number in simplest form.
$2 + 0.3 + 0.02 = 2.32 = 2\frac{8}{25}$; $2\frac{8}{25}$ lb

Exercise 7 • page 68

90   12-7 Practice A

Lesson 8 Comparing and Ordering Decimals

Objective

- Compare and order decimals to hundredths.

Lesson Materials

- Blank Hundredths Grid (BLM)
- Place-value discs: ones, tenths, and hundredths
- Place-value cards: ones, tenths, and hundredths

Think

Allow students to choose between place-value cards, discs, or the Blank Hundredths Grid (BLM) to represent the pumpkin weights.

Record student strategies for comparing numbers on the board and discuss the methods students used.

Learn

Have students compare their solutions from **Think** with the ones shown in the textbook.

Emma reminds students to begin comparing digits in the greatest place.

Ask students why Dion thinks of 2.4 as equal to 2.40. (We can append a zero to the end and not change the value of the number).

Students should see that we can compare decimals the same way we compare whole numbers. Start with the digit in the highest place and compare. If the values are the same, compare the digits in the next highest place, etc.

40 hundredths is greater than 37 hundredths.

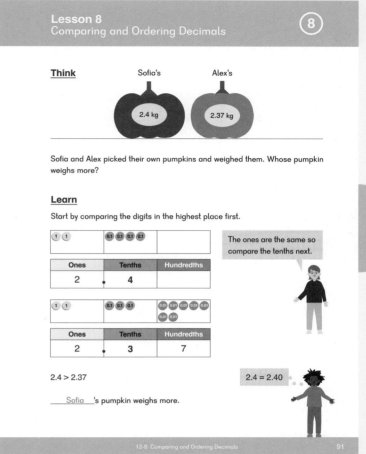

Do

1 – **3** For each question, discuss the different models shown to help students compare the decimals.

2 (a) Ensure students understand that although there are more discs in the hundredths place, we only need to compare the tenths place to see that 0.52 is greater than 0.48.

(b) and (c) Ask students which place we need to look at to compare the decimals.

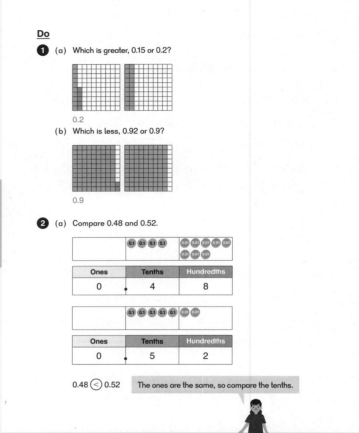

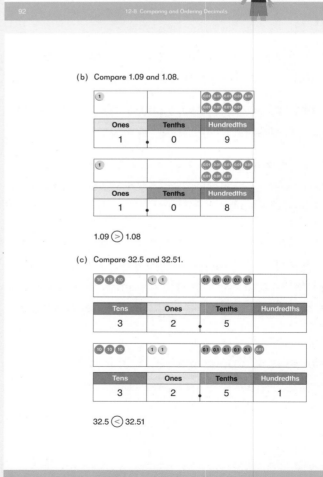

3 If students need additional help on these problems, have them use place-value discs.

4—**8** Students should be able to solve the problems independently.

5 and **7** These problems can be turned into an activity by having students copy the numbers onto index cards to put the numbers in order.

If students have difficulty with these problems, have them use place-value cards to build the numbers.

6 Sofia converts $\frac{2}{5}$ to a decimal to compare it to the decimal 0.38.

Dion converts both numbers to fractions with denominators of 100 to compare.

Activity

▲ Hundredths Battle

Materials: Deck of cards (tens and face cards removed), or Number Cards (BLM) 0—9, Decimal Battle Mat (BLM)

Each student turns over one card representing the number of tenths at the same time and places it in the tenths place on the mat. Each player then places a second card on the mat to represent the number of hundredths. The player with the greatest number collects the cards. Play continues until a player is out of cards.

Example round:

Player 1: 0.46   Player 2: 0.16

Exercise 8 · page 70

3

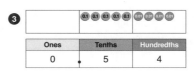

Ones	Tenths	Hundredths
0	5	4

(a) What number is 0.1 more than 0.54?
0.64
(b) What number is 0.01 less than 0.54?
0.53
(c) What number should be added to 0.54 to get 0.6?
0.06
(d) What number should be added to 0.54 to get 1?
0.46

> 54 hundredths + ? hundredths = 100 hundredths

4 What sign, > or <, goes in each ◯?

(a) 0.74 ⊙ 0.69   (b) 0.86 ⊙ 0.88

(c) 0.3 ⊙ 0.28   (d) 3.4 ⊙ 0.92

(e) 4.01 ⊙ 4   (f) 75.6 ⊙ 75.58

(g) 16.9 ⊙ 4.87   (h) 4.35 ⊙ 43.5

94

---

5 Order the numbers from least to greatest.

(a) 132, 1.32, 13.2   (b) 28.84, 28.34, 28.05, 28.3
1.32, 13.2, 132   28.05, 28.3, 28.34, 28.84
(c) 1.8, 1.75, 1.9, 1.81   (d) 10.84, 108.4, 10.09, 100.9
1.75, 1.8, 1.81, 1.9   10.09, 10.84, 100.9, 108.4

6 Compare $\frac{2}{5}$ and 0.38.

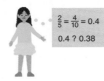

$\frac{2}{5} = \frac{4}{10} = 0.4$

0.4 ? 0.38

$\frac{2}{5} = \frac{4}{10} = \frac{40}{100}$

$0.38 = \frac{38}{100}$

$\frac{40}{100}$? $\frac{38}{100}$

$\frac{2}{5}$ ⊙ 0.38

95

7 Order the numbers from least to greatest.

(a) $\frac{1}{2}$, 0.4, 0.75, $\frac{3}{5}$ 0.4, $\frac{1}{2}$, $\frac{3}{5}$, 0.75

(b) 4.34, $4\frac{3}{4}$, $3\frac{45}{50}$, 3.6   3.6, $3\frac{45}{50}$, 4.34, $4\frac{3}{4}$

(c) 0.99, $\frac{93}{100}$, 0.94, $\frac{19}{20}$ $\frac{93}{100}$, 0.94, $\frac{19}{20}$, 0.99

(d) $\frac{4}{5}$, 4.5, $\frac{5}{4}$, 5.4 $\frac{4}{5}$, $\frac{5}{4}$, 4.5, 5.4

8 Alex ran $\frac{3}{5}$ km. Sofia ran 0.8 km. Who ran farther?
$\frac{3}{5}$ = 0.6; 0.8 > 0.6; Sofia

Exercise 8 · page 70

Lesson 9 Rounding Decimals

Objective

- Round decimals given in tenths to the nearest whole number.

Think

Pose the **Think** problem and ask students to recall what they remember about rounding numbers.

If necessary, ask students:

- "What numbers are the dogs' weights between?"
- "Can you place the dogs' weights on a number line?"

Learn

Ask students why Emma points out that the dogs weights are each between 3 kg and 4 kg. (So that she can draw a number line with increments between 3 and 4). Emma has included a midpoint between 3 and 4 of 3.5 on her number line. This will help her place each dog's weight in the correct location on the number line.

Bailey

The number line is divided into 10 increments of one-tenth, or 0.1, to help place 3.28 in the correct location.

The location of 3.28 on a number line makes it easy to see that it is rounded to 3 when rounding to the nearest whole number.

Alex points out that to round to the nearest tenth, we need to look at the digit in the next place value to the right, the hundredths place. This number line is divided into increments of 0.01. 3.28 is between 3.2 and 3.3.

The location of 3.28 on a number line makes it easy to see that it is rounded to 3.3 when rounding to the nearest tenth.

Think

Bailey 3.28 kg

Mila 3.85 kg

Sheriff 3.54 kg

A veterinarian weighed three dogs. Round the weight of each dog to the nearest whole number of kilograms, and to the nearest tenth of a kilogram.

Learn

All the weights are between 3 kg and 4 kg.

Bailey   Sheriff   Mila

3 ——————————————— 4

Bailey

3.28

3 ——————— 3.5 ——————— 4

The digit in the tenths place tells us which whole number the decimal is closest to. 3.28 kg is closer to 3 kg than to 4 kg.

3.28 kg is 3 kg when rounded to the nearest whole number of kilograms.

Rounding to the nearest whole number means we are rounding to the ones place.

97

3.28

3.2 ——————— 3.25 ——————— 3.3

The digit in the hundredths place tells us which tenth the decimal is closest to. 3.28 kg is closer to 3.3 kg than to 3.2 kg.

3.28 kg is 3.3 kg when rounded to the nearest tenth of a kilogram.

Rounding to the nearest tenth is the same as rounding to 1 decimal place.

Mila

Ask students:

- "What increments is this number line divided into and why?" (Tenths, so that we can round to the nearest tenth.)
- "What is the nearest whole number of kilograms to 3.85?" (4)
- "How do we round a number that is halfway between two increments?" (Round it to the next greatest tenth.)
- "What is the nearest tenth of a kilogram to 3.85?" (3.9)

To help us find Mila's weight to the nearest tenth of a kilogram, the number line is divided into increments of 0.01. 3.85 is exactly halfway between 3.8 and 3.9.

When a number is exactly halfway between two numbers in the place we are rounding to, we round the number up.

Sheriff

Ask students:

- "What increments is this number line divided into and why." (Also tenths, so that we can round to the nearest tenth.)
- "What is the nearest whole number of kilograms to 3.54?" (4)
- "What is the nearest tenth of a kilogram to 3.54?" (3.5)

Students should see that rounding decimals works in the same manner as rounding whole numbers.

Mila

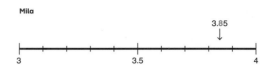

3.85 kg is 4 kg when rounded to the nearest whole number of kilograms.

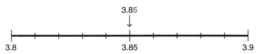

3.85 kg is halfway between 3.8 kg and 3.9 kg, so we round up.
3.85 kg is 3.9 kg when rounded to the nearest tenth of a kilogram.

Sheriff

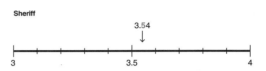

3.54 kg is 4 kg when rounded to the nearest whole number of kilograms.

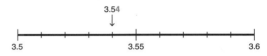

3.54 kg is 3.5 kg when rounded to 1 decimal place.

Do

1—**4** For each question, discuss the different number lines shown to help students round the decimals correctly.

2 Students should know that rounding to the nearest pound means rounding to the nearest whole number, i.e. the nearest 1 lb.

3 Since we are rounding to the nearest 0.1, the number line has increments of 0.01.

4 Help students see that in rounding to the nearest tenth, they are rounding to 10, because 10.0 = 10.

Do

1 A leaf is 12.37 cm long.

(a) Round the length of the leaf to the nearest centimeter.

The leaf is 12 cm when rounded to the nearest centimeter.

(b) Round the length of the leaf to 1 decimal place.

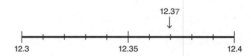

The leaf is 12.4 cm when rounded to 1 decimal place.

2 A horse weighs 840.5 lb. Round the weight of the horse to the nearest pound.

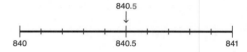

The weight of the horse is 841 lb when rounded to the nearest pound.

3 Round each number to 1 decimal place.

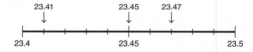

(a) 23.41 is 23.4 when rounded to 1 decimal place.

(b) 23.45 is 23.5 when rounded to 1 decimal place.

(c) 23.47 is 23.5 when rounded to 1 decimal place.

4 Round 10.02 to 1 decimal place.

 When we round to 1 decimal place, we include a digit in the first decimal place in the answer, even if it is 0.

10.02 is 10.0 when rounded to 1 decimal place.

5 (a) Round 4.25 to 1 decimal place. 4.3

(b) Round 4.25 to a whole number. 4

6 — 9 Students should be able to work these problems independently.

Activity

▲ Three in a Row – Round It

Materials: Three in a Row – Round It Game Board (BLM), deck of cards, counters

In each round, players draw three cards. They then arrange the cards into a number with ones and some hundredths using a counter as the decimal point. Aces are ones. Tens and face cards are zero.

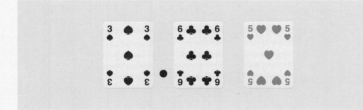

Players round their numbers to the nearest tenth to capture a space on the game board.

Play continues until a player has three counters in a row, column, or in a diagonal.

Sample game:

Player 1 (green) draws 6, 3, 5. She chooses the number 3.65 and rounds it to 3.7. She then marks that number on the game board.

Player 2 (red) draws 5, 7, 1. He chooses the number 1.57 and rounds it to 1.6. He marks 1.6 on the game board.

Players draw new cards and the game continues until one player has three marks in a row horizontally, vertically, or diagonally.

Ask students what strategies they could use to win the game. They may choose to create their first rounded numbers to be positioned far away from other players' marked numbers. They may choose to create numbers that will block their opponents from marking adjacent numbers.

---

6 Round each decimal to a whole number.

(a) 0.6   1   (b) 4.5   5

(c) 17.6   18   (d) 0.19   0

(e) 3.52   4   (f) 60.93   61

7 Round each decimal to 1 decimal place.

(a) 0.82   0.8   (b) 2.34   2.3

(c) 7.07   7.1   (d) 5.55   5.6

(e) 15.63   15.6   (f) 172.03   172.0

8

McTOWNSVILLEBURGH
CITY LIMIT
POP 1.7 MILLION   ELEV 52 FT

There are 1.7 million people in a city. Which is a closer estimate of the number of people in the city, 1 million or 2 million people?
2 million people

9 Alex rounded a number with 2 decimal places to 1 decimal place and got 2.3. What are the possible numbers Alex could have rounded?
Any number between 2.25 and 2.34.

Exercise 9 • page 73

0.1	0.2	0.3	0.4	0.5	0.6	0.7	0.8	0.9	1.0
1.1	1.2	1.3	1.4	1.5	✗	1.7	1.8	1.9	2.0
2.1	2.2	2.3	2.4	2.5	2.6	2.7	2.8	2.9	3.0
3.1	3.2	3.3	3.4	3.5	3.6	✗	3.8	3.9	4.0
4.1	4.2	4.3	4.4	4.5	4.6	4.7	4.8	4.9	5.0
5.1	5.2	5.3	5.4	5.5	5.6	5.7	5.8	5.9	6.0
6.1	6.2	6.3	6.4	6.5	6.6	6.7	6.8	6.9	7.0
7.1	7.2	7.3	7.4	7.5	7.6	7.7	7.8	7.9	8.0
8.1	8.2	8.3	8.4	8.5	8.6	8.7	8.8	8.9	9.0
9.1	9.2	9.3	9.4	9.5	9.6	9.7	9.8	9.9	10

Exercise 9 • page 73

Lesson 10 Practice B

Objective

- Practice concepts from the chapter.

After students complete the **Practice** in the textbook, have them continue to practice working with fractions and decimals with activities from the chapter.

4 (f)–(h) Remind students that they do not need to round the numbers to the nearest tenth first, just to the nearest whole number.

---

1 (a) What number is 0.1 less than 0.85?
0.75
(b) What number is 0.01 more than 0.85?
0.86
(c) What number should be added to 0.85 to get 1?
0.15

2 What sign, >, <, or =, goes in each ◯?

(a) 8.09 $<$ 8.9   (b) 3.4 $=$ 3.40

(c) 64.3 $>$ 21.28   (d) 100 $>$ 1.00

3 Order the numbers from least to greatest.

(a) 0.4, $\frac{3}{10}$, 0.7, $\frac{8}{10}$ $\frac{3}{10}$, 0.4, 0.7, $\frac{8}{10}$

(b) 1, 0.45, 0, 0.09   0, 0.09, 0.45, 1

(c) 4, 0.4, 0.04, 0.44   0.04, 0.4, 0.44, 4

(d) $3\frac{7}{10}$, 2.9, $2\frac{5}{10}$, 3.3 $2\frac{5}{10}$, 2.9, 3.3, $3\frac{7}{10}$

(e) $5\frac{3}{100}$, 5.3, 3.5, $3\frac{5}{100}$ $3\frac{5}{100}$, 3.5, $5\frac{3}{100}$, 5.3

(f) $3\frac{1}{2}$, $\frac{3}{2}$, $2\frac{3}{5}$, 2.35 $\frac{3}{2}$, 2.35, $2\frac{3}{5}$, $3\frac{1}{2}$

---

4 Round each decimal to a whole number.

(a) 0.2   0   (b) 0.7   1

(c) 4.5   5   (d) 19.4   19

(e) 58.5   59   (f) 1.62   2

(g) 45.08   45   (h) 100.51 101

5 Round each number to 1 decimal place.

(a) 0.53   0.5   (b) 0.47   0.5

(c) 0.25   0.3   (d) 1.09   1.1

(e) 3.47   3.5   (f) 93.93   93.9

(g) 6.95   7.0   (h) 38.97   39.0

6 A watermelon weighs 5.8 kg. About how much does the watermelon weigh to the nearest kilogram?
6 kg

7 Usain ran the 100 m dash in 10.49 seconds.

(a) Express his time to the nearest tenth of a second.
10.5 sec
(b) Express his time to the nearest second.
10 sec

Brain Works

★ Hex

Materials: Hex Board (BLM) in a dry erase sleeve, two colored dry erase markers

Each player chooses a color and a side (black or white). On each turn, players color in one empty hexagon. Once chosen, the hexagon cannot change color.

The first player to form a connected path of hexagons using his color from one side of the board to the other wins.

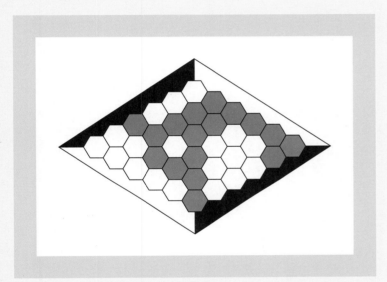

In the sample game, blue has completed a connecting path first.

Exercise 10 • page 76

104

8 Dion, Sofia, and Emma each swam 200 m. Their times in minutes are shown here.

Dion	2.78 min
Sofia	2.73 min
Emma	2.75 min

(a) Who swam the fastest?
Sofia

(b) Express each time to 1 decimal point.
Dion: 2.8 min; Sofia: 2.7 min; Emma: 2.8 min

9 A flagpole is 4.98 m tall.

(a) Express the height of the flagpole to the nearest tenth of a meter.
5.0 m

(b) Express the height of the flagpole to the nearest meter.
5 m

10 Mei played tennis for 0.5 hours.

(a) Express this time in hours as a fraction in simplest form.
$\frac{1}{2}$ h

(b) Express this time in minutes.
30 min

11 Alice is 4.25 ft tall.

(a) Express her height in feet as a mixed number in simplest form.
$4\frac{1}{4}$ ft

(b) Express her height in feet and inches.
4 ft 3 in

Exercise 10 · page 76

104   12-10 Practice B

Chapter 12 Decimals

Exercise 1

Basics

1 Complete the table.

	Fraction	Decimal
	$\frac{1}{10}$	0.1
	$\frac{3}{10}$	0.3
	$\frac{7}{10}$	0.7
	$\frac{9}{10}$	0.9

2 Write a decimal to make the equations true.

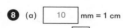

(a) $0.4 + \boxed{0.6} = 1$ (b) $1 - 0.4 = \boxed{0.6}$

Practice

3 Shade each square to show the decimal.

(a) 0.5   (b) 0.8

4 Write the decimal indicated by each arrow.

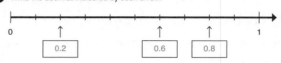

    0.2   0.6   0.8

5 Write the decimals represented by the place-value discs.

(a)

Ones	Tenths
0	8

(b)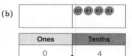

Ones	Tenths
0	4

6 Write each fraction as a decimal.

(a) $\frac{3}{10} = \boxed{0.3}$ (b) $\frac{1}{10} = \boxed{0.1}$

(c) $\frac{9}{10} = \boxed{0.9}$ (d) $\frac{40}{100} = \boxed{0.4}$

7 Max ran 0.7 km. He wants to run 1 km. How much farther does he have to run?

$1 - 0.7 = 0.3$

0.3 km

8 (a) $\boxed{10}$ mm = 1 cm

(b) 1 mm = $\boxed{\frac{1}{10}}$ cm

(c) 1 mm = $\boxed{0.1}$ cm

(d) 4 mm = $\boxed{0.4}$ cm

Challenge

9 1 deciliter (dL) is $\frac{1}{10}$ of 1 liter. Pierre has a bottle with 1 L of water. He drank 2 deciliters of water.

(a) Express the amount he drank as a fraction of a liter.

$\frac{2}{10}$ L

(b) Express the amount he drank in liters as a decimal.

0.2 L

(c) Express the amount of water left in liters as a decimal.

0.8 L

Teacher's Guide 4B Chapter 12

Exercise 2

Basics

1

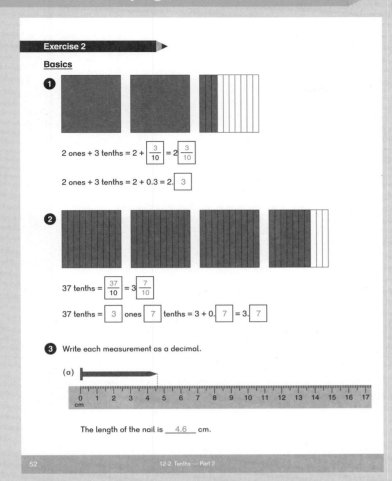

2 ones + 3 tenths = 2 + $\boxed{\dfrac{3}{10}}$ = 2$\boxed{\dfrac{3}{10}}$

2 ones + 3 tenths = 2 + 0.3 = 2.$\boxed{3}$

2

37 tenths = $\boxed{\dfrac{37}{10}}$ = 3$\boxed{\dfrac{7}{10}}$

37 tenths = $\boxed{3}$ ones $\boxed{7}$ tenths = 3 + 0.$\boxed{7}$ = 3.$\boxed{7}$

3 Write each measurement as a decimal.

(a)

The length of the nail is ___4.6___ cm.

(b)

The block weighs ___2.4___ kg.

(c)

There is a total of ___3.5___ L of water.

4 Write the decimals represented by the place-value discs.

(a)

Tens	Ones	Tenths
	5	5

(b)

Tens	Ones	Tenths
9	6	7

Practice

5 Write the decimals indicated by each arrow.

(a)

| 0.6 | 1.5 | 2.4 | 3.8 |

(b)

| 18.3 | 19.5 | 20.2 | 21.6 |

6 Write each number indicated by the place-value discs as a decimal and as a mixed number (or whole number).

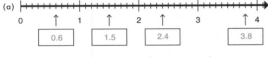 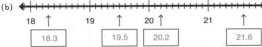

	Decimal	Mixed Number
	1.9	$1\frac{9}{10}$
	9.1	$9\frac{1}{10}$
	2.1	$2\frac{1}{10}$
	50.7	$50\frac{7}{10}$

7 Complete the number patterns.

(a)

| 3.7 | 3.8 | 3.9 | 4.0 | 4.1 | 4.2 |

(b)

| 10.2 | 10.1 | 10.0 | 9.9 | 9.8 | 9.7 |

(c)

| 38.2 | 39.2 | 40.2 | 41.2 | 42.2 | 43.2 |

8 (a) 9 + 0.4 = $\boxed{9.4}$ (b) 60 + 1 + 0.8 = $\boxed{61.8}$

(c) 0.5 + 30 = $\boxed{30.5}$ (d) 900 + 8 + 0.1 = $\boxed{908.1}$

(e) 20 + 9 + $\boxed{0.7}$ = 29.7 (f) 0.5 + $\boxed{4}$ = 4.5

Challenge

9 Write >, <, or = in each ◯.

(a) $4\frac{3}{10}$ ⊘ 3.4   (b) 70 ⊘ 7.0

(c) 21 tenths ⊜ 2.1   (d) 6.7 ⊘ $\frac{60}{10}$

(e) 6 ⊘ 0.6   (f) 1.3 ⊘ 130 tenths

10 (a) 12.3 = $\boxed{123}$ tenths   (b) 132.4 = $\boxed{1,324}$ tenths

Teacher's Guide 4B Chapter 12

Exercise 3

Basics

1 Complete the table.

	Fraction	Decimal
	$\frac{1}{100}$	0.01
	$\frac{7}{100}$	0.07
	$\frac{7}{10} + \frac{9}{100}$	0.79
	$\frac{43}{100}$	0.43

2 Shade each square to show the decimal.

(a) 0.28

(b) 0.92

Practice

3 Write the decimals indicated by each arrow.

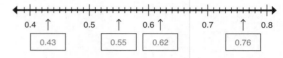

0.4 ↑	0.5	↑	0.6 ↑	0.7	↑	0.8

| 0.43 | | 0.55 | 0.62 | | 0.76 | |

4 Write the decimals represented by the place-value discs.

(a)

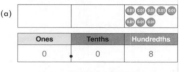

Ones	Tenths	Hundredths
0	0	8

(b)

Ones	Tenths	Hundredths
0	7	5

5 Complete the table.

	Decimal	Fraction
	0.17	$\frac{17}{100}$
	0.82	$\frac{82}{100}$

6 Complete the number patterns.

(a) | 0.17 | 0.18 | 0.19 | 0.2 | 0.21 | 0.22 |

(b) | 0.64 | 0.63 | 0.62 | 0.61 | 0.6 | 0.59 |

7 Write the decimal.

(a) $\frac{6}{100}$ = 0.06

(b) $\frac{56}{100}$ = 0.56

(c) $\frac{8}{10} + \frac{7}{100}$ = 0.87

(d) 0.6 + 0.08 = 0.68

(e) 1 − 0.65 = 0.35

(f) 0.51 + 0.49 = 1

8 Express each length as a decimal.

(a) 4 cm = 0.04 m

(b) 99 cm = 0.99 m

Teacher's Guide 4B Chapter 12

Exercise 4

Basics

1 Complete the table.

	Fraction	Decimal
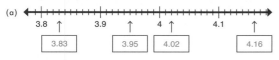	$1 + \dfrac{3}{10} + \dfrac{6}{100}$	1.36
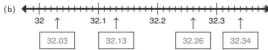	$2 + \dfrac{64}{100}$	2.64
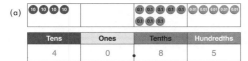	$2\dfrac{8}{100}$	2.08
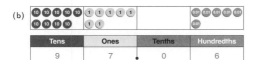	$1 + \dfrac{5}{10} + \dfrac{5}{100}$	1.55
	$\dfrac{133}{100}$	1.33

2 Shade the squares to show the decimal.

(a) 1.28

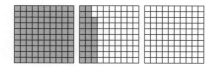

(b) 2.71

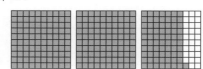

3 (a) Write the decimal represented by the place-value discs.

Tens	Ones	Tenths	Hundredths
7	5	8	4

(b) The digit __7__ is in the tens place. Its value is __70__.

(c) The digit __5__ is in the ones place. Its value is __5__.

(d) The digit __8__ is in the __tenths__ place. Its value is 0.8.

(e) The digit 4 is in the __hundredths__ place. Its value is __0.04__.

(f) 70 + 5 + 0.8 + 0.04 = | 75.84 |

Practice

4 Write the decimal indicated by each arrow.

(a)

3.8   3.9   4   4.1

| 3.83 | | 3.95 | 4.02 | | 4.16 |

(b)

32   32.1   32.2   32.3

| 32.03 | 32.13 | | 32.26 | 32.34 |

5 Write the decimals represented by the place-value discs. Then write each number in expanded form.

(a)

Tens	Ones	Tenths	Hundredths
4	0	8	5

Expanded form: 40 + 0.8 + 0.05

(b)

Tens	Ones	Tenths	Hundredths
9	7	0	6

Expanded form: 90 + 7 + 0.06

6 Complete the number patterns.

(a)

| 4.97 | 4.98 | 4.99 | 5 | 5.01 | 5.02 |

(b)

| 8.62 | 8.61 | 8.6 | 8.59 | 8.58 | 8.57 |

(c)

| 29.62 | 29.72 | 29.82 | 29.92 | 30.02 | 30.12 |

7 Write the decimal.

(a) $7\dfrac{9}{100}$ = | 7.09 |

(b) $3\dfrac{56}{100}$ = | 3.56 |

(c) $\dfrac{170}{100}$ = | 1.7 |

(d) 7 + 0.6 + 0.08 = | 7.68 |

(e) 500 + 0.8 + 0.04 = | 500.84 |

(f) 30 + 7 + | 0.3 | + 0.01 = 37.31

(g) | 0.65 | + 6 + 40 = 46.65

(h) six and four hundredths = | 6.04 |

Exercise 5

Basics

1 Express 0.8 as a fraction in simplest form.

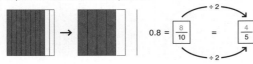

$$0.8 = \frac{8}{10} = \frac{4}{5}$$

2 Express 0.45 as a fraction in simplest form.

$$0.45 = \frac{45}{100} = \frac{9}{20}$$

3 Express 0.32 as a fraction in simplest form.

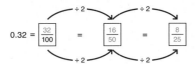

$$0.32 = \frac{32}{100} = \frac{16}{50} = \frac{8}{25}$$

4 Express 4.48 as a mixed number in simplest form.

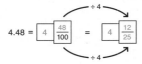

$$4.48 = 4\frac{48}{100} = 4\frac{12}{25}$$

Practice

5 Finish labeling each tick mark with a decimal and with a fraction in simplest form.

6 Match.

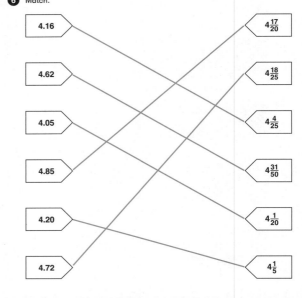

4.16		$4\frac{17}{20}$
4.62		$4\frac{18}{25}$
4.05		$4\frac{4}{25}$
4.85		$4\frac{31}{50}$
4.20		$4\frac{1}{20}$
4.72		$4\frac{1}{5}$

7 Write each decimal as a fraction or mixed number in simplest form.

(a) 6.4 $6\frac{2}{5}$

(b) 0.85 $\frac{17}{20}$

(c) 8.08 $8\frac{2}{25}$

(d) 10.54 $10\frac{27}{50}$

8 A beaker contains 2.35 L of solution. Express this amount in liters as a mixed number in simplest form.

$2\frac{7}{20}$ L

9 A package weighs 7.64 kg. Express this weight in kilograms as a mixed number in simplest form.

$7\frac{16}{25}$ kg

10 A football is 10.5 in long and the white stripe is 2.25 in from the end of the ball. Express each measurement in inches as a mixed number in simplest form.

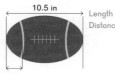

Length of football: $10\frac{1}{2}$ in
Distance for white stripe: $2\frac{1}{4}$ in

Exercise 6

Basics

1 Express $\frac{1}{2}$ as a decimal.

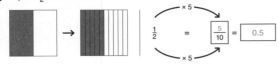

$\frac{1}{2} = \boxed{\frac{5}{10}} = \boxed{0.5}$

2 Express $\frac{17}{20}$ as a decimal.

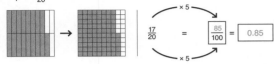

$\frac{17}{20} = \boxed{\frac{85}{100}} = \boxed{0.85}$

3 Express $\frac{9}{5}$ as a decimal.

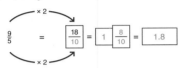

$\frac{9}{5} = \boxed{\frac{18}{10}} = 1\boxed{\frac{8}{10}} = \boxed{1.8}$

4 Express $7\frac{6}{25}$ as a decimal.

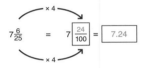

$7\frac{6}{25} = 7\boxed{\frac{24}{100}} = \boxed{7.24}$

Practice

5 Express each fraction as a decimal.

$\frac{1}{2} = \boxed{0.5}$

$\frac{1}{4} = \boxed{0.25}$ | $\frac{3}{4} = \boxed{0.75}$

$\frac{1}{5} = \boxed{0.2}$ | $\frac{2}{5} = \boxed{0.4}$ | $\frac{3}{5} = \boxed{0.6}$ | $\frac{4}{5} = \boxed{0.8}$

$\frac{1}{20} = \boxed{0.05}$ | $\frac{7}{20} = \boxed{0.35}$ | $\frac{13}{20} = \boxed{0.65}$ | $\frac{19}{20} = \boxed{0.95}$

$\frac{1}{25} = \boxed{0.04}$ | $\frac{7}{25} = \boxed{0.28}$ | $\frac{13}{25} = \boxed{0.52}$ | $\frac{24}{25} = \boxed{0.96}$

$\frac{1}{50} = \boxed{0.02}$ | $\frac{7}{50} = \boxed{0.14}$ | $\frac{13}{50} = \boxed{0.26}$ | $\frac{49}{50} = \boxed{0.98}$

6 A football weighs $14\frac{2}{5}$ oz. Express the weight of the football as a decimal.
14.4 oz

7 The wingspan of a house swallow is $8\frac{3}{4}$ in. Express this length as a decimal.
8.75 in

Exercise 7

Check

1 In the number 98.95:

(a) The value of the digit in the tenths place is ___0.9___.

(b) The value of the digit in the tens place is ___100___ times the value of the digit in the tenths place.

(c) The digit with a value of 0.05 is in the ___hundredths___ place.

(d) Write the number in expanded form.
90 + 8 + 0.9 + 0.05

2 (a) $8 + \boxed{0.2} + 0.06 = 8.26$

(b) $\boxed{0.04} + 0.6 + 72 = 72.64$

3 Express each value as a fraction or as a mixed number in simplest form.

(a) 0.3 $\frac{3}{10}$

(b) 0.07 $\frac{7}{100}$

(c) 0.21 $\frac{21}{100}$

(d) 4.79 $4\frac{79}{100}$

(e) 8.90 $8\frac{9}{10}$

(f) 6.5 $6\frac{1}{2}$

(g) 6.15 $6\frac{3}{20}$

(h) 11.04 $11\frac{1}{25}$

4 Express each value as a decimal.

(a) $\frac{4}{10}$ 0.4

(b) $10\frac{7}{10}$ 10.7

(c) $\frac{25}{100}$ 0.25

(d) $7\frac{52}{100}$ 7.52

(e) $\frac{37}{10}$ 3.7

(f) $\frac{620}{100}$ 6.2

(g) $2\frac{3}{4}$ 2.75

(h) $6\frac{17}{20}$ 6.85

(i) $\frac{7}{2}$ 3.5

(j) $\frac{32}{25}$ 1.28

5 (a) What number is 2 hundredths more than 3.99?
4.01

(b) What number is 2 tenths more than 3.99?
4.19

(c) What number is 2 hundredths less than 6.01?
5.99

(d) What number is 2 tenths less than 6.01?
5.81

Challenge

6 Express each value as a decimal.

(a) $3 + \frac{2}{5} + \frac{2}{25}$ 3.48

(b) $8 + \frac{1}{2} + \frac{3}{50}$ 8.56

Exercise 8

Basics

1 Shade the squares to show each decimal. Then write > or < in each ◯.

(a)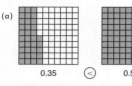

0.35 ⓛ< 0.53

(b)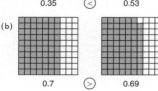

0.7 ⓛ> 0.69

2 Circle the digits in the greatest place that are different in each number. Then write > or < in each ◯.

(a)

Ones	Tenths	Hundredths
1	⑤	2
1	⑧	1

0.5 ⓛ< 0.8

1.52 ⓛ< 1.81

(b)

Ones	Tenths	Hundredths
4	6	⑦
4	6	⓪

0.07 ⓛ> 0

4.67 ⓛ> 4.6

3 Write any missing digits, then write > or < in each ◯.

(a) Compare $3\frac{4}{5}$ and 3.45

$3\frac{4}{5}$ = 3.⬚8 │ 3.⬚8 ⓛ> 3.45 │ $3\frac{4}{5}$ ⓛ> 3.45

(b) Compare $2\frac{1}{8}$ and 2.75

2.75 = 2 ⬚$\frac{3}{4}$ │ $2\frac{1}{8}$ ⓛ< 2 ⬚$\frac{3}{4}$ │ $2\frac{1}{8}$ ⓛ< 2.75

(c) Compare $6\frac{4}{7}$ and 7.19

6 ⓛ< 7 │ $6\frac{4}{7}$ ⓛ< 7.19

Practice

4 Write >, <, or = in each ◯.

(a) 1.5 ⓛ< 1.8

(b) 6.52 ⓛ> 5.62

(c) 1.8 ⓛ> 1.72

(d) 4.15 ⓛ< 41.5

(e) 2.3 ⓛ> $\frac{23}{100}$

(f) $2\frac{1}{4}$ ⓛ> 2.2

5 Write the numbers in decreasing order.

(a) 8.89, 88.9, 9.88, 8.98   88.9, 9.88, 8.98, 8.89

(b) 0.57, $\frac{1}{3}$, 0.77, $1\frac{2}{3}$ $1\frac{2}{3}$, 0.77, 0.57, $\frac{1}{3}$

6 Write the numbers in increasing order.

(a) 7.4, 7.04, 4.7, 7.7   4.7, 7.04, 7.4, 7.7

(b) 132.89, 321.98, 132.98, 132.8   132.8, 132.89, 132.98, 321.98

(c) 2.7, $2\frac{4}{5}$, $2\frac{3}{4}$, 2.07   2.07, 2.7, $2\frac{3}{4}$, $2\frac{4}{5}$

Challenge

7 Use all of the following digits and the decimal point.

6, 1, 5, .

(a) Write the greatest number less than 100.
65.1

(b) Write the least number.
1.56

Exercise 9

Basics

1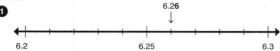

(a) Which number is 6.26 closer to, 6.2 or 6.3? 6.3

(b) 6.26 is __6.3__ when rounded to the nearest tenth.

(c) Look at the digit in the __hundredths__ place to round to the nearest tenth.

2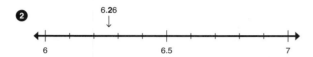

(a) Which number is 6.26 closer to, 6 or 7? 6

(b) 6.26 is __6__ when rounded to a whole number.

(c) Look at the digit in the __tenths__ place to round to a whole number.

3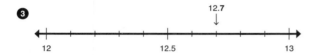

12.7 is __13__ when rounded to a whole number.

4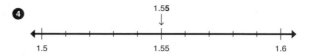

1.55 is halfway between 1.5 and __1.6__, so we round up.

1.55 is __1.6__ when rounded to 1 decimal place.

5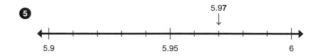

5.97 is __6.0__ when rounded to 1 decimal place.

Practice

6 Answer using the given decimals above the number line.

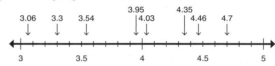

(a) Which decimals are 3 when rounded to a whole number?
3.06, 3.3

(b) Which decimals are 4 when rounded to a whole number?
3.54, 3.95, 4.03, 4.35, 4.46

(c) Which decimals are 4.5 when rounded to 1 decimal place?
4.46

(d) Which decimals are 4.0 when rounded to 1 decimal place?
3.95, 4.03

7 Round each decimal to 1 decimal place and to a whole number.

Decimal	1 Decimal Place	Whole Number
6.89	6.9	7
0.64	0.6	1
9.65	9.7	10
402.87	402.9	403
36.04	36.0	36

Challenge

8 Fill in the missing digit so that the number rounds to 2 when rounded to a whole number and 2.5 when rounded to 1 decimal place.

2 . 4 5

9 What is the least number with two decimal places that rounds to 2 when rounded to the nearest tenth?
1.95

Exercise 10 • pages 76–78

Check

1 Complete the number patterns.

(a)

3.08	3.1	3.12	3.14	3.16	3.18

(b)

11.07	11.05	11.03	11.01	10.99	10.97

(c)

19.3	19.6	19.9	20.2	20.5	20.8

2 Write > or < in each ◯.

(a) 16.4 ⊙> 14.8

(b) 12.02 ⊙< 12.20

(c) 2.3 ⊙> $\frac{23}{50}$

(d) $2\frac{7}{40}$ ⊙< 2.7

3 Write the numbers in increasing order.

(a) 6.07, 7.06, 6.7, 7.6   6.07, 6.7, 7.06, 7.6

(b) 2.92, $2\frac{3}{5}$, $\frac{29}{10}$, $2\frac{43}{50}$ $2\frac{3}{5}$, $2\frac{43}{50}$, $\frac{29}{10}$, 2.92

4 A monarch butterfly's wingspan measures 8.93 cm.

(a) Round this number to a tenth of a centimeter.
8.9 cm

(b) Round this number to a whole number of centimeters.
9 cm

5 Consider the following numbers.

7.08, 6.98, 7.14, 6.03, 7.03

(a) Which number is closest to 7?
6.98

(b) Which number is closest to 7.1?
7.08

6 Use all of the digits and a decimal point for each number.

3, 4, 5, .

(a) Write a number that is between 3.35 and 3.53.
3.45

(b) Write two numbers that round to 3.5 when rounded to 1 decimal place.
3.45, 3.54

(c) Write two numbers that round to 4 when rounded to a whole number.
3.54, 4.35

7 What decimal is the same distance from 6.3 as it is from 6.4 on the number line?
6.35

Challenge

8 List all the numbers with 1 decimal place that round to 5 when rounded to a whole number.

4.5, 4.6, 4.7, 4.8, 4.9, 5.0, 5.1, 5.2, 5.3, 5.4

9 List all the numbers with two decimal places that round to 3.4 when rounded to 1 decimal place.

3.35, 3.36, 3.37, 3.38, 3.39, 3.40, 3.41, 3.42, 3.43, 3.44

Suggested number of class periods: 10–11

	Lesson	Page	Resources		Objectives
	Chapter Opener	p. 119	TB:	p. 105	Review addition and subtraction of money and consider ways to add or subtract decimals.
1	Adding and Subtracting Tenths	p. 120	TB: WB:	p. 106 p. 79	Add and subtract decimals with tenths using mental math.
2	Adding Tenths with Regrouping	p. 122	TB: WB:	p. 109 p. 81	Add decimals to the tenths place with regrouping.
3	Subtracting Tenths with Regrouping	p. 125	TB: WB:	p. 113 p. 83	Subtract decimals to the tenths place.
4	Practice A	p. 128	TB: WB:	p. 117 p. 86	Practice adding and subtracting decimals to the tenths place.
5	Adding Hundredths	p. 129	TB: WB:	p. 119 p. 88	Add decimals to the hundredths place.
6	Subtracting from 1 and 0.1	p. 132	TB: WB:	p. 123 p. 90	Subtract one-place and two-place decimals less than 1 from 1. Subtract two-place decimals less than 0.1 from 0.1.
7	Subtracting Hundredths	p. 134	TB: WB:	p. 126 p. 92	Subtract decimals to hundredths.
8	Money, Decimals, and Fractions	p. 137	TB: WB:	p. 130 p. 95	Relate money notation to decimals. Estimate, add, and subtract money amounts using the vertical algorithm.
9	Practice B	p. 139	TB: WB:	p. 134 p. 98	Practice adding and subtracting decimals to the hundredths place.
	Review 3	p. 141	TB: WB:	p. 136 p. 101	Review concepts from Chapter 1 through Chapter 13.
	Workbook Solutions	p. 143			

In Dimensions Math 2A and 3A, students learned both mental math strategies and algorithms for addition and subtraction of whole numbers. In this chapter, those skills are further developed with decimals to the hundredths place.

Students will use basic mental math strategies for adding and subtracting tenths. They will first add and subtract tenths with regrouping between place values, then extend these skills to hundredths.

Since decimals are written using the base ten number system, the algorithms for decimals work the same as for whole numbers. Digits are lined up vertically by place value and are added or subtracted from the least place to the greatest place.

The decimal point always separates a decimal into its whole number component and its fractional or decimal component. It is therefore always placed between the ones and tenths places. Students will eventually align digits vertically by place value.

Throughout the lessons, students are encouraged to estimate before solving. Estimation helps students avoid errors by determining if their answers are reasonable.

In this chapter, students will begin to add numbers with tenths to numbers with hundredths. When subtracting a decimal with hundredths from a decimal with tenths, students can write a 0 in the hundredths place to help them be sure they are adding or subtracting the correct digits (for example, $3.5 - 1.87 = 3.50 - 1.87$).

For students struggling with the place value representation of decimals, use place-value mats and discs to review the concept that digits in places one column to the left are ten times the value of the same digit to the right, and digits in places one column to the right are one-tenth the value of the same digit to the left.

Mental Math for Addition and Subtraction

Students will see that the same mental math strategies used for whole number addition and subtraction can also be used with decimals.

Example: 3.6 + 1.5

If we think of the numbers as 36 tenths and 15 tenths, this becomes an easier problem.

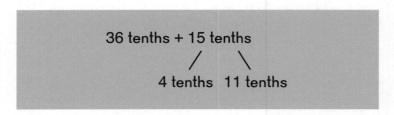

36 tenths + 15 tenths = 40 tenths + 11 tenths
= 51 tenths = 5.1

Example: 0.45 − 0.18

45 hundredths − 18 hundredths
= 45 hundredths − 20 hundredths + 2 hundredths
= 27 hundredths = 0.27

Addition Algorithm

A general procedure for demonstrating the addition algorithm with place-value discs is shown here.

Example: 2.75 + 1.55

Add the hundredths:

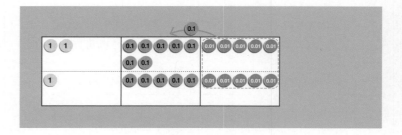

5 hundredths + 5 hundredths = 10 hundredths

Regroup 10 hundredths as 1 tenth.

Add the tenths including any regrouped tenths:

$$\begin{array}{r} 1 \\ 2.7\,5 \\ +\ \ 1.5\,5 \\ \hline 0 \end{array}$$

7 tenths + 5 tenths + 1 tenth = 13 tenths

Regroup 13 tenths as 1 one and 3 tenths.

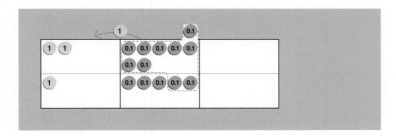

Put a decimal point between the tenths and the ones places.

Add the ones, including any regrouped ones:

$$\begin{array}{r} 1\ 1 \\ 2.7\,5 \\ +\ \ 1.5\,5 \\ \hline .3\,0 \end{array}$$

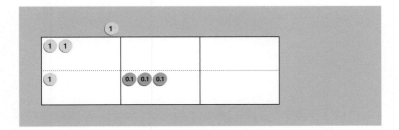

2 ones + 1 one + 1 one = 4 ones

2.75 + 1.55 = 4.30 = 4.3

At this point, students can omit trailing zeros from the answer. For example, they can write the answer 4.30 as 4.3 because 4 ones and 30 hundredths = 4 ones and 3 tenths.

$$\begin{array}{r} 1\ 1 \\ 2.7\,5 \\ +\ \ 1.5\,5 \\ \hline 4.3\,0 \end{array}$$

Subtraction Algorithm

Example: 1.45 − 0.78

Subtract the hundredths:

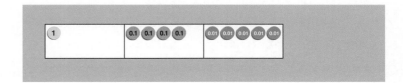

There are not enough hundredths in the hundredths place to subtract 8 hundredths.

Regroup 1 tenth as 10 hundredths.
45 hundredths is now 3 tenths and 15 hundredths.

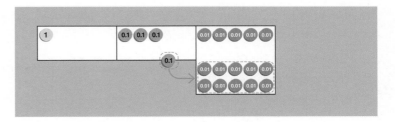

15 hundredths − 8 hundredths = 7 hundredths

Write the difference of 7 hundredths below the line in the hundredths column.

Subtract the tenths:

$$\begin{array}{r} 3\ 15 \\ 1.\cancel{4}\cancel{5} \\ -\ \ 0.7\,8 \\ \hline 7 \end{array}$$

There are not enough tenths to subtract 7 tenths. Regroup 1 one as 10 tenths. There are now 13 tenths.

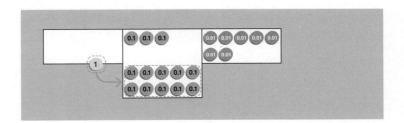

13 tenths − 7 tenths = 6 tenths

Write the difference of 6 tenths below the line in the tenths column. Put a decimal point between the tenths and ones place.

$$\begin{array}{r} 13\ 15 \\ \cancel{1}.\cancel{4}\cancel{5} \\ -\ \ 0.7\,8 \\ \hline 0.6\,7 \end{array}$$

1.45 − 0.78 = 0.67

Money

Lesson 8 uses money as a way to practice decimal computations to the hundredths.

Coins and bills are not all base ten (for example, 5-dollar bills and quarters), but we use the base ten system when writing money quantities. We can use the same procedures for adding and subtracting decimals. When expressing values as dollars, answers will always have two decimal places.

Materials

- 10-sided die
- Counters
- Deck of cards
- Place-value discs
- Play bills, pennies, dimes
- Whiteboards

Blackline Masters

- Hundredths Chart (BLM)
- Magic Squares (BLM)
- Number Cards (BLM)

Activities

Games and activities included in this chapter are designed to provide practice with adding and subtracting decimals. The included activities can be used after students complete the **Do** questions, or anytime additional practice is needed.

Chapter Opener

Objective

- Review addition and subtraction of money and consider ways to add or subtract decimals.

Have students discuss Mei's question. Ask them to recall what they have learned about adding money and how that relates to what they now know about decimals.

Students should understand that the decimal point is always between the dollars and cents. When we add money, we are adding cents to cents and dollars to dollars. If there are more than 100 cents, we can convert cents to dollars or dollars and cents.

Continue to Lesson 1.

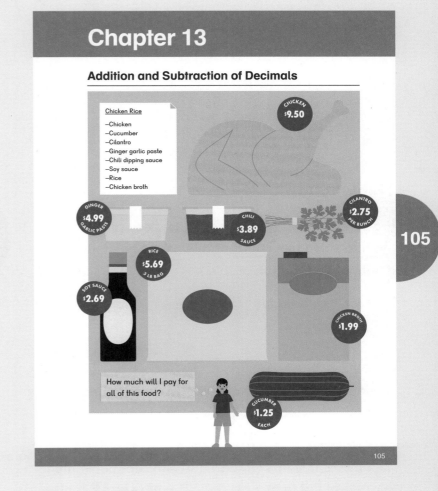

Lesson 1 Adding and Subtracting Tenths

Objective

- Add and subtract decimals with tenths using mental math.

Lesson Materials

- Place-value discs: ones and tenths

Think

Provide students with place-value discs and use them to solve the **Think** problems. They should write an equation for each problem.

Discuss the methods students used.

Learn

Students should see that it is easy to add (and subtract) the decimals in these problems as we are adding and subtracting like units, tenths.

Alex thinks it is easy to add and subtract decimals by thinking of the tenths as units: 5 tenths and 3 tenths.

(b) Just as in earlier grades when students subtracted 3 dogs from 5 dogs, 3 cm from 5 cm, and 3 thousands from 5 thousands, they can subtract 3 tenths from 5 tenths: 5 tenths − 3 tenths = 2 tenths.

Have students compare their solutions from **Think** with the ones shown in the textbook.

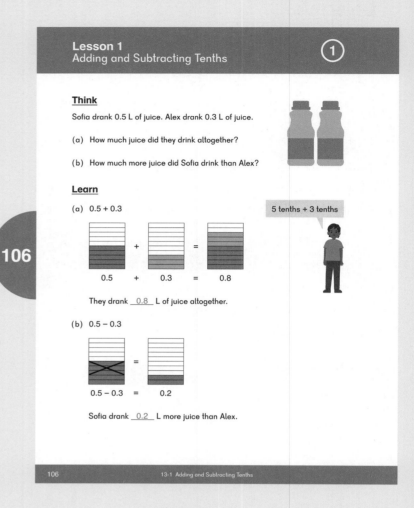

106

Do

❶—❹ Discuss these problems with students. Have them use the place-value discs to help solve the problems if necessary.

❸ Students should see that 10 tenths can be regrouped as 1 one (similar to regrouping 10 ones as 1 ten).

❹ Students can think in terms of the place value units. 1 one is regrouped as 10 tenths.

❻ Just as 13 ones − 7 ones is 6 ones, 13 tenths − 7 tenths is 6 tenths.

❼—❽ Students should be able to solve these problems independently.

Exercise 1 • page 79

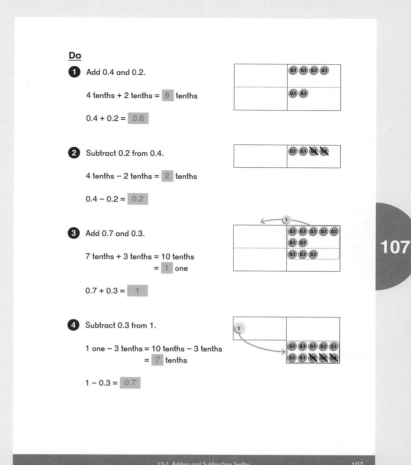

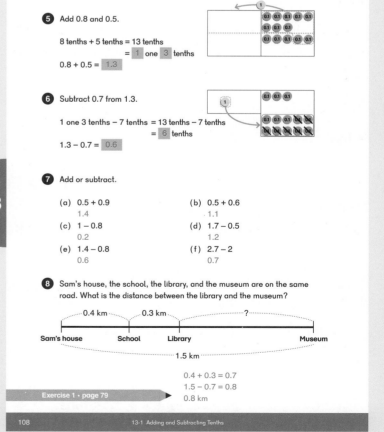

Lesson 2 Adding Tenths with Regrouping

Objective

- Add decimals to the tenths place with regrouping.

Lesson Materials

- Place-value discs: tens, ones, and tenths

Think

Provide students with place-value discs and pose the **Think** problem.

Discuss Sofia's estimation. Ask students if her estimate will be greater or less than the actual sum. Since she is rounding both numbers up, the exact answer will be less than the estimated answer.

Students can use place-value discs or any other known strategy to add the numbers together.

Record their strategies on the board and discuss the methods students used.

Learn

Have students compare their solutions from **Think** with the ones shown in the textbook. Discuss the two methods shown.

Method 1

In Dimensions Math 1, students learned how to "make 10" when adding two single digit numbers together. In Dimensions Math 2, they learned to "make 100." Here, they are learning to "make 1." Once the numbers are expressed as units of tenths, students can use mental math to add them together, for example:

$$27 \text{ tenths} + 15 \text{ tenths}$$
$$\diagup \quad \diagdown$$
$$3 \text{ tenths} \quad 12 \text{ tenths}$$

27 tenths + 15 tenths = 30 tenths + 12 tenths
= 42 tenths = 4.2

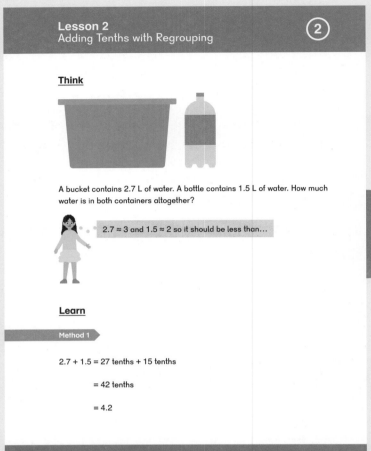

Lesson 2
Adding Tenths with Regrouping   ②

Think

A bucket contains 2.7 L of water. A bottle contains 1.5 L of water. How much water is in both containers altogether?

2.7 ≈ 3 and 1.5 ≈ 2 so it should be less than…

Learn

Method 1

2.7 + 1.5 = 27 tenths + 15 tenths

= 42 tenths

= 4.2

13-2 Adding Tenths with Regrouping   109

109

Method 2

As we saw in Chapter 12, decimals are an extension of the base ten system, so the same vertical algorithm works for adding decimals.

Students should be fluent with the addition algorithm for whole numbers. Discuss how the algorithm is similar for decimals.

Just as when adding whole numbers with the algorithm, we always add like units. In the same way, with decimals, we add ones to ones and tenths to tenths.

When 10 tenths are regrouped as 1 one, we can write the regrouped digit above the digits in the ones place.

Ask students what Dion means when he says we line up the place values. (We line up the ones and the tenths and the decimal goes between them.)

Do

❶ — ❸ Discuss the problems with students. Emma reminds students to estimate their answers first. This will help them see if their final answers are reasonable.

❸ Ask students why Mei puts a 0 in the tenths place. 4.6 has one decimal place and 27 has none, which is why Mei is expressing 27 as 27.0 in order for both numbers that we are adding to have the same number of decimal places.

Having the same number of decimal places when adding helps students keep the digits in each place value aligned. It will also help when they start subtracting with regrouping.

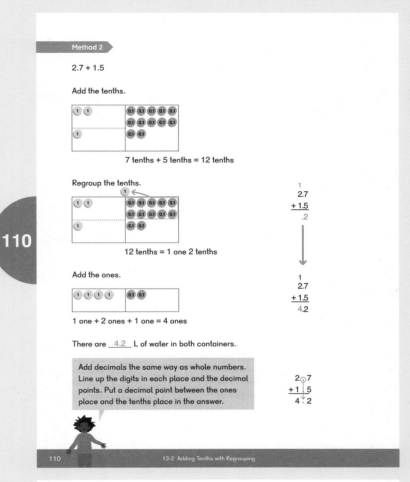

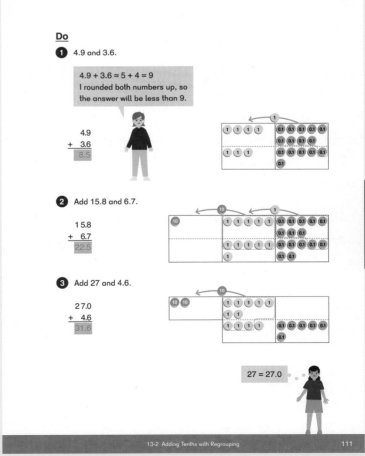

4 Alex reminds students that using the algorithm, we add in the least place first, then the next greater place, and so on.

5 — **6** Students should be able to work these problems independently.

Activity

▲ Greatest Addition

Materials: 10-sided die or Number Cards (BLM) 0—9

Have students draw a personal game board, as shown below, on paper or a dry erase board.

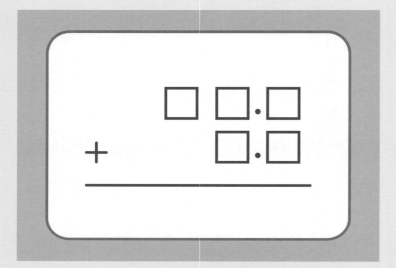

Players take turns rolling the die or drawing a card. On each turn, they place the number drawn in one of the empty boxes. When the boxes are filled, they add the two numbers.

The player with the greatest final sum in each round scores a point. The first player with five points is the winner.

Exercise 2 • page 81

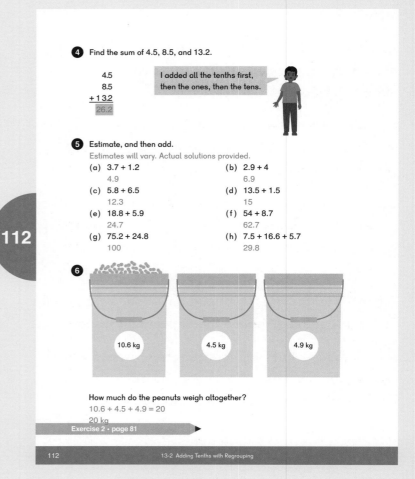

4 Find the sum of 4.5, 8.5, and 13.2.

4.5
8.5
+ 13.2
26.2

I added all the tenths first, then the ones, then the tens.

5 Estimate, and then add.
Estimates will vary. Actual solutions provided.
(a) 3.7 + 1.2
   4.9
(b) 2.9 + 4
   6.9
(c) 5.8 + 6.5
   12.3
(d) 13.5 + 1.5
   15
(e) 18.8 + 5.9
   24.7
(f) 54 + 8.7
   62.7
(g) 75.2 + 24.8
   100
(h) 7.5 + 16.6 + 5.7
   29.8

6

10.6 kg   4.5 kg   4.9 kg

How much do the peanuts weigh altogether?
10.6 + 4.5 + 4.9 = 20
20 kg

Exercise 2 • page 81

112

Lesson 3 Subtracting Tenths with Regrouping

Objective

• Subtract decimals to the tenths place.

Lesson Materials

• Place-value discs: tens, ones, and tenths

Think

Provide students with place-value discs and pose the **Think** problem. Discuss Sofia's comment and have students estimate their answers before solving.

Students can use place-value discs, the algorithm, or any other known strategy to subtract.

Record their strategies on the board and discuss the methods students used.

Learn

Have students compare their solutions from **Think** with the ones shown in the textbook. Discuss the two methods shown.

Method 1

Ask students why the numbers are expressed as tenths. They should see that they can use mental math to subtract 18 from 35.

For example:

35 tenths − 18 tenths = 35 tenths − 20 tenths + 2 tenths = 17 tenths = 1.7

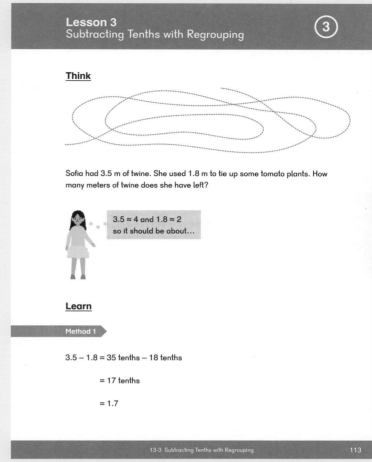

Method 2

The vertical algorithm for subtraction of decimals is the same as for whole numbers.

Students should be fluent with the subtraction algorithm for whole numbers. Discuss how the algorithm is similar for decimals.

When 1 one is regrouped as 10 tenths, we can record the new number of tenths in the algorithm above the digits in the tenths place.

Ask students what Dion can do to get more tenths in the tenths place. (He can regroup 1 one as 10 tenths.)

Emma reminds students to write the decimal point in the answer. By now, students should know that a decimal point is always written between the ones and the tenths places.

Alex uses addition to check his work the same way we check answers when we subtract whole numbers.

Do

❶—❹ Discuss the problems with students.

Sofia reminds students to estimate their answers first. This will help them see if their final answers are reasonable.

Students who need additional help can use the place-value discs to find the actual answer.

❷ Ask students how this problem is different from previous problems. Students should see that they will be regrouping in two places: from tens to ones and from ones to tenths.

❸ Dion tells students to put a 0 in the tenths place to have the same number of decimal places in both numbers.

When he regroups, he will have 7 ones and 10 tenths.

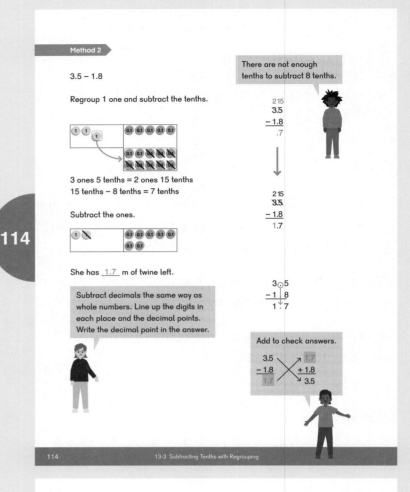

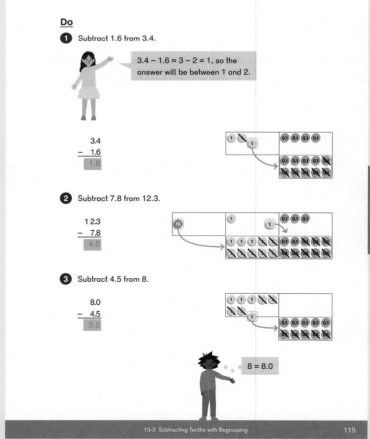

④—⑤ Allow students to use place-value discs if they need additional practice understanding regrouping. Most students should be working with just the algorithm.

Activity

▲ Least Difference

Materials: 10-sided die or Number Cards (BLM) 0–9

Have students draw a personal gameboard, as shown below, on paper or a dry erase board.

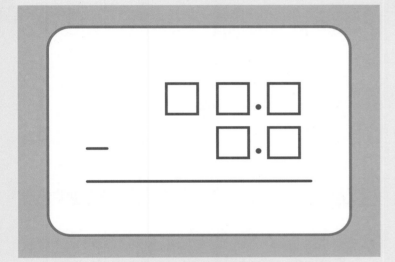

Players take turns rolling the die or drawing a card. On each turn, they place the number drawn in one of the empty boxes on the gameboard. When the boxes are filled, they subtract the second number from the first.

The player with the least difference in each round scores a point.

The first player with five points is the winner.

Exercise 3 · page 83

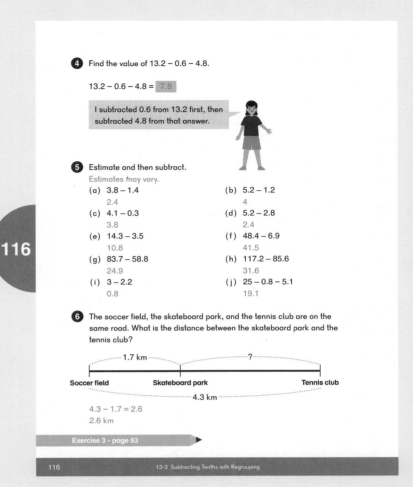

④ Find the value of 13.2 − 0.6 − 4.8.

13.2 − 0.6 − 4.8 = 7.8

I subtracted 0.6 from 13.2 first, then subtracted 4.8 from that answer.

⑤ Estimate and then subtract.
Estimates may vary.

(a) 3.8 − 1.4
2.4

(b) 5.2 − 1.2
4

(c) 4.1 − 0.3
3.8

(d) 5.2 − 2.8
2.4

(e) 14.3 − 3.5
10.8

(f) 48.4 − 6.9
41.5

(g) 83.7 − 58.8
24.9

(h) 117.2 − 85.6
31.6

(i) 3 − 2.2
0.8

(j) 25 − 0.8 − 5.1
19.1

⑥ The soccer field, the skateboard park, and the tennis club are on the same road. What is the distance between the skateboard park and the tennis club?

4.3 − 1.7 = 2.6
2.6 km

Exercise 3 · page 83

116   13-3 Subtracting Tenths with Regrouping

116

Lesson 4 Practice A

Objective

- Practice adding and subtracting decimals to the tenths place.

After students complete the **Practice** in the textbook, have them continue to practice adding and subtracting decimals with activities from the chapter.

2–**6** Encourage students to draw bar models if they need help understanding the problems.

2

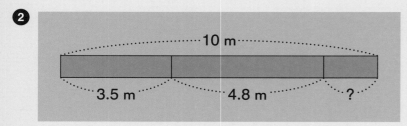

3

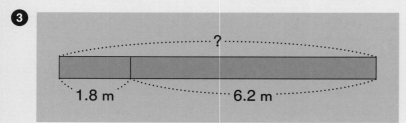

5

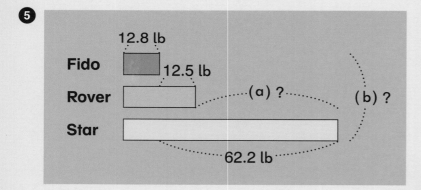

Exercise 4 • page 86

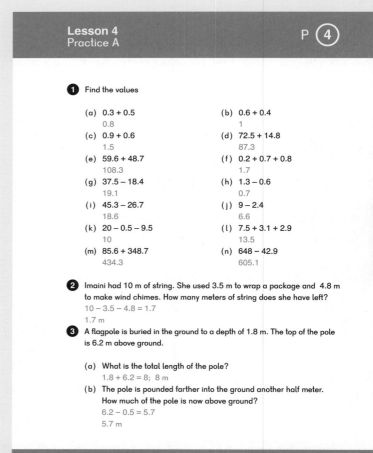

1 Find the values

(a) 0.3 + 0.5
   0.8
(b) 0.6 + 0.4
   1
(c) 0.9 + 0.6
   1.5
(d) 72.5 + 14.8
   87.3
(e) 59.6 + 48.7
   108.3
(f) 0.2 + 0.7 + 0.8
   1.7
(g) 37.5 – 18.4
   19.1
(h) 1.3 – 0.6
   0.7
(i) 45.3 – 26.7
   18.6
(j) 9 – 2.4
   6.6
(k) 20 – 0.5 – 9.5
   10
(l) 7.5 + 3.1 + 2.9
   13.5
(m) 85.6 + 348.7
   434.3
(n) 648 – 42.9
   605.1

2 Imaini had 10 m of string. She used 3.5 m to wrap a package and 4.8 m to make wind chimes. How many meters of string does she have left?
10 – 3.5 – 4.8 = 1.7
1.7 m

3 A flagpole is buried in the ground to a depth of 1.8 m. The top of the pole is 6.2 m above ground.

(a) What is the total length of the pole?
   1.8 + 6.2 = 8; 8 m
(b) The pole is pounded farther into the ground another half meter. How much of the pole is now above ground?
   6.2 – 0.5 = 5.7
   5.7 m

13-4 Practice A   117

117

4 The pharmacy, the music store, and the farmers market are on the same street.

(a) How far is the pharmacy from the farmers market?
   21.3 + 9.8 = 31.1; 31.1 m
(b) How much farther is the music store from the pharmacy than it is from the farmers market?
   21.3 – 9.8 = 11.5; 11.5 m

5

118

Fido weighs 12.8 lb. Rover weighs 12.5 lb more than Fido. Fido weighs 62.2 lb less than Star.   Rover: 12.8 + 12.5 = 25.3
                                                                  Star: 12.8 + 62.2 = 75
(a) How much more does Star weigh than Rover?
   75 – 25.3 = 49.7; 49.7 lb
(b) What is the total weight of all three dogs?
   12.8 + 25.3 + 75 = 113.1; 113.1 lb

6 One rod is 3.8 m long and the other rod is 5.2 m long. They are bound together with part of each rod overlapping. The total length is 8.1 m. How many meters is the overlap?

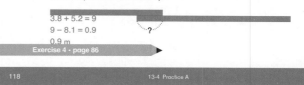

3.8 + 5.2 = 9
9 – 8.1 = 0.9
0.9 m

Exercise 4 • page 86

118   13-4 Practice A

Objective

- Add decimals to the hundredths place.

Lesson Materials

- Place-value discs: ones, tenths, and hundredths

Think

Provide students with place-value discs and pose the **Think** problem. Discuss Alex's comment and have students estimate their answer before solving. Since both numbers are less than 1 kg, the answer has to be less than 2 kg.

Students can use place-value discs, the algorithm, or any other known strategy to add the numbers together.

Record their strategies on the board and discuss the methods students used.

Learn

Have students compare their solutions from **Think** with the ones shown in the textbook. Discuss the two methods shown.

Method 1

Ask students why the numbers are expressed as hundredths. They should see that they can use mental math to add 47 hundredths + 35 hundredths.

For example:

47 hundredths + 35 hundredths

/ \

3 hundredths   32 hundredths

47 hundredths + 35 hundredths

= 50 hundredths + 32 hundredths

= 82 hundredths = 0.82

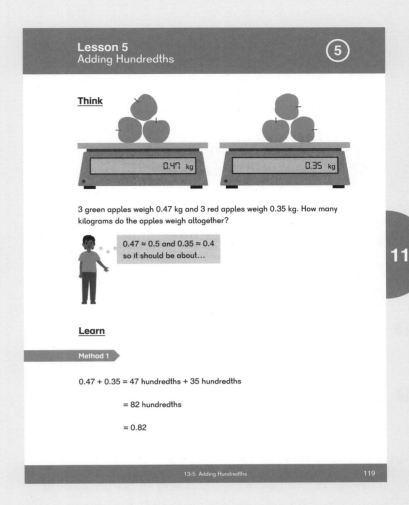

Lesson 5
Adding Hundredths ⑤

Think

3 green apples weigh 0.47 kg and 3 red apples weigh 0.35 kg. How many kilograms do the apples weigh altogether?

0.47 ≈ 0.5 and 0.35 ≈ 0.4 so it should be about...

Learn

Method 1

$0.47 + 0.35 = 47 \text{ hundredths} + 35 \text{ hundredths}$

$= 82 \text{ hundredths}$

$= 0.82$

13-5 Adding Hundredths   119

119

Method 2

The vertical algorithm can be used in the same way as previous decimal problems. Again, we begin by adding from right to left.

Have students work along with place-value discs as the steps are modeled.

Relate the process with place-value discs to the notations on the algorithm where the regrouped hundredths are recorded.

Do

❶ — ❹ Discuss the problems with students.

Estimates may vary depending on student estimates.

❶ Two possible estimates:

$0.80 + 0.15 = 0.95$
$0.8 + 0.2 = 1.0$

If students estimate using 0.8 and 0.2, they should realize that the answer will be less than 1 because they rounded both numbers up.

❸ Dion points out that we can put a 0 in the hundredths place so that both numbers have the same number of digits. This will help students align the digits correctly and add in the correct place values.

Ask students what numbers they think Emma used to estimate. Emma estimated both 3.45 and 2.8 as 3. Since 2.8 is closer to 3 than 3.45, her estimate is on the low side, so the answer must be a little more than 6.

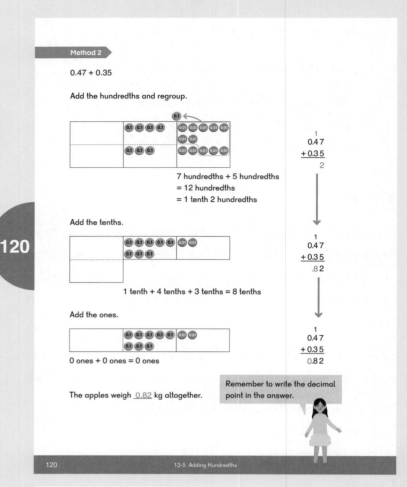

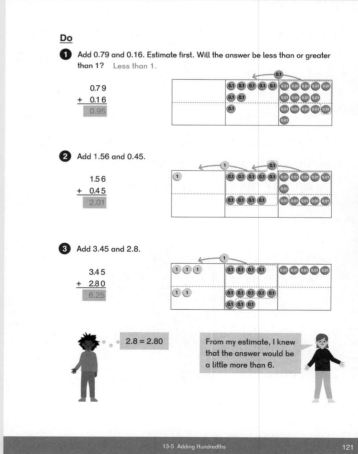

④ Ask students why we can omit the trailing zero in 76.50. (Because 76 and fifty hundredths = 76 and five tenths.)

⑤—⑥ Students should be able to work these problems independently.

Activity

▲ Greatest Addition

Materials: 10-sided die or Number Cards (BLM) 0—9

Modify the gameboard from the game in Lesson 2 to include hundredths:

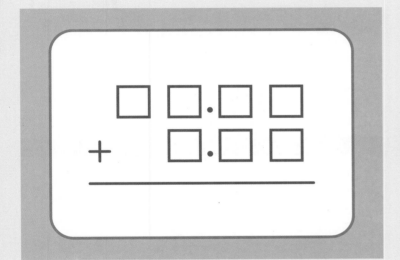

The rules are the same.

Exercise 5 • page 88

---

④ Add 48.63 and 27.87.

76.50 = 76.5

$$\begin{array}{r} 48.63 \\ +27.87 \\ \hline 76.50 \end{array}$$

⑤ Estimate and then add.
Estimates may vary.
(a) 0.05 + 0.04
0.09
(b) 0.36 + 0.25
0.61
(c) 5.72 + 1.63
7.35
(d) 8 + 6.75
14.75
(e) 18.39 + 2.61
21
(f) 1.43 + 0.9
2.33
(g) 12.4 + 0.53
12.93
(h) 43.01 + 6.9
49.91

122

⑥

Swimmer	Time (min)
Mei	1.08
Alex	0.59
Dion	1.76
Emma	0.53

Mei, Alex, Dion, and Emma each swam one length of the pool in a relay race. Their individual times in minutes are shown in the table. What is their total combined time in minutes for the race?
1.08 + 0.59 + 1.76 + 0.53 = 3.96
3.96 min

Exercise 5 • page 88

Lesson 6 Subtracting from 1 and 0.1

Objectives

- Subtract one-place and two-place decimals less than 1 from 1.
- Subtract two-place decimals less than 0.1 from 0.1.

Lesson Materials

- Place-value discs: ones, tenths, and hundredths

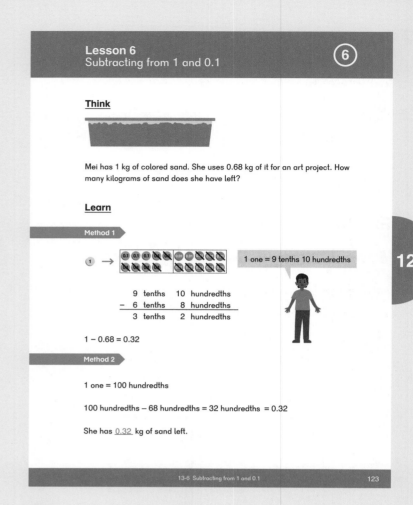

Think

Provide students with place-value discs and pose the **Think** problem.

Students can use place-value discs, the algorithm, or any other known strategy to subtract.

Discuss the methods students used.

Learn

Have students compare their solutions from **Think** with the ones shown in the textbook. Discuss the two methods shown.

Method 1

Alex knows that just as 1 hundred could be regrouped as 9 tens and 10 ones, we can regroup 1 one as 9 tenths and 10 hundredths.

Students can see this with the discs.

Discuss the regrouping shown with the place-value discs from 1 one to 9 tenths and 10 hundredths. This is the same as when students added two numbers to make 1 hundred or 1 thousand. For 0.68, think of how many more hundredths are needed to make 10 hundredths and how many more tenths are needed to make 9 tenths because 9 tenths + 10 hundredths = 1 one.

Method 2

If students think of 1 one as 100 hundredths, they can use mental math to subtract.

Do

①—④ Discuss the problems with students.

① Sofia thinks about 1 tenth as 10 hundredths.

② and **⑤** can be turned into activities by having students copy the numbers onto index cards to match the pairs.

⑥ Dion splits 2 tenths into 1 tenth and 1 tenth. He can then subtract 5 hundredths from 10 hundredths to get 5 hundredths and add back in the 0.1.

⑦ Emma also uses a mental math strategy. She splits 3 into 2 and 1 and subtracts 0.35 from 1.

⑧—⑨ Students should be able to work these problems independently.

Exercise 6 · page 90

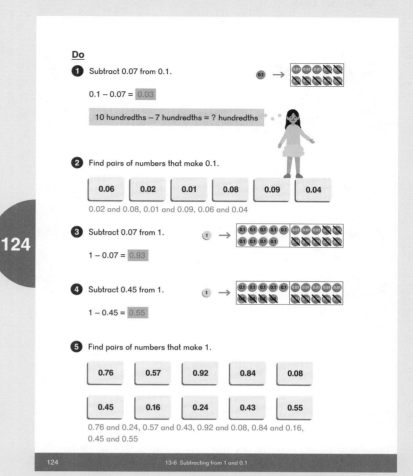

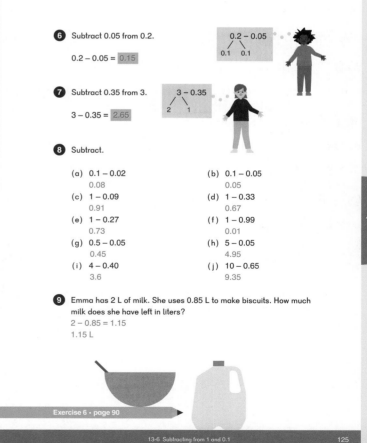

Lesson 7 Subtracting Hundredths

Objective

- Subtract decimals to hundredths.

Lesson Materials

- Place-value discs: tens, ones, tenths, and hundredths

Think

Provide students with place-value discs and pose the **Think** problem. Discuss Mei's comment and have students estimate their answers before solving.

Students can use place-value discs, the algorithm or any other known strategy to subtract.

Discuss the methods students used.

Learn

Have students compare their solutions from **Think** with the one shown in the textbook.

Ask students what Alex will need to do to subtract. He will need to regroup 1 tenth into 10 hundredths.

Ask students where we can record the new number of hundredths in the hundredths column in the algorithm.

Next, regroup 1 one as 10 tenths. Record the new number of tenths in the tenths column in the algorithm.

Dion encourages students to check their work by using addition.

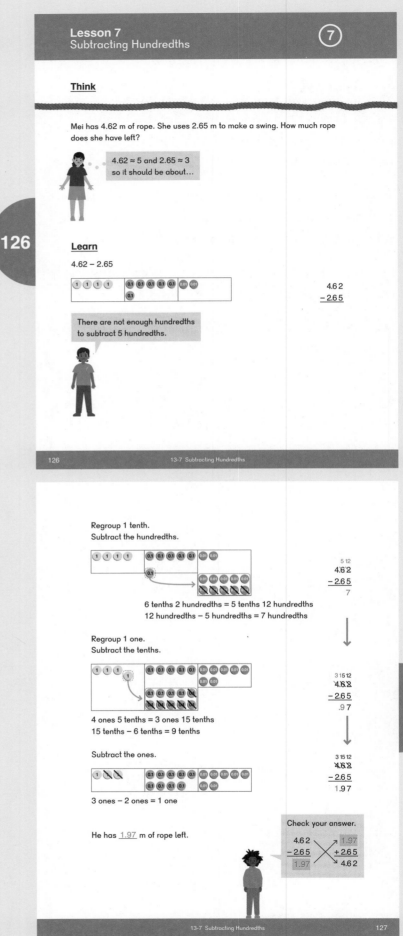

Do

❶—❹ Discuss the problems with students.

❷ Ask students why Emma is thinking 4.1 = 4.10. They should know that they can append a zero to the hundredths place so that there will be the same number of decimal places in both numbers.

Ask students how Mei estimated an answer close to 3. A reasonable estimate would be 4 − 1.

❸ We are subtracting a two-place decimal, so we can write 10 as 10.00 to help align the digits when writing the problem vertically.

128

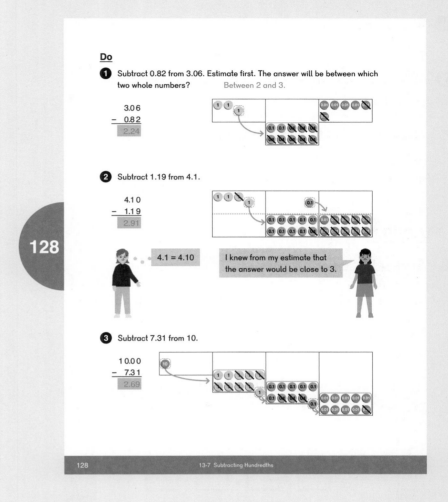

4 Alex writes 19 as 19.00 in order to subtract using the same number of decimal places in both numbers.

5 — **6** Students should solve these problems independently.

Allow students to use place-value discs if they need additional practice understanding regrouping. Most students should be working with just the algorithm.

Activity

▲ Least Difference

Materials: 10-sided die or Number Cards (BLM) 0−9

Modify the gameboard from the game in Lesson 3 to include hundredths:

The rules are the same.

Exercise 7 · page 92

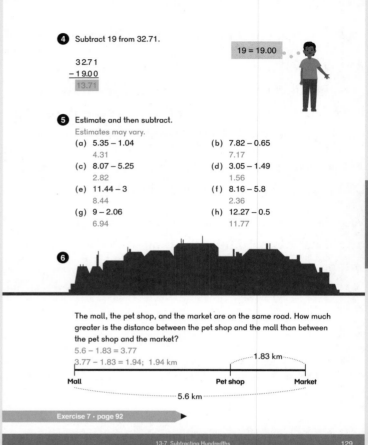

4 Subtract 19 from 32.71.

$$32.71$$
$$-19.00$$
$$13.71$$

19 = 19.00

5 Estimate and then subtract.
Estimates may vary.
(a) 5.35 − 1.04
    4.31
(b) 7.82 − 0.65
    7.17
(c) 8.07 − 5.25
    2.82
(d) 3.05 − 1.49
    1.56
(e) 11.44 − 3
    8.44
(f) 8.16 − 5.8
    2.36
(g) 9 − 2.06
    6.94
(h) 12.27 − 0.5
    11.77

6

The mall, the pet shop, and the market are on the same road. How much greater is the distance between the pet shop and the mall than between the pet shop and the market?
5.6 − 1.83 = 3.77
3.77 − 1.83 = 1.94; 1.94 km

1.83 km

Mall   Pet shop   Market

5.6 km

Exercise 7 · page 92

13-7 Subtracting Hundredths   129

129

Lesson 8 Money, Decimals, and Fractions

Objectives

- Relate money notation to decimals.
- Estimate, add, and subtract money amounts using the vertical algorithm.

Lesson Materials

- Play bills, pennies, dimes

Think

Pose the **Think** problems and have students try to solve the problems independently. Students can use play bills and coins to solve the problems if necessary.

Discuss the methods students used.

Learn

Have students compare their solutions from **Think** with the one shown in the textbook. Discuss the examples with students.

(a) We know that 100 cents makes 1 dollar. Therefore, a penny, 1 cent, is 1 hundredth of a dollar.

We can write 1 cent as $0.01.

(b) We write 1 dime as $0.10. We know there are 10 tenths in 1 one, and 10 dimes in $1, so a dime (10 cents) is $\frac{1}{10}$ of $1.

We can write the fraction $\frac{1}{10}$ to show that a dime is $\frac{1}{10}$ of a dollar.

Students should relate 0.10 to $\frac{10}{100}$.

Sofia points out U.S. dollars and cents are written with 2 decimal places.

(c) Students can use the addition algorithm to add amounts of money the same way they have been adding other decimals, as Dion points out.

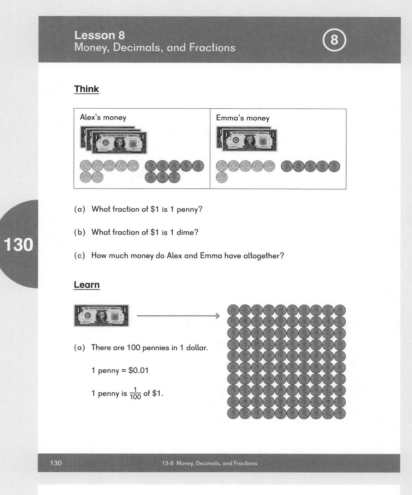

Think

Alex's money   Emma's money

(a) What fraction of $1 is 1 penny?

(b) What fraction of $1 is 1 dime?

(c) How much money do Alex and Emma have altogether?

Learn

(a) There are 100 pennies in 1 dollar.

   1 penny = $0.01

   1 penny is $\frac{1}{100}$ of $1.

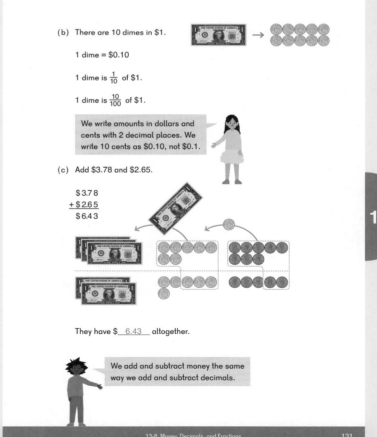

(b) There are 10 dimes in $1.

   1 dime = $0.10

   1 dime is $\frac{1}{10}$ of $1.

   1 dime is $\frac{10}{100}$ of $1.

> We write amounts in dollars and cents with 2 decimal places. We write 10 cents as $0.10, not $0.1.

(c) Add $3.78 and $2.65.

   $3.78
   + $2.65
   $6.43

They have $ __6.43__ altogether.

> We add and subtract money the same way we add and subtract decimals.

131

Do

1 — 6 Discuss the problems with students.

2 Because Emma knows that there are 4 quarters in a dollar, and a dollar is 100 cents, then 1 quarter is $\frac{1}{4}$ of a dollar, thus the name "quarter."

3 If students do not know how many nickels make a dollar, ask, "How many nickels make 50 cents?"

4 Mei estimates her answer will be about 30 cents or $0.30.

6 Ask students why Dion is thinking of $5 = $5.00. When a number is given in dollars only, in order to have the same number of decimal places in both numbers, we can write a decimal point and 00 cents so that $5 has two decimal places. Then we can use the algorithm method to subtract $2.43.

7 — 8 Students should be able to work these problems independently.

Exercise 8 • page 95

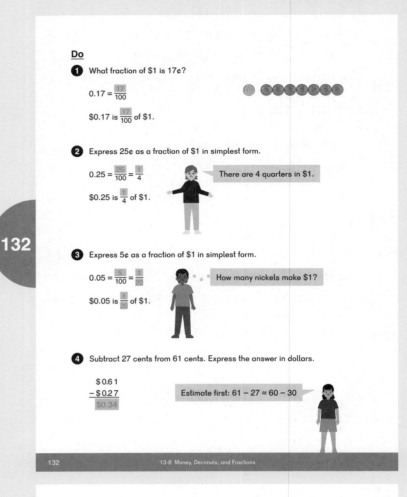

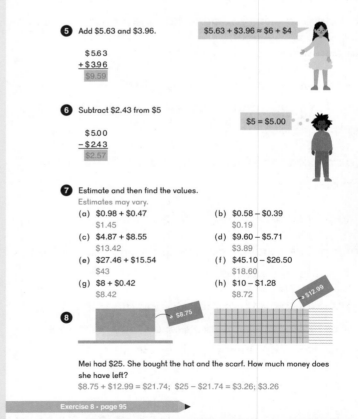

Teacher's Guide 4B Chapter 13   © 2019 Singapore Math Inc.

Lesson 9 Practice B

Objective

- Practice adding and subtracting decimals to the hundredths place.

After students complete the **Practice** in the textbook, have them continue to practice adding and subtracting decimals with activities from the chapter.

Encourage students to draw bar models if they need additional help understanding the problems.

4

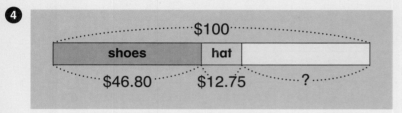

$100

shoes	hat	

$46.80 $12.75   ?

7

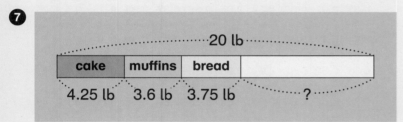

20 lb

cake	muffins	bread	

4.25 lb   3.6 lb   3.75 lb   ?

8

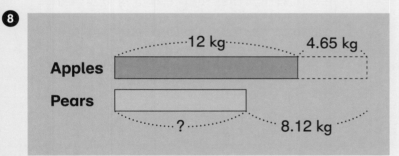

12 kg   4.65 kg

Apples

Pears

?   8.12 kg

9

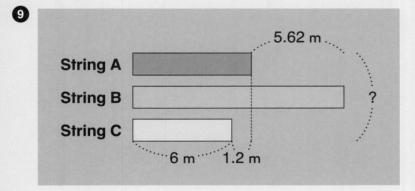

5.62 m

String A

String B   ?

String C

6 m   1.2 m

Lesson 9
Practice B   P ⑨

1 Estimate and then find the values.
Estimates may vary.
(a) 2.63 + 1.34   (b) 0.68 + 0.56
    3.97   1.24
(c) 0.4 + 0.97   (d) 6.07 + 2.16
    1.37   8.23
(e) 85.79 + 26.28   (f) 36.78 + 0.6 + 7
    112.07   44.38
(g) 50.34 − 6.13   (h) 30.01 − 12.34
    44.21   17.67
(i) 1 − 0.92   (j) 5 − 2.03
    0.08   2.97
(k) 1.45 − 0.57   (l) 9.6 − 3.28
    0.88   6.32
(m) 72 − 8.09   (n) 10.3 − 2.05 − 6.8
    63.91   1.45

2 (a) Express 50¢ as a fraction of $1 in simplest form.
$\frac{1}{2}$
(b) Express 8 nickels as a fraction of $1 in simplest form.
$\frac{2}{5}$
(c) Express 45¢ as a fraction of $1 in simplest form.
$\frac{9}{20}$

3 Josef bought a comic book for $7.95 and a picture book for $15.28. How much did he spend?
$7.95 + $15.28 = $23.23
$23.23

134   13-9 Practice B

4

Daniel had $100. He bought some shoes for $46.80 and a hat for $12.75. How much money does he have left?
$46.80 + $12.75 = $59.55
$100 − $59.55 = $40.45; $40.45

5 Dana had $47.32. She spent $32.07. Then she earned another $8. How much money does she have now?
$47.32 − $32.07 = $15.25
$15.25 + $8 = $23.25; $23.25

6 Brianna says she has six and four-fifths dollars. How much money does she have?
$6.80

7 A baker had 20 lb of flour. He used 4.25 lb to make a cake, 3.6 lb to make muffins, and 3.75 lb to make bread. How many pounds of flour does he have left?
20 − 4.25 − 3.6 − 3.75 = 8.4
8.4 lb

8 A basket of apples weighed 8.12 kg more than a basket of pears. After 4.65 kg of apples were removed from the basket of apples, it weighed 12 kg. How much does the basket of pears weigh?
Basket of apples: 12 + 4.65 = 16.65
Basket of pears: 16.65 − 8.12 = 8.53; 8.53 kg

9 String A is 5.62 m shorter than String B and 1.2 m longer than String C. String C is 6 m long. How long are the three strings altogether?
String A: 1.2 + 6 = 7.2
String B: 7.2 + 5.62 = 12.82
12.82 + 7.2 + 6 = 26.02
26.02 m

Exercise 9 · page 98

13-9 Practice B   135

134

135

Activities

▲ Magic Squares

Materials: Magic Squares (BLM)

Arrange the cards in a 3 × 3 array so that every column and row adds up to the same value.

Solutions:

Puzzle 1

0.2	0.7	0.6
0.9	0.5	0.1
0.4	0.3	0.8

Puzzle 2

1.3	0.8	1.5
1.4	1.2	1
0.9	1.6	1.1

Puzzle 3

3.4	3.5	3.0
2.9	3.3	3.7
3.6	3.1	3.2

▲ Three in a Row

Materials: Hundredths Chart (BLM), deck of cards, counters

In each round, players draw 4 cards. They make the 4 numbers on their cards into any 2 two-place decimal numbers. For example, a player who draws 7, 4, 3, and 1 could make the numbers 0.47 and 0.13. Tens and face cards can be considered 0.

Players add or subtract the two numbers to capture a space on the game board. Play continues until a player has three counters in a row, column, or diagonal.

Sample game:

Round 1: Player 1 (green) draws 2, 3, 8, 9. She makes the numbers 0.98 and 0.23 and subtracts. She marks 0.75 on the game board. Player 2 (red) draws 3, 1, 0, 5. He makes the numbers 0.53 and 0.01 and adds. He marks 0.54 on the game board.

Round 2: Players draw new cards.

Player 1 draws 6, 1, 7, 3. Looking at the spaces available on the Hundredths Chart (BLM), she rearranges the numbers until she has 0.73 − 0.16 so she can mark 0.57 on the game board.

Player 2 draws 2, 5, 4, 2. Thinking strategically, he moves the numbers around until he has 0.52 + 0.24 so he can mark 0.76 on the game board. On Player 1's next turn, she will try to create numbers and add or subtract so that she can mark 0.66 and win the game.

If that does not happen, on Player 2's next turn, he will try to create numbers and add or subtract so that he can mark 0.65 and win the game.

0.01	0.02	0.03	0.04	0.05	0.06	0.07	0.08	0.09	0.1
0.11	0.12	0.13	0.14	0.15	0.16	0.17	0.18	0.19	0.2
0.21	0.22	0.23	0.24	0.25	0.26	0.27	0.28	0.29	0.3
0.31	0.32	0.33	0.34	0.35	0.36	0.37	0.38	0.39	0.4
0.41	0.42	0.43	0.44	0.45	0.46	0.47	0.48	0.49	0.5
0.51	0.52	0.53	⊗	0.55	0.56	⊗	0.58	0.59	0.6
0.61	0.62	0.63	0.64	0.65	0.66	0.67	0.68	0.69	0.7
0.71	0.72	0.73	0.74	⊗	⊗	0.77	0.78	0.79	0.8
0.81	0.82	0.83	0.84	0.85	0.86	0.87	0.88	0.89	0.9
0.91	0.92	0.93	0.94	0.95	0.96	0.97	0.98	0.99	1

Exercise 9 • page 98

Review 3

Objective

- Review concepts from Chapter 1 through Chapter 13.

Use the cumulative review to practice and reinforce content and skills from the first 13 chapters of Dimensions Math 4A and 4B.

---

①

| 32,574 | 450,096 | 632.57 | 40.25 |

What does the digit 5 stand for in each number?
500; 50,000; 0.5; 0.05
Write each number in expanded form.
30,000 + 2,000 + 500 + 70 + 4; 400,000 + 50,000 + 90 + 6
600 + 30 + 2 + 0.5 + 0.07; 40 + 0.2 + 0.05

② Write each value as a whole number or a decimal.

(a) 60 hundreds   6,000
(b) 60 hundredths   0.6
(c) 200 tens   2,000
(d) 200 tenths   20

③ Estimate and then find the values.
Estimates may vary.

(a) 86,956 + 7,872
94,828
(b) 103,424 − 63,527
39,897
(c) 2,052 × 30
61,560
(d) 302 ÷ 7
43 R 1 (or $43\frac{1}{7}$)
(e) 87 × 652
56,724
(f) 2,014 ÷ 4
503 R 2 (or $503\frac{1}{2}$)
(g) 0.7 + 0.5
1.2
(h) 2.4 − 1.9
0.5
(i) 43.7 + 2.31
46.01
(j) 20.02 − 11.45
8.57
(k) 45.87 + 54.13
100
(l) 100 − 0.7
99.3

136

---

④ (a) Find the first four common multiples of 3, 4, and 6.
12, 24, 36, 48
(b) Find the common factors of 18, 24, and 30.
1, 2, 3, 6
(c) Find all the prime numbers less than 30.
2, 3, 5, 7, 11, 13, 17, 19, 23, 29

⑤ Express the values as a fraction or mixed number in simplest form.

(a) $\frac{3}{4} + \frac{7}{12}$ $1\frac{1}{3}$
(b) $6\frac{1}{3} - \frac{7}{9}$ $5\frac{5}{9}$
(c) $4\frac{3}{5} - 1\frac{1}{10}$ $3\frac{1}{2}$
(d) $\frac{5}{6} \times 18$ 15
(e) $8 \times \frac{7}{20}$ $2\frac{4}{5}$
(f) $\frac{5}{12} \times 20$ $8\frac{1}{3}$

⑥ Find the area and perimeter of each shape.

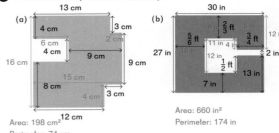

(a) 13 cm, 4 cm, 3 cm, 6 cm, 2 cm, 4 cm, 9 cm, 16 cm, 9 cm, 15 cm, 8 cm, 4 cm, 3 cm, 12 cm
Area: 198 cm²
Perimeter: 74 cm

(b) 30 in, $\frac{2}{3}$ ft, $\frac{5}{6}$ ft, $\frac{3}{4}$ ft, 12 in, 11 in 4 in, 27 in, 12 in, 2 in, $\frac{1}{2}$ ft, 13 in, 7 in
Area: 660 in²
Perimeter: 174 in

137

⑦ The perimeter of a rectangular painting is 30 ft. The width of the painting is $2\frac{1}{3}$ ft. What is the area of the painting in square inches?
30 ft = 360 in; $2\frac{1}{3}$ ft = 28 in
360 − 28 − 28 = 304
Length: 304 ÷ 2 = 152
152 × 28 = 4,256; 4,256 in²

Encourage students to draw bar models if they need help understanding the problems.

10

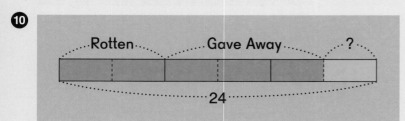

11

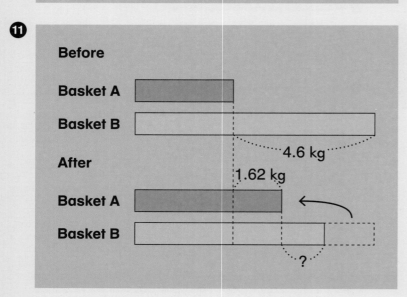

Exercise 10 • page 101

---

8 Express each decimal as a mixed number in simplest form and each mixed number as a decimal.

(a) 2.4 $2\frac{2}{5}$ (b) 40.08 $40\frac{2}{25}$ (c) 6.35 $6\frac{7}{20}$

(d) $2\frac{9}{100}$ 2.09   (e) $3\frac{3}{25}$ 3.12   (f) $10\frac{1}{5}$ 10.2

9 Some students recorded the distance their paper airplanes traveled and then shared their data.

4.3 m	4.4 m		3.85 m
4 m 30 cm	$4\frac{2}{5}$ m	5.04 m	385 cm
$5\frac{3}{4}$ m	4 m 3 cm	$3\frac{3}{4}$ m	5.8 m
5.75 m	4.03 m	3.75 m	

(a) What is the difference in meters between the shortest and longest distance?
5.8 − 3.75 = 2.05;   2.05 m (or $2\frac{1}{20}$ m)

(b) How many airplanes traveled less than 4 m 50 cm?
4 m 50 cm = 4.5 m
5 airplanes

10 Natasha had 24 plums. $\frac{1}{3}$ of them were rotten and had to be thrown away. She gave $\frac{3}{4}$ of the remainder to her friends and ate the rest. How many plums did she eat?
Rotten: $\frac{1}{3}$ × 24 = 8;   Remainder: 24 − 8 = 16;   Friends: $\frac{3}{4}$ × 16 = 12
Plums she ate: 16 − 12 = 4;   4 plums

11 There are two baskets of plums. Basket A weighs 4.6 kg less than Basket B. 1.62 kg of plums was transferred from Basket B to Basket A. How much more does Basket B now weigh than Basket A?
4.6 − 1.62 − 1.62 = 1.36
1.36 kg

Exercise 10 • page 101

138

Chapter 13 Addition and Subtraction of Decimals

Exercise 1

Basics

1 6 tenths + 3 tenths = [9] tenths

0.6 + 0.3 = [0.9]

2 6 tenths + 4 tenths = [10] tenths = [1] one

0.6 + 0.4 = [1]

3 6 tenths + 7 tenths = [13] tenths = [1] one [3] tenths

0.6 + 0.7 = [1.3]

4 8 tenths − 6 tenths = [2] tenths

0.8 − 0.6 = [0.2]

5 1 one − 6 tenths = [10] tenths − 6 tenths = [4] tenths

1 − 0.6 = [0.4]

6 1 one 4 tenths − 6 tenths = [14] tenths − 6 tenths = [8] tenths

1.4 − 0.6 = [0.8]

Practice

7 Add or subtract.

(a) 0.3 + 0.4 = [0.7]   (b) 0.5 + 0.6 = [1.1]

(c) 0.9 + 0.8 = [1.7]   (d) 0.7 + 0.6 = [1.3]

(e) 0.7 − 0.5 = [0.2]   (f) 1.7 − 0.9 = [0.8]

(g) 1.2 − 0.7 = [0.5]   (h) 1.4 − 0.8 = [0.6]

8 Write the missing values.

(a) 0.5 + [0.7] = 1.2   (b) [1.2] + 0.6 = 1.8

(c) 1.3 − [0.8] = 0.5   (d) [1] − 0.6 = 0.4

Challenge

9 Add or subtract using mental math.

(a) 7.8 + 0.9 = [8.7]

(b) 4.8 + 0.8 = [5.6]

(c) 6.1 − 0.9 = [5.2]

(d) 9.4 − 0.7 = [8.7]

(e) 0.2 + 0.5 + 0.6 + 0.9 + 0.8 + 0.4 + 0.5 + 0.1 + 0.7 = [4.7]

Exercise 2

Basics

1 (a) Estimate the sum of 4.6 and 6.8.

4.6 + 6.8 ≈ 5 + 7 = [12]

(b) Find the sum of 4.6 and 6.8. ⟶

4.6 + 6.8 = 11.4

$$\begin{array}{r} 1 \\ 4\ .\ 6 \\ +\quad 6\ .\ 8 \\ \hline 1\ 1\ .\ 4 \end{array}$$

2 (a) Estimate the sum of 45 and 6.8.
Estimates may vary.

(b) Find the sum of 45 and 6.8. ⟶

45 + 6.8 = 51.8

$$\begin{array}{r} 1 \\ 4\ 5\ .\ 0 \\ +\qquad 6\ .\ 8 \\ \hline 5\ 1\ .\ 8 \end{array}$$

3 (a) Estimate the sum of 24.7 and 9.5.
Estimates may vary.

(b) Find the sum of 24.7 and 9.5. ⟶

24.7 + 9.5 = 34.2

$$\begin{array}{r} 1\ 1 \\ 2\ 4\ .\ 7 \\ +\qquad 9\ .\ 5 \\ \hline 3\ 4\ .\ 2 \end{array}$$

Practice

4 Add. Remember to estimate first.

(a) 9.3 + 6.8

$$\begin{array}{r} 9.3 \\ +\ 6.8 \\ \hline 1\ 6.1 \end{array}$$

(b) 8.3 + 16.8

$$\begin{array}{r} 8.3 \\ +\ 16.8 \\ \hline 2\ 5.1 \end{array}$$

(c) 15.8 + 3.3

$$\begin{array}{r} 15.8 \\ +\ 3.3 \\ \hline 1\ 9.1 \end{array}$$

(d) 5.4 + 3.6

$$\begin{array}{r} 5.4 \\ +\ 3.6 \\ \hline 9.0 \end{array}$$

(e) 82 + 9.4

$$\begin{array}{r} 8\ 2.0 \\ +\ 9.4 \\ \hline 9\ 1.4 \end{array}$$

(f) 6.9 + 5.3 + 2.6

$$\begin{array}{r} 6.9 \\ 5.3 \\ +\ 2.6 \\ \hline 1\ 4.8 \end{array}$$

5 To make a dye, Aurora mixed 0.6 L of vinegar with 1.8 L of beet juice and 1.3 L of choke cherry juice. How many liters of red dye did she make?

0.6 + 1.8 + 1.3 = 3.7

3.7 L

Exercise 3

Basics

1 (a) Estimate the value of 8.2 − 2.8.

$8.2 - 2.8 \approx 8 - 3 =$ ☐ 5

(b) Subtract 2.8 from 8.2. ⟶

$8.2 - 2.8 = 5.4$

$$\begin{array}{r} 7\;\;12 \\ \cancel{8}.\cancel{2} \\ -\;\;2.8 \\ \hline 5\,|\,4 \end{array}$$

2 (a) Estimate the value of 47 − 6.8.
Estimates may vary.

(b) Subtract 6.8 from 47. ⟶

$47 - 6.8 = 40.2$

$$\begin{array}{r} 6\;\;10 \\ 4\;\;\cancel{7}.\cancel{0} \\ -\;\;6.8 \\ \hline 4\,|\,0\,|\,2 \end{array}$$

3 (a) Estimate the value of 24.7 − 9.5.
Estimates may vary.

(b) Subtract 9.5 from 24.7 ⟶

$24.7 - 9.5 = 15.2$

$$\begin{array}{r} 1\;\;14 \\ \cancel{2}\;\;\cancel{4}.7 \\ -\;\;9.5 \\ \hline 1\,|\,5\,|\,2 \end{array}$$

Practice

4 Subtract. Remember to estimate first.

(a) 9.3 − 6.8

$$\begin{array}{r} 9.3 \\ -\;6.8 \\ \hline 2.5 \end{array}$$

(b) 18.3 − 4.8

$$\begin{array}{r} 1\,8.3 \\ -\;\;4.8 \\ \hline 1\,3.5 \end{array}$$

(c) 25.8 − 17.3

$$\begin{array}{r} 2\,5.8 \\ -\,1\,7.3 \\ \hline 8.5 \end{array}$$

(d) 21.9 − 5.3

$$\begin{array}{r} 2\,1.9 \\ -\;\;5.3 \\ \hline 1\,6.6 \end{array}$$

(e) 51.4 − 3

$$\begin{array}{r} 5\,1.4 \\ -\;\;3.0 \\ \hline 4\,8.4 \end{array}$$

(f) 82 − 9.4

$$\begin{array}{r} 8\,2.0 \\ -\;\;9.4 \\ \hline 7\,2.6 \end{array}$$

5 A car's gas tank can hold 15 gallons of gas. It had 1.2 gallons of gas. Then Paul added 11.3 gallons. How many more gallons of gas must be added for it to be full?

$15 - 1.2 - 11.3 = 2.5$

2.5 gallons

6 Jada jogged 3.5 km on Saturday. On Sunday she jogged 1.2 km less than on Saturday. On Saturday, Sunday, and Monday she jogged a total of 8.4 km. How far did she jog on Monday?

Sunday: $3.5 - 1.2 = 2.3$

$8.4 - 3.5 - 2.3 = 2.6$

2.6 km

Challenge

7 There are two strips of paper, one of which is 20.5 cm long. When the two strips of paper are glued together with an overlap of 6.8 cm, the total length is 40 cm. How long is the other strip of paper?

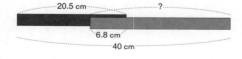

20.5 cm   ?

6.8 cm

40 cm

$40 - 20.5 = 19.5$

$19.5 + 6.8 = 26.3$

26.3 cm

Exercise 4

Check

1 Add or subtract.

(a) 7.8 + 6.8
14.6

(b) 9.2 − 6.8
2.4

(c) 14.8 + 7.3
22.1

(d) 45.2 − 6.7
38.5

(e) 74.7 + 5.3
80

(f) 12.9 − 8
4.9

(g) 112.6 + 5.8
118.4

(h) 12 − 2.1
9.9

(i) 10.2 + 28.7 + 5.5
44.4

2 Express the sum of $6\frac{1}{2}$, 4.2, $\frac{3}{5}$, and 8.2 as a decimal.
$6\frac{1}{2}$ = 6.5
$\frac{3}{5}$ = 0.6
6.5 + 4.2 + 0.6 + 8.2 = 19.5
19.5

3 An airline charges an extra baggage fee if a suitcase weighs more than 50 lb. A suitcase by itself weighs 12.8 lb. How much weight can be added to the suitcase so it will still be 5 lb under 50 lb?
50 − 5 = 45
45 − 12.8 = 32.2
32.2 lb

4 Jasper weighed himself on the scale and found that he weighed 128.6 lb. Then he weighed both himself and his suitcase and found that together they weighed 185.3 lb. Does the suitcase weigh more or less than 50 lb, and by how much?
185.3 − 128.6 = 56.7
56.7 − 50 = 6.7
6.7 lb more

5 The capacity of a bottle is 4.2 L. It has $1\frac{3}{5}$ L of water in it now. How much water must be added to fill it? Express the answer as a decimal.
$1\frac{3}{5}$ = 1.6
4.2 − 1.6 = 2.6
2.6 L

Exercise 5

Basics

1 (a) Estimate the sum of 0.78 and 0.23.

0.78 + 0.23 ≈ 0.8 + 0.2 = [1]

(b) Find the sum of 0.78 and 0.23. ⟶
0.78 + 0.23 = 1.01

```
    1  1
   0 . 7  8
 + 0 . 2  3
   1 . 0  1
```

2 (a) Estimate the sum of 5.65 and 6.8.

5.65 + 6.8 ≈ 6 + 7 = [13]

(b) Find the sum of 5.65 and 6.8. ⟶
5.65 + 6.8 = 12.45

```
       1
   5 . 6  5
 + 6 . 8  0
  1 2 . 4  5
```

3 (a) Estimate the sum of 0.81 and 29.5.

0.81 + 29.5 ≈ 1 + 30 = [31]

(b) Find the sum of 0.81 and 29.5. ⟶
0.81 + 29.5 = 30.31

```
      1  1
  2 9 . 5  0
 +   0 . 8  1
  3 0 . 3  1
```

Practice

4 Add. Remember to estimate first.

(a) 0.65 + 0.85
```
    0 . 6 5
 +  0 . 8 5
    1 . 5
```

(b) 8.32 + 16.8
```
    8 . 3 2
 + 1 6 . 8 0
  2 5 . 1 2
```

(c) 15.81 + 7.32
```
  1 5 . 8 1
 +  7 . 3 2
  2 3 . 1 3
```

(d) 8.95 + 0.67
```
    8 . 9 5
 +  0 . 6 7
    9 . 6 2
```

(e) 73 + 9.48
```
  7 3 . 0 0
 +  9 . 4 8
  8 2 . 4 8
```

(f) 2.56 + 5.3 + 0.62
```
    2 . 5 6
    5 . 3 0
 +  0 . 6 2
    8 . 4 8
```

5 In a laboratory, 3 chemicals were weighed and then mixed together before adding water to the mixture. Chemical A weighed 6.91 g, Chemical B weighed 7.37 g, and Chemical C weighed 0.80 g. What is the total weight of the three chemicals?
6.91 + 7.37 + 0.80 = 15.08
15.08 g

Exercise 6

Basics

1 Cross off discs to show the answer.

(a) Subtract 7 from 10.

10 − 7 = ☐ 3

(b) Subtract 0.07 from 0.1.

1 tenth − 7 hundredths = ☐ 10 hundredths − 7 hundredths

= ☐ 3 hundredths

0.1 − 0.07 = ☐ 0.03

(c) Subtract 0.07 from 0.2.

0.2 − 0.07 = ☐ 0.13

2 (a) 50 + ☐ 40 = 90   (b) 0.5 + ☐ 0.4 = 0.9

(c) 3 + ☐ 7 = 10   (d) 0.03 + ☐ 0.07 = 0.1

(e) 53 + ☐ 47 = 100   (f) 0.53 + ☐ 0.47 = 1

(g) 100 − 53 = ☐ 47   (h) 1 − 0.53 = ☐ 0.47

(i) 200 − 53 = ☐ 147   (j) 2 − 0.53 = ☐ 1.47

Practice

3 (a) 0.1 − 0.09 = ☐ 0.01   (b) 0.1 − 0.04 = ☐ 0.06

(c) 0.1 − 0.02 = ☐ 0.08   (d) ☐ 0.05 + 0.05 = 0.1

(e) 0.5 − 0.06 = ☐ 0.44   (f) 0.4 − 0.01 = ☐ 0.39

4 (a) 1 − 0.85 = ☐ 0.15   (b) 1 − 0.89 = ☐ 0.11

(c) 1 − 0.44 = ☐ 0.56   (d) 1 − 0.72 = ☐ 0.28

(e) 0.17 + ☐ 0.83 = 1   (f) ☐ 0.72 + 0.28 = 1

(g) 3 − 0.25 = ☐ 2.75   (h) 4 − 0.33 = ☐ 3.67

Challenge

5 Add or subtract using mental math.

(a) 3.76 + 0.99 = ☐ 4.75

(b) 7.87 + 0.98 = ☐ 8.85

(c) 3.7 + 0.98 = ☐ 4.68

(d) 1.5 − 0.98 = ☐ 0.52

(e) 5.22 + 3.99 = ☐ 9.21

(f) 7.07 − 3.98 = ☐ 3.09

Basics

1 (a) Estimate the value of 4.13 − 0.68.

$4.13 − 0.68 ≈ 4 − 0.7 = \boxed{3.3}$

(b) Subtract 0.68 from 4.13. ⟶
$4.13 − 0.68 = 3.45$

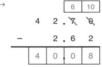

	3	10	13
	̶4̶ .	̶1̶	̶3̶
−	0 .	6	8
	3	4	5

2 (a) Estimate the value of 23.46 − 7.8.
Estimates may vary.
(b) Subtract 7.8 from 23.46. ⟶
$23.46 − 7.8 = 15.66$

	1	12	14	
	̶2̶	̶3̶ .	̶4̶	6
−		7 .	8	0
	1	5 .	6	6

3 (a) Estimate the value of 42.7 − 2.62.
Estimates may vary.
(b) Subtract 2.62 from 42.7. ⟶
$42.7 − 2.62 = 40.08$

		6	10
4	2 .	̶7̶	̶0̶
−	2 .	6	2
4	0 .	0	8

Practice

4 Subtract. Remember to estimate first.

(a) 0.61 − 0.38

	0 .	6	1
−	0 .	3	8
	0 .	2	3

(b) 8.32 − 0.49

	8 .	3	2
−	0 .	4	9
	7 .	8	3

(c) 15.18 − 7.32

1	5 .	1	8
−	7 .	3	2
	7 .	8	6

(d) 8.35 − 0.6

	8 .	3	5
−	0 .	6	0
	7 .	7	5

(e) 73 − 9.48

7	3 .	0	0
−	9 .	4	8
6	3 .	5	2

(f) 5.03 − 4.56

	5 .	0	3
−	4 .	5	6
	0 .	4	7

5 A beaker is filled with 1.2 L of a salt solution. 0.37 L of the solution was poured out from it. How many liters of solution are still in the beaker?
$1.2 − 0.37 = 0.83$
0.83 L

6 In a science experiment, students hung a 100 g weight on a string and measured the time it took for a pendulum to swing back and forth once.

Trial	Length of string (m)	Time (s)
A	0.15	0.83
B	0.5	1.5
C	0.9	1.93

(a) What was the difference in the length of string between Trial A and Trial B and between Trial B and Trial C?
Trial A and Trial B: 0.5 − 0.15 = 0.35; 0.35 m
Trial B and Trial C: 0.9 − 0.5 = 0.4; 0.4 m

(b) What is the difference in time between Trial A and Trial B and between Trial B and Trial C?
Trial A and Trial B: 1.5 − 0.83 = 0.67; 0.67 s
Trial B and Trial C: 1.93 − 1.5 = 0.43; 0.43 s

(c) Did the time increase or decrease as the length of the string increased?
Increase

(d) What is the length of string in centimeters for each trial?
Trial A: 15 cm
Trial B: 50 cm
Trial C: 90 cm

Teacher's Guide 4B Chapter 13

Exercise 8

Basics

1 Complete the table to express the value of each coin in dollars and as a fraction of $1 in simplest form.

Coin	Dollars	Fraction of $1
Penny	$0.01	$\frac{1}{100}$
Nickel	$0.05	$\frac{1}{20}$
Dime	$0.10	$\frac{1}{10}$
Quarter	$0.25	$\frac{25}{100} = \boxed{\frac{1}{4}}$
50-cent coin	$0.50	$\frac{1}{2}$

2 Add $4.75 and $6.35.

```
    $4 . 7 5
+   $6 . 3 5
    $11 . 1 0
```

3 Clara had $10. She then spent $4.27. How much money does she have left?

```
    $1 0 . 0 0
-     $4 . 2 7
      $5 . 7 3
```

Practice

4 Express each of the following in dollars and as a fraction of $1 in simplest form.

	Dollars	Fraction of $1
15¢	$0.15	$\frac{3}{20}$
52¢	$0.52	$\frac{13}{25}$
7 nickels	$0.35	$\frac{7}{20}$
2 quarters, 5 nickels	$0.75	$\frac{3}{4}$
1 quarter, 1 dime, 1 penny	$0.36	$\frac{9}{25}$

5 Add or subtract.

(a) $11.56 − $5.56
$6.00 or $6

(b) $81.35 − $9
$72.35

(c) $6.21 + $0.38
$6.59

(d) $87.32 + $0.69
$88.01

(e) $20.18 + $7.32
$27.50

(f) $42 − $9.48
$32.52

6 Franco had $2. He spent $1.60. What fraction of the money does he have left?

$2 − $1.60 = $0.40

$\frac{40}{200} = \frac{1}{5}$

$\frac{1}{5}$ of the money

7 Aisha bought two books and a bookmark. One book cost $5.45, the other book cost $8.28, and the bookmark cost $1.99. She paid with a $20 bill. How much change did she receive?

$5.45 + $8.28 + $1.99 = $15.72
$20 − $15.72 = $4.28
$4.28

Challenge

8 Hannah has $34.50 more than Clemens. Clemens has $132.30. Paula has $14.80 less than Clemens. They want to combine their money to buy a raft that costs $449.29. How much more money do they need?

Hannah
Clemens $132.30
Paula $34.50 $449.29
Money needed $14.80

Hannah: $132.30 + $34.50 = $166.80
Paula: $132.30 − $14.80 = $117.50
$166.80 + $117.50 + $132.30 = $416.60
$449.29 − $416.60 = $32.69
$32.69 more

Exercise 9

Check

1 (a) $0.1 - 0.07 =$ 0.03

(b) $1 - 0.06 =$ 0.94

(c) $1 - 0.28 =$ 0.72

(d) $1 - 0.44 =$ 0.56

(e) $0.08 +$ 0.02 $= 0.1$

(f) 0.81 $+ 0.19 = 1$

(g) $5 - 0.85 =$ 4.15

(h) $10 - 0.33 =$ 9.67

2 Express each of the following in dollars and as a fraction of $1 in simplest form.

	Dollars	Fraction of $1
30¢	$0.30	$\frac{3}{10}$
92¢	$0.92	$\frac{23}{25}$
3 dimes, 3 nickels	$0.45	$\frac{9}{20}$
1 quarter, 5 nickels, 6 pennies	$0.56	$\frac{14}{25}$
2 quarters, 1 dime, 5 pennies	$0.65	$\frac{13}{20}$

3 75¢ is what fraction of $5?

$\frac{75}{500} = \frac{3}{20}$

4 Follow the arrows and fill in the missing numbers. Write + or − in each ◯.

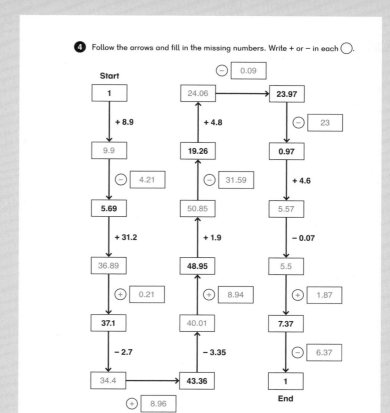

5 Express the sum of $6\frac{7}{20}$, 2.4, $\frac{8}{25}$, and 4.12 as a decimal.

$6\frac{7}{20} = 6.35$

$\frac{8}{25} = 0.32$

$6.35 + 2.4 + 0.32 + 4.12 = 13.19$

13.19

6 Bron bought a pad of watercolor paper that cost $17.30 and a set of watercolor paints. The paints cost $4.31 more than the paper. He paid with two $20 bills. How much change did he receive?

$17.30 + $4.31 = $21.61

$40 − $21.61 − $17.30 = $1.09

$1.09

7 Tiara grew three pumpkins in different areas of her yard. She weighed the pumpkins 3 weeks before she harvested them, and then again the day she harvested them. The total weight of the three pumpkins when she harvested them was 28.7 kg. The table shows the results. Complete the table. Which pumpkin grew the most over the 3 weeks?   Pumpkin B

	Starting weight	Weight after 3 weeks	Difference in weight
Pumpkin A	8.6 kg	9.24 kg	0.64 kg
Pumpkin B	7.26 kg	10.89 kg	3.63 kg
Pumpkin C	6.74 kg	8.57 kg	1.83 kg

Teacher's Guide 4B Chapter 13

Exercise 10

Check

1 | 854.6 | 89.05 | 70.54 | 504.2 |

(a) What does the digit 5 stand for in each number?
854.6: 5 tens; 89.05: 5 hundredths; 70.54: 5 tenths
504.2: 5 hundreds

(b) Write each number in expanded form.
854.6: 800 + 50 + 4 + 0.6; 89.05: 80 + 9 + 0.05
70.54: 70 + 0.5 + 0.04; 504.2: 500 + 4 + 0.2

(c) Write each number as a mixed number in simplest form.
854.6: $854\frac{3}{5}$; 89.05: $89\frac{1}{20}$; 70.54: $70\frac{27}{50}$; 504.2: $504\frac{1}{5}$

2 Write >, <, or = in each ◯.

(a) $4\frac{3}{5} - 1\frac{1}{10}$ ⊘ $10.6 - 7.4$

(b) $12 - 10.2$ ⊘ $8 \times \frac{7}{20}$

(c) $13.35 - 9.6$ ⊜ $1\frac{1}{2} + 2\frac{1}{4}$

(d) $\frac{5}{6} \times 18$ ⊘ $10.55 + 5.68$

(e) 7 m 8 cm + 4 m 20 cm ⊘ 7.8 m + 4.2 m

---

3 This table shows the rainfall, in inches, for each month over one year in a city.

Month	Jan	Feb	Mar	Apr	May	Jun	Jul	Aug	Sep	Oct	Nov	Dec
Rainfall (in)	4.7	3	3.2	2.7	2.5	1.5	1.2	1.2	1.8	3.7	5.8	4.2

(a) Graph this information below.

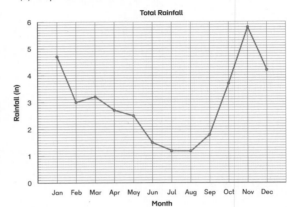

(b) Which month had the most rainfall?
November

(c) Between which months was there a monthly increase in rainfall?
August and November

(d) Which months had the same amount of rainfall?
July and August

(e) What was the total amount of rainfall in inches for the year?
35.5 in

(f) The total amount of rainfall for the year is how many inches less than 3 feet?
36 in − 35.5 in = 0.5 in
0.5 in

(g) What fraction of the months had more than $1\frac{1}{4}$ inches of rain?
All except July and August.
$\frac{10}{12} = \frac{5}{6}$

4 The perimeter of a rectangular picture frame is 100 in. The width of the frame is 1 ft 8 in.

(a) Express the length of the frame in feet and inches.
1 ft 8 in = 20 in; 100 in − 20 in − 20 in = 60 in; 60 in ÷ 2 = 30 in
30 in = 2 ft 6 in

(b) Express the length of the frame in feet as a mixed number.
$2\frac{1}{2}$ ft

(c) Express the length of the frame in feet as a decimal.
2.5 ft

---

5 Find the area in square centimeters and perimeter in centimeters of the following figure.

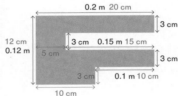

Area:
20 × 3 = 60
5 × 3 = 15
10 × 3 = 30
60 + 60 + 15 + 30 = 165
165 cm²
Perimeter:
20 + 3 + 15 + 3 + 15 + 3 + 10 + 3 + 10 + 12 = 94
94 cm

6 Aaron needs 1,000 yd of paracord, a type of rope, to make a hammock. He has two 1,000-ft spools of paracord, three 250-ft spools of paracord, and a 20-yd length of paracord. How many feet of paracord does he still need?

1,000 yd = 3,000 ft
20 yd = 60 ft
1,000 + 1,000 + 250 + 250 + 250 + 60 = 2,810
3,000 − 2,810 = 190
190 ft

7 There are between 50 and 90 children at a sports event. They can be divided into 6 equal groups or 8 equal groups. How many children are there?

Multiples of 6: 54, 60, 66, 72, 78, 84, 90

Multiples of 8: 56, 64, 72, 80, 88

72 children

8 A bin of nails weighs 14 kg 210 g. The bin by itself weighs 2 kg 300 g. 4 kg 30 g of nails were removed. What is the weight of the nails left in the bin? Express the answer in compound units.

14 kg 210 g − 2 kg 300 g = 11 kg 910 g

11 kg 910 g − 4 kg 30 g = 7 kg 880 g

7 kg 880 g

9 Violet spent $\frac{1}{3}$ of her money on a book and $3.60 on a snack. She had $12.40 left. How much money did she have to start with?

Book		

$3.60 + $12.40 = $16

2 units ⟶ $16

1 units ⟶ $16 ÷ 2 = $8

3 units ⟶ 3 × $8 = $24

$24

Challenge

10 Two bags of beans together weighed 15.82 kg. Bag A weighed 7.45 kg. After some beans were transferred from Bag B to Bag A, Bag A weighed 10 kg. What is the weight of Bag B now? Express the answer as a decimal.

Bag B: 15.82 − 7.45 = 8.37

Amount transferred: 10 − 7.45 = 2.55

Bag B after: 8.37 − 2.55 = 5.82

5.82 kg

11 This square is formed by 16 identical small rectangles. The perimeter of each small rectangle is 10 cm. What is the area of the square?

We can see from the figure that the length of each small rectangle is four times the width.

Length: 4 cm

Width: 1 cm

Area of each rectangle:

4 × 1 = 4

4 cm²

Area of square:

4 × 16 = 64

64 cm²

12 Owen has a 3-quart and a 5-quart jar. He wants to measure 1 gal of water. How can he use the jars he has to do this?

Fill up the 3 qt jar, pour it into the 5 qt jar. Refill 3 qt jar and fill up the 5 qt jar with it, leaving 1 qt in the 3 qt jar. Pour out the 5 qt jar, pour the 1 qt from the 3 qt jar into the 5 qt jar. Refill the 3 qt jar. Pour into the 5 qt jar. This makes 4 qt, or 1 gal.

Notes

Suggested number of class periods: 9–10

	Lesson	Page	Resources		Objectives
	Chapter Opener	p. 159	TB:	p. 139	Investigate multiplying decimals.
1	Multiplying Tenths and Hundredths	p. 160	TB: WB:	p. 140 p. 107	Multiply one-place and two-place decimals less than 1 by a one-digit whole number.
2	Multiplying Decimals by a Whole Number — Part 1	p. 163	TB: WB:	p. 143 p. 109	Multiply a one-place decimal by a one-digit whole number.
3	Multiplying Decimals by a Whole Number — Part 2	p. 167	TB: WB:	p. 147 p. 112	Multiply a two-place decimal by a one-digit whole number.
4	Practice A	p. 170	TB: WB:	p. 151 p. 115	Practice multiplying decimals.
5	Dividing Tenths and Hundredths	p. 171	TB: WB:	p. 153 p. 117	Divide a one-place or two-place decimal by a one-digit whole number.
6	Dividing Decimals by a Whole Number — Part 1	p. 174	TB: WB:	p. 156 p. 119	Divide a one-place decimal by a one-digit whole number.
7	Dividing Decimals by a Whole Number — Part 2	p. 177	TB: WB:	p. 160 p. 122	Divide a two-place decimal by a one-digit whole number.
8	Dividing Decimals by a Whole Number — Part 3	p. 179	TB: WB:	p. 164 p. 125	Divide decimals to hundredths in cases where the quotient has a different number of decimal places than the dividend.
9	Practice B	p. 182	TB: WB:	p. 168 p. 127	Practice division with decimals to hundredths.
	Workbook Solutions	p. 184			

In Dimensions Math 3A and 4A, students learned both mental math strategies and standard algorithms for multiplication and division of whole numbers. In this chapter, students will build on prior knowledge of both mental math strategies and standard algorithms for multiplying a decimal to hundredths by a one-digit whole number.

Students will also build on prior knowledge of mental math and standard algorithms for dividing decimals to hundredths by a one-digit whole number. At this level, quotients will only be whole numbers, or one-place decimals, or two-place decimals. There will not be a remainder after the hundredths are divided.

In this chapter the whole number is the multiplier (number of parts) and the decimal is the multiplicand (number in each part). Thus 0.64 × 3 is thought of as 0.64 multiplied by 3, 3 groups of 0.64, or 0.64 + 0.64 + 0.64.

Students have learned that when multiplying two factors, the order does not change the product. For convenience and consistency with earlier chapters on multiplication of whole numbers, the multiplier is written as the second factor in this chapter.

In Dimensions Math 5, students will learn to solve problems where we consider a whole number multiplied by a decimal: 3 × 0.64 or 3 multiplied 0.64 times.

Throughout the lessons, students are encouraged to estimate before solving. Estimation helps avoid errors with decimals. A common error is writing the decimal point in the wrong place in the answer. Estimation prior to solving should minimize that problem.

Mental Math for Multiplication

Students will see that the same mental math strategies used for whole number multiplication can also be used for multiplication of a decimal by a whole number. Multiples of ones, tenths, and hundredths can easily be solved by thinking of simple computations.

For example, 2.6 × 3 can be thought of as 26 tenths multiplied by 3.

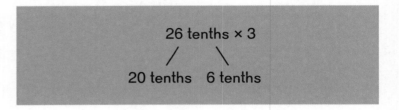

26 tenths × 3 = 60 tenths + 18 tenths
= 78 tenths = 7.8

Standard Multiplication Algorithm

In Lessons 1–4, students will multiply a decimal number by a whole number. Students will use place-value discs to help them see that the algorithm for decimals works the same way as for whole numbers.

Example: 0.64 × 3

Estimate first. 0.64 is about 0.6.

6 tenths × 3 = 18 tenths = 1.8

The answer should be more than 1.8.

Estimated values can vary. Students should realize that since 0.64 is less than 1, the product will be less than 3.

Multiply the hundredths by 3 and regroup:

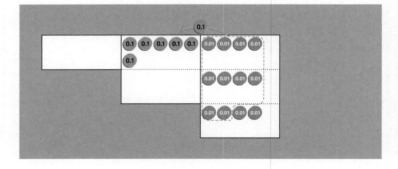

4 hundredths × 3 = 12 hundredths

12 hundredths = 1 tenth and 2 hundredths

Multiply the tenths by 3 and regroup:

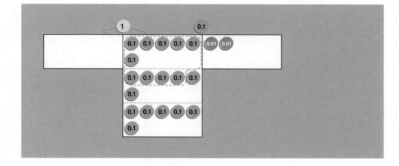

6 tenths × 3 = 18 tenths

Add the regrouped tenths:
18 tenths + 1 tenths = 19 tenths

19 tenths = 1 one and 9 tenths

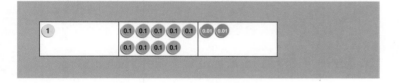

0.64 × 3 = 1.92

Using place-values discs with decimals helps students find the product with the vertical algorithm. This is similar to how they work with whole numbers by focusing on place value.

The decimal point at the end of a computation always goes between the ones and tenths:

$$\begin{array}{r} \overset{1}{0.6}4 \\ \times\quad 3 \\ \hline 1.92 \end{array}$$

In the addition and subtraction algorithm for decimals, the digits for each number are aligned vertically by place value. In the multiplication algorithm they are aligned on the right. When multiplying a decimal by a whole number, the decimal point in the product will be aligned vertically with the decimal point in the decimal multiplicand. In this example, 0.64 is the multiplicand.

A shortcut way to think about this is to realize that the product has the same number of digits after the decimal point as the decimal multiplicand. Some of these digits may be 0, so the final answer can be simplified. For example, 0.25 × 8 = 2.00 = 2.

In Dimensions Math 5, students will learn where the decimal point should go when multiplying a decimal by a decimal.

In this chapter, the multiplication algorithm will be written with the decimal number on top, as shown in the example on this page.

Mental Math for Division

Mental math strategies used for whole number division can also be used for division of a decimal number. Quotients of tens, ones, tenths, and hundredths can easily be solved by thinking of simple computations involving one or two digit numbers. For example, 4.8 ÷ 6 can be thought of as 48 tenths ÷ 6.

48 tenths ÷ 6 = 8 tenths = 0.8

Standard Division Algorithm

In lessons 5–8, students will learn the standard algorithm for dividing a decimal number by a whole number. Students will use place-value discs to see the similarity to the standard algorithm for dividing whole numbers.

The algorithm is introduced with problems that many students can solve mentally.

Example: 1.62 ÷ 3

Divide the ones by 3.

We cannot divide 1 one disc into 3 equal groups. Regroup the 1 one disc as 10 tenths discs.

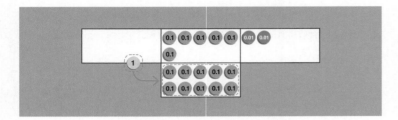

There are now 16 tenths to divide into 3 groups.

Divide the tenths by 3:

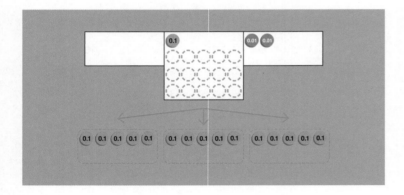

16 tenths ÷ 3 = 5 tenths and 1 tenth remaining. Regroup the 1 tenth disc as 10 hundredths discs. There are now 12 hundredths to divide into 3 groups.

Divide the hundredths by 3:

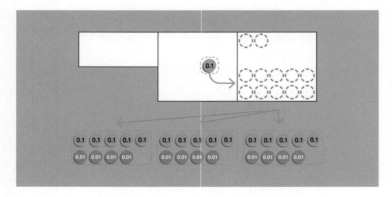

12 hundredths ÷ 3 = 4 hundredths

Students can easily see that there are 0 ones, 5 tenths and 4 hundredths in each of the 3 groups:

1.62 ÷ 3 = 0.54

To tie the place value discs representation to the division algorithm:

$$3\overline{)1.62}$$

Divide the greatest place value, in this case, ones.

Regroup 1 one as 10 tenths. There are now 16 tenths. Record a 0 in the ones place in the quotient for 0 ones.

$$\begin{array}{r} 0 \\ 3\overline{)1.62} \end{array}$$

Divide the tenths by 3.

16 tenths ÷ 3 = 5 tenths and 1 tenth remaining.

Record a decimal point and a 5 in the tenths place in the quotient.

Regroup 1 tenth as 10 hundredths. There are now 12 hundredths.

$$\begin{array}{r} 0.5 \\ 3\overline{)1.62} \\ \underline{15} \\ 12 \end{array}$$

Place a 12 in the algorithm, representing 12 hundredths.

Divide the hundredths by 3:

12 hundredths ÷ 3 = 4 hundredths

Record 4 in the hundredths place in the quotient.

1.62 ÷ 3 = 0.54

```
      0.5 4
  3 ) 1.6 2
      1 5
      ───
        1 2
        1 2
        ───
          0
```

We can check the answer with multiplication:

```
    0.5 4
  ×     3
  ───────
    1.6 2
```

Decimal division where the number of decimal places in the quotient goes beyond two decimal places or where quotients are rounded is covered in Dimensions Math 5.

Materials

- 10-sided die
- Place-value discs
- Play bills and coins
- Take-out menus from restaurants
- Whiteboards

Blackline Masters

- Decimal Division Cards (BLM)
- Grocery Shopping (BLM)
- Kaboom Cards (BLM)
- Mental Math Decimal Duel Scoring Sheet (BLM)
- Number Cards (BLM)

Activities

Games and activities included in this chapter provide practice for multiplying and dividing decimals. They can be used after students complete the **Do** questions, or anytime additional practice is needed.

Notes

Chapter Opener

Objective

- Investigate multiplying decimals.

Lesson Materials

- Play bills and coins

Have students discuss Mei's question.

Students should realize that the most efficient way to answer Mei's question is to multiply or divide, but they have only multiplied and divided whole numbers. Some students may suggest using repeated addition. Students confident with mental math may be able to find the cost of three pounds of each type of fruit. In this chapter, they will learn how to multiply a decimal number by a whole number.

Continue to Lesson 1.

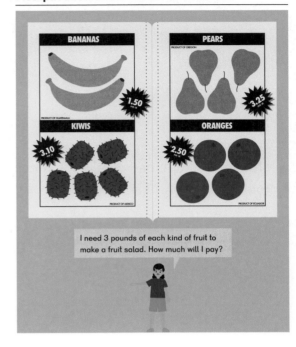

Chapter 14

Multiplication and Division of Decimals

I need 3 pounds of each kind of fruit to make a fruit salad. How much will I pay?

139

Lesson 1 Multiplying Tenths and Hundredths

Objective

- Multiply one-place and two-place decimals less than 1 by a one-digit whole number.

Lesson Materials

- Place-value discs: ones, tenths, and hundredths

Think

Provide students with place-value discs and pose the **Think** problems.

Students may use the place-value discs, the algorithm, or any other known strategy to solve the problem.

Discuss the methods students used.

Learn

Have students compare their solutions from **Think** with the ones shown in the textbook. Discuss the examples shown.

Students should see that:

4 ones × 3 = 12 ones = 12

4 tenths × 3 = 12 tenths = 1.2

4 hundredths × 3 = 12 hundredths = 0.12

Ask students to share patterns they see. When there is one decimal place in a factor, there is one decimal place in the product. When there are two decimal places in one of the factors, there are two decimal places in the product.

As with whole numbers, when there are more than ten in one place, we regroup. In (a), 10 tenths are regrouped into 1 one. In (b), 10 hundredths are regrouped into 1 tenth.

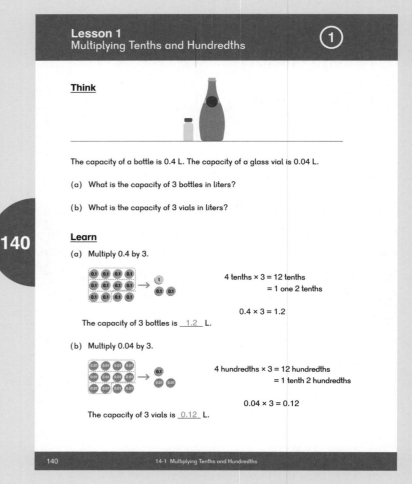

Lesson 1
Multiplying Tenths and Hundredths ①

Think

The capacity of a bottle is 0.4 L. The capacity of a glass vial is 0.04 L.

(a) What is the capacity of 3 bottles in liters?

(b) What is the capacity of 3 vials in liters?

Learn

(a) Multiply 0.4 by 3.

4 tenths × 3 = 12 tenths
= 1 one 2 tenths

0.4 × 3 = 1.2

The capacity of 3 bottles is __1.2__ L.

(b) Multiply 0.04 by 3.

4 hundredths × 3 = 12 hundredths
= 1 tenth 2 hundredths

0.04 × 3 = 0.12

The capacity of 3 vials is __0.12__ L.

140   14-1 Multiplying Tenths and Hundredths

Do

❶ — **❸** Have students continue to use place-value discs to work through the problems as needed.

In **❶**, students can find the answer to 2 × 3 to help them solve the problems, then use that basic fact to find the product of 2 tenths and 2 hundredths. In **❷** and **❸** students should see that they need to regroup.

❷ Ask students to think of 0.5 as $\frac{1}{2}$, "What is $\frac{1}{2}$ multiplied by 4 or 4 times $\frac{1}{2}$?"

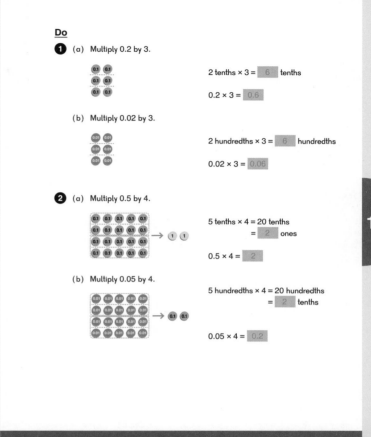

4 — 6 Students should be able to solve these problems independently.

Activity

▲ Mental Math Duel

Materials: Number Cards (BLM) 0—9 (multiple sets), Mental Math Decimal Duel Scoring Sheet (BLM)

Players take turns drawing cards until they each have twelve cards. They then fill up the twelve boxes in the scoring sheet with the numbers on their cards. All numbers on each card must be used and used only once. Once players have filled out their scoring sheets, they complete the multiplication equations and add the four products together.

The player with the greatest sum is the winner.

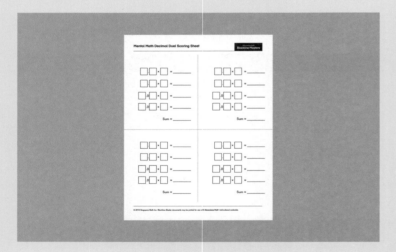

Exercise 1 • page 107

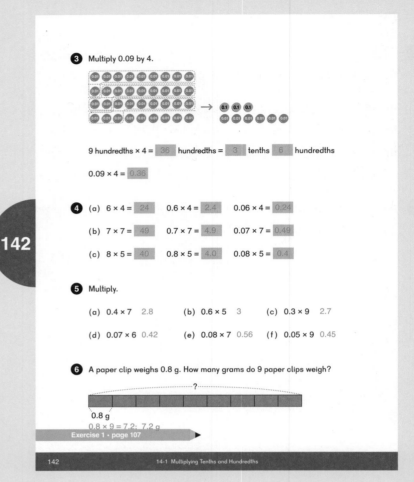

3 Multiply 0.09 by 4.

9 hundredths × 4 = 36 hundredths = 3 tenths 6 hundredths

0.09 × 4 = 0.36

4 (a) 6 × 4 = 24   0.6 × 4 = 2.4   0.06 × 4 = 0.24

(b) 7 × 7 = 49   0.7 × 7 = 4.9   0.07 × 7 = 0.49

(c) 8 × 5 = 40   0.8 × 5 = 4.0   0.08 × 5 = 0.4

5 Multiply.

(a) 0.4 × 7   2.8   (b) 0.6 × 5   3   (c) 0.3 × 9   2.7

(d) 0.07 × 6   0.42   (e) 0.08 × 7   0.56   (f) 0.05 × 9   0.45

6 A paper clip weighs 0.8 g. How many grams do 9 paper clips weigh?

0.8 g

0.8 × 9 = 7.2; 7.2 g

Exercise 1 • page 107

142   14-1 Multiplying Tenths and Hundredths

Objective

- Multiply a one-place decimal by a one-digit whole number.

Lesson Materials

- Place-value discs: tens, ones, and tenths

Think

Provide students with place-value discs and pose the **Think** problem.

Discuss Dion's comments about estimating the answer. Ask students if they think the product will be closer to 6 or 9, and why.

Record their strategies on the board and discuss the methods students used.

Learn

Have students compare their solutions from **Think** with the ones shown in the textbook. Discuss the two methods shown.

Method 1

The number 2.4 is 24 tenths. Students can multiply 24 tenths by 3:

24 tenths × 3
20 tenths   4 tenths

24 tenths × 3 = 60 tenths + 12 tenths = 72 tenths

= 70 tenths + 2 tenths

= 7 ones 2 tenths = 7.2

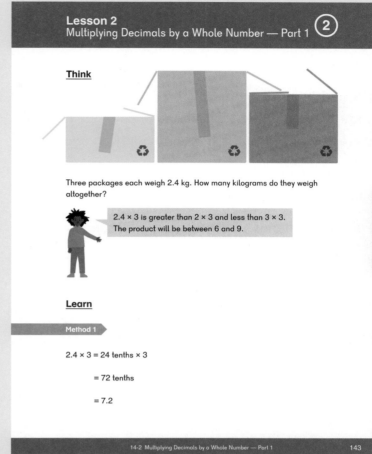

Lesson 2
Multiplying Decimals by a Whole Number — Part 1 ②

Think

Three packages each weigh 2.4 kg. How many kilograms do they weigh altogether?

2.4 × 3 is greater than 2 × 3 and less than 3 × 3.
The product will be between 6 and 9.

143

Learn

Method 1

2.4 × 3 = 24 tenths × 3

= 72 tenths

= 7.2

14-2 Multiplying Decimals by a Whole Number — Part 1   143

Method 2

Have students work along with place-value discs as the steps are modeled.

When 10 tenths are regrouped as 1 one, we can write the regrouped 1 above the ones place to help us remember to add it in after multiplying ones.

Show the following algorithm on the board and go through the computation with the class.

For 24 × 3, first multiply the ones and regroup them:

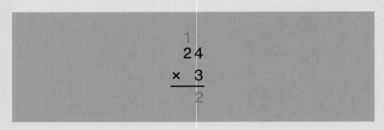

Next, multiply the tens and add the regrouped 1:

$$
\begin{array}{r}
\overset{1}{2}4 \\
\times\ \ 3 \\
\hline
72
\end{array}
$$

The computation steps for 2.4 × 3 are shown in the textbook.

Discuss similarities (digits are lined up the same way, order of computing and regrouping is the same) and differences (decimal point is included in the computation and answer of 2.4 × 3). Emphasize the importance of including the decimal point and placing it correctly when multiplying decimal numbers.

Students should see that the steps in the algorithm are the same with decimals as whole numbers. We multiply from the least to the greatest place value.

144

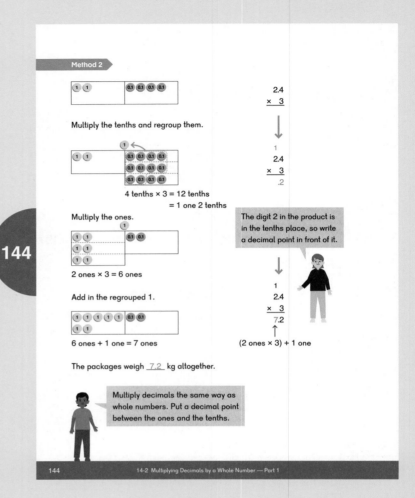

Do

①—**④** Have students continue to use place-value discs to work through the problems as needed. They should estimate the product before solving the problem.

① Mei reminds students to estimate the product first. This will help them see if their final product is reasonable.

② A common error is for students to forget to record the decimal in the product. Estimation helps us see if the answer is reasonable.

③ Sofia reminds students that 17.0 is the same value as 17.

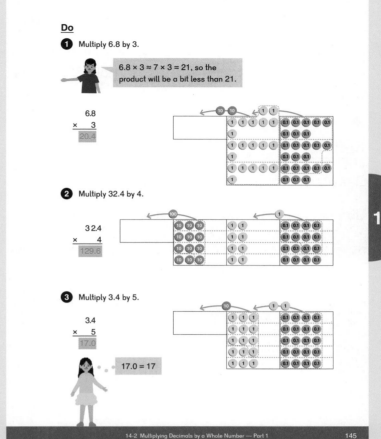

⑤ — ⑥ Students should be able to solve these problems independently.

⑤ Throughout all of these problems, students should see that the product is a one-place decimal (before it is simplified).

Activity

▲ Greatest Product

Materials: 10-sided die or Number Cards (BLM) 0–9

Have students draw personal gameboards as shown below on paper or dry erase boards:

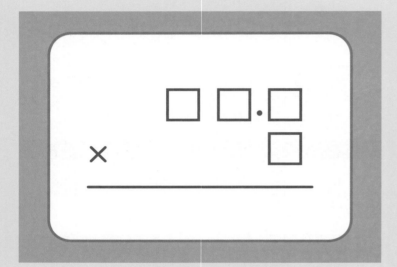

Players take turns rolling the die or drawing a card. On each turn, they place the number drawn in one of the empty boxes on the gameboard. When the boxes are filled, they find the product of the numbers.

The player with the greatest final product in each round scores a point.

The first player with five points is the winner.

Exercise 2 • page 109

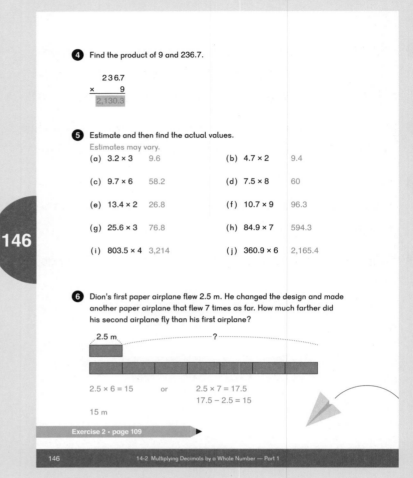

④ Find the product of 9 and 236.7.

$$\begin{array}{r} 236.7 \\ \times \qquad 9 \\ \hline 2{,}130.3 \end{array}$$

⑤ Estimate and then find the actual values.
Estimates may vary.

(a) 3.2 × 3   9.6   (b) 4.7 × 2   9.4

(c) 9.7 × 6   58.2   (d) 7.5 × 8   60

(e) 13.4 × 2   26.8   (f) 10.7 × 9   96.3

(g) 25.6 × 3   76.8   (h) 84.9 × 7   594.3

(i) 803.5 × 4 3,214   (j) 360.9 × 6 2,165.4

⑥ Dion's first paper airplane flew 2.5 m. He changed the design and made another paper airplane that flew 7 times as far. How much farther did his second airplane fly than his first airplane?

2.5 × 6 = 15   or   2.5 × 7 = 17.5
                                     17.5 − 2.5 = 15

15 m

Exercise 2 • page 109

146   14-2 Multiplying Decimals by a Whole Number — Part 1

Lesson 3 Multiplying Decimals by a Whole Number — Part 2

Objective

- Multiply a two-place decimal by a one-digit whole number.

Lesson Materials

- Place-value discs: tens, ones, tenths, and hundredths

Think

Provide students with place-value discs and pose the **Think** problem.

Students should note that in this problem, they are multiplying decimals in the hundredths. Discuss Mei's estimate.

Record their strategies on the board and discuss the methods students used.

Learn

Have students compare their solutions from **Think** with the ones shown in the textbook. Discuss the two methods shown.

Method 1

The number 0.45 is thought of as 45 hundredths. Students can multiply 45 hundredths by 3:

45 hundredths × 3

/ \

40 hundredths   5 hundredths

45 hundredths × 3 = 120 hundredths + 15 hundredths
= 135 hundredths = 1 one, 3 tenths, 5 hundredths
= 1.35

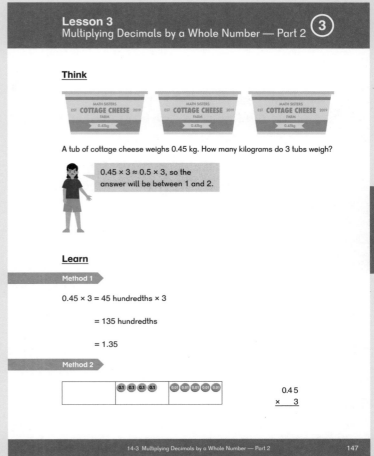

Method 2

Have students work along with place-value discs as the steps are modeled.

Students should see that the steps in the algorithm with two-place decimals are the same as with whole numbers and with one-place decimals. Since we are multiplying hundredths by a whole number, the product is a two-place decimal (before it is simplified).

Dion reminds students where to place the decimal point in the final product.

Do

❶ — ❹ Have students continue to use place-value discs to work through the problems as needed.

❶ Emma reminds students to estimate the product first. This will help them get an idea of the size of the product and see if their final answers are reasonable.

❷ — ❸ Sofia and Alex remind students that we can remove the final zeros without changing the value.

In ❷, the product is a two-place decimal number simplified to a one-place decimal number.

In ❸, the product is a two-place decimal number simplified to a whole number.

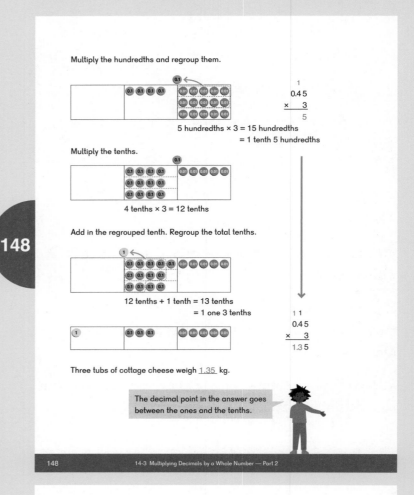

Multiply the hundredths and regroup them.

$$5 \text{ hundredths} \times 3 = 15 \text{ hundredths}$$
$$= 1 \text{ tenth } 5 \text{ hundredths}$$

Multiply the tenths.

$$4 \text{ tenths} \times 3 = 12 \text{ tenths}$$

Add in the regrouped tenth. Regroup the total tenths.

$$12 \text{ tenths} + 1 \text{ tenth} = 13 \text{ tenths}$$
$$= 1 \text{ one } 3 \text{ tenths}$$

Three tubs of cottage cheese weigh <u>1.35</u> kg.

The decimal point in the answer goes between the ones and the tenths.

148

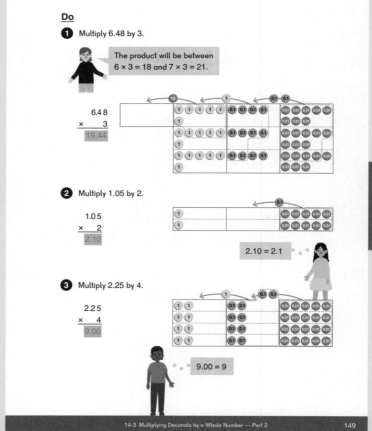

Do

❶ Multiply 6.48 by 3.

The product will be between $6 \times 3 = 18$ and $7 \times 3 = 21$.

$$\begin{array}{r} 6.48 \\ \times \quad 3 \\ \hline 19.44 \end{array}$$

❷ Multiply 1.05 by 2.

$$\begin{array}{r} 1.05 \\ \times \quad 2 \\ \hline 2.10 \end{array}$$

2.10 = 2.1

❸ Multiply 2.25 by 4.

$$\begin{array}{r} 2.25 \\ \times \quad 4 \\ \hline 9.00 \end{array}$$

9.00 = 9

149

4 In prior problems, Sofia and Alex simplified by removing the trailing zeros. Dion reminds students how to write the answer in dollars and cents.

5 Students should be able to work these problems independently.

Activities

▲ Greatest Product

Materials: 10-sided die or Number Cards (BLM) 0—9

Modify the gameboard from Lesson 2 for numbers in the hundredths:

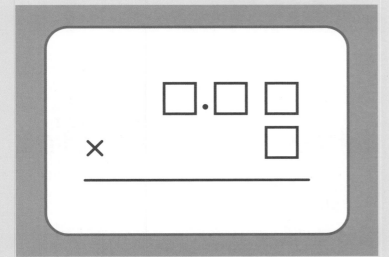

The rules are the same.

▲ Order Up!

Materials: Take-out menus from restaurants

Students take turns being the customer and waiter. The customer orders two menu items. The waiter prepares a bill and calculates the total cost of the order. The customer checks the bill to ensure the calculations were done correctly.

Exercise 3 • page 112

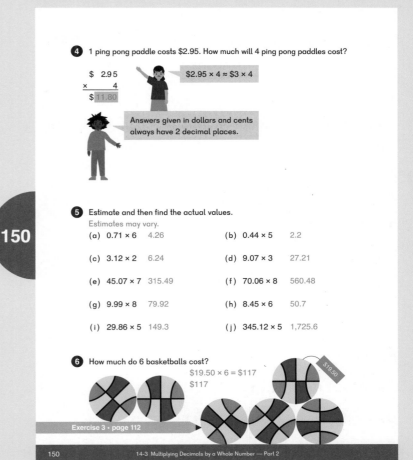

4 1 ping pong paddle costs $2.95. How much will 4 ping pong paddles cost?

$$\begin{array}{r} \$\ 2.95 \\ \times\qquad 4 \\ \hline \$\ 11.80 \end{array}$$

$2.95 × 4 ≈ \$3 × 4$

Answers given in dollars and cents always have 2 decimal places.

5 Estimate and then find the actual values.
Estimates may vary.

(a) 0.71 × 6   4.26

(b) 0.44 × 5   2.2

(c) 3.12 × 2   6.24

(d) 9.07 × 3   27.21

(e) 45.07 × 7   315.49

(f) 70.06 × 8   560.48

(g) 9.99 × 8   79.92

(h) 8.45 × 6   50.7

(i) 29.86 × 5   149.3

(j) 345.12 × 5 1,725.6

6 How much do 6 basketballs cost?
$19.50 × 6 = $117
$117

$19.50

Exercise 3 • page 112

150   14-3 Multiplying Decimals by a Whole Number — Part 2

Lesson 4 Practice A

Objective

- Practice multiplying decimals.

After students complete the **Practice** in the textbook, have them continue to practice multiplying decimals with activities from the chapter.

5 (a) Students can estimate 4 × $7 = $28 for cookies and 5 × $5 = $25 for juice to see that $40 will not be enough money.

For additional practice, have students revisit the Chapter Opener and find the cost of the fruit Mei needs to make a fruit salad.

Activity

▲ Greatest and Least

Materials: Number Cards (BLM) 1–9

Using four of the digits 1–9 once, what is the greatest product that can be made?

Do the same to find the least possible product.

Greatest product: 8.76 × 9 = 78.84
Least product: 2.34 × 1 = 2.34

Exercise 4 • page 115

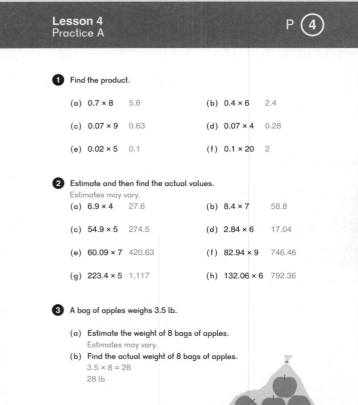

Lesson 4
Practice A

P ④

1 Find the product.

   (a) 0.7 × 8   5.6   (b) 0.4 × 6   2.4

   (c) 0.07 × 9   0.63   (d) 0.07 × 4   0.28

   (e) 0.02 × 5   0.1   (f) 0.1 × 20   2

2 Estimate and then find the actual values.
Estimates may vary.
   (a) 6.9 × 4   27.6   (b) 8.4 × 7   58.8

   (c) 54.9 × 5   274.5   (d) 2.84 × 6   17.04

   (e) 60.09 × 7   420.63   (f) 82.94 × 9   746.46

   (g) 223.4 × 5   1,117   (h) 132.06 × 6   792.36

3 A bag of apples weighs 3.5 lb.

   (a) Estimate the weight of 8 bags of apples.
      Estimates may vary.
   (b) Find the actual weight of 8 bags of apples.
      3.5 × 8 = 28
      28 lb

151

---

4 A bag of flour costs $5.65 and a bag of sugar costs $4.58. A bakery buys 5 bags of flour and 5 bags of sugar.

   (a) Estimate the total cost.
       Estimates may vary.
   (b) Find the actual total cost.
       $5.65 × 5 = $28.25; $4.58 × 5 = $22.90
       $28.25 + $22.90 = $51.15; $51.15

5 Emma wants to buy 4 boxes of cookies and 5 bottles of juice for a birthday party. A box of cookies costs $6.89 and a bottle of juice costs $5.30. She has $40.

   (a) Does she have enough money? Estimates may vary.
       Rounding down, 6 × 4 = 24, 5 × 5 = 25, she needs more than $49.
   (b) Determine how much money she will have left over, or how much more money she will need.
       $6.89 × 4 = $27.56; $5.30 × 5 = $26.50
       $27.56 + $26.50 = $54.06; $54.06 − $40 = $14.06; $14.06 more

6 Last week, Camilla ran 2.5 miles a day for 5 days. This week, she ran 3.75 miles a day for 4 days.

   (a) In which week did she run farther?
       2.5 × 5 = 12.5; 3.75 × 4 = 15; this week
   (b) How much farther did she run?
       15 − 12.5 = 2.5
       2.5 miles farther

7 A bottle of shampoo costs $6.85. A bottle of conditioner costs 90¢ more than the bottle of shampoo. Elena bought 2 of each. How much did she spend?
$6.85 + $0.90 = $7.75; $6.85 + $7.75 = $14.60; $14.60 × 2 = $29.20
$29.20

Exercise 4 • page 115

152

Lesson 5 Dividing Tenths and Hundredths

Objective

- Divide a one-place or two-place decimal by a one-digit whole number.

Lesson Materials

- Place-value discs: ones, tenths, and hundredths

Think

Provide students with place-value discs and pose the **Think** problem.

Discuss the methods students used.

Learn

Have students compare their solutions from **Think** with the ones shown in the textbook. Discuss the examples shown.

Have students work along with place-value discs as the steps are modeled.

(a) We cannot divide the 1 one disc into 3 equal groups of ones. 1 one disc is regrouped as 10 tenths discs to make a total of 12 tenths, which can be divided into 3 equal groups of tenths.

(b) We cannot divide 1 tenth disc into 3 equal groups of tenths. 1 tenth disc is regrouped as 10 hundredths discs, to make a total of 12 hundredths, which can be divided into 3 equal groups of hundredths.

Ask students how solving problem (a) helps to solve problem (b).

Emma and Sofia think about the problem as a missing factor problem: 4 tenths × what number = 12 tenths? 4 hundredths × what number = 12 hundredths?

Students may have used mental math to solve the problems without the discs:

12 ÷ 3 = 4, so 12 tenths ÷ 3 = 4 tenths and 12 hundredths ÷ 3 = 4 hundredths.

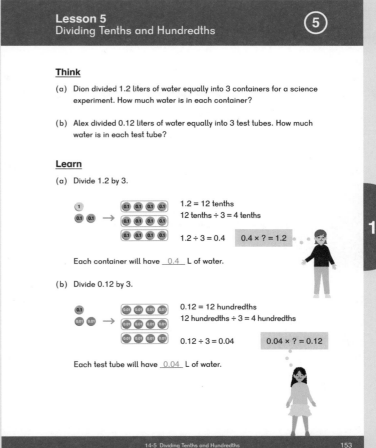

Think

(a) Dion divided 1.2 liters of water equally into 3 containers for a science experiment. How much water is in each container?

(b) Alex divided 0.12 liters of water equally into 3 test tubes. How much water is in each test tube?

Learn

(a) Divide 1.2 by 3.

1.2 = 12 tenths
12 tenths ÷ 3 = 4 tenths

1.2 ÷ 3 = 0.4   0.4 × ? = 1.2

Each container will have __0.4__ L of water.

(b) Divide 0.12 by 3.

0.12 = 12 hundredths
12 hundredths ÷ 3 = 4 hundredths

0.12 ÷ 3 = 0.04   0.04 × ? = 0.12

Each test tube will have __0.04__ L of water.

Do

1—**3** Have students continue to use place-value discs to work through the problems as needed.

2 (a) 2 ones cannot be divided into 4 equal groups of ones.

Students could also solve this problem mentally by realizing that 2 = 20 tenths and 20 tenths ÷ 4 = 5 tenths.

(b) Ask student what patterns they see from **1** (a) to **1** (b) and **2** (a) to **2** (b).

154

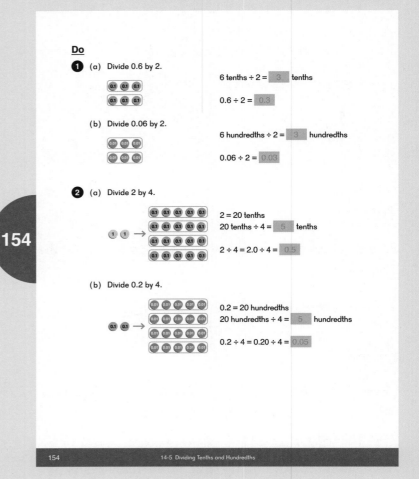

3 Alex thinks of the tenths as units so he can calculate mentally the same way as with whole numbers. Since 4.5 = 45 tenths, we can divide the same way we divide 45 by 5.

4 Mei is thinking of hundredths as units so she can also divide mentally.

5—**6** Students should be able to solve these problems independently.

5 Ask students to notice patterns between the three problems in each row. Have them focus on the place values of each problem.

This will help them think about the place value when calculating with the algorithm in the next lessons.

Activity

▲ **Decimal Division Kaboom**

Materials: Decimal Division Cards (BLM), Kaboom Cards (BLM)

Shuffle the Decimal Division Cards (BLM) and three Kaboom Cards (BLM) together, and place them facedown in a pile. Players take turns drawing a card and saying the answer to the division equation.

If a student answers correctly, she keeps the card. If she answers incorrectly, the card is returned to the pile. When a student draws a Kaboom Card (BLM), he returns all collected cards to the pile.

The player with the most cards at the end of the allotted time wins.

Exercise 5 • page 117

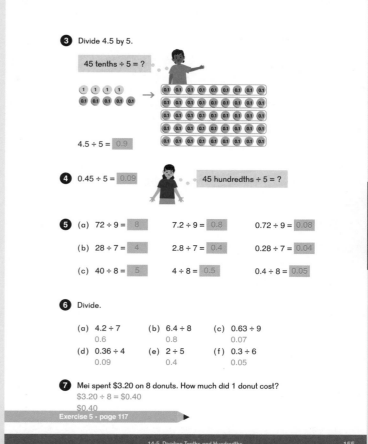

3 Divide 4.5 by 5.

45 tenths ÷ 5 = ?

4.5 ÷ 5 = 0.9

4 0.45 ÷ 5 = 0.09   45 hundredths ÷ 5 = ?

5 (a) 72 ÷ 9 = 8   7.2 ÷ 9 = 0.8   0.72 ÷ 9 = 0.08

(b) 28 ÷ 7 = 4   2.8 ÷ 7 = 0.4   0.28 ÷ 7 = 0.04

(c) 40 ÷ 8 = 5   4 ÷ 8 = 0.5   0.4 ÷ 8 = 0.05

6 Divide.

(a) 4.2 ÷ 7   (b) 6.4 ÷ 8   (c) 0.63 ÷ 9
    0.6   0.8   0.07
(d) 0.36 ÷ 4   (e) 2 ÷ 5   (f) 0.3 ÷ 6
    0.09   0.4   0.05

7 Mei spent $3.20 on 8 donuts. How much did 1 donut cost?
$3.20 ÷ 8 = $0.40
$0.40

Exercise 5 • page 117

14-5 Dividing Tenths and Hundredths   155

155

Lesson 6 Dividing Decimals by a Whole Number — Part 1

Objective

- Divide a one-place decimal by a one-digit whole number.

Lesson Materials

- Place-value discs: tens, ones, and tenths

Think

Provide students with place-value discs and pose the **Think** problem. Have students try to solve the problem independently.

Discuss Alex's estimate.

Ask students if the quotient will be closer to 2 or 3. They should see that 7.2 is closer to 6 than to 9, so the quotient should be closer to 2 than 3.

Discuss the methods students used.

Learn

Have students compare their solutions from **Think** with the ones shown in the textbook. Discuss the two methods shown.

Method 1

Dion divides 72 tenths by 3 the same way he would divide 72 by 3.

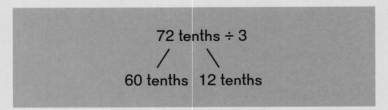

72 tenths ÷ 3 = 20 tenths + 4 tenths = 24 tenths = 2.4

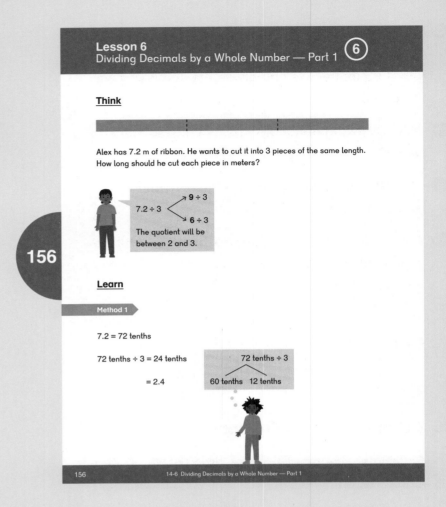

Method 2

Have students work along with place-value discs as the steps are modeled.

Students should see that the steps in the algorithm are the same with decimals as with whole numbers. It is a repeated process of dividing the value of the digit in each place by the dividend and then regrouping the remainder.

Mei reminds students how to check their answers.

Discuss Emma's comment.

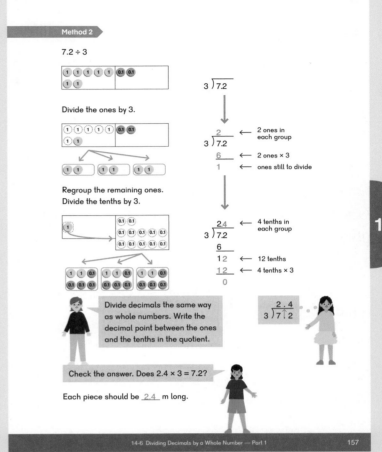

Do

①—② Have students continue to use place-value discs to work through the problems as needed.

① 3 ones do not divide evenly into 2 equal groups of ones. Divide 2 ones into 2 equal groups of ones. 1 one remains.

1 one cannot be divided into 2 equal groups of ones. Regroup the 1 one as 10 tenths. There are now 16 tenths, which can be divided into 2 equal groups of tenths.

② 3 tens do not divide evenly into 2 equal groups of tens. Divide 2 tens into 2 equal groups of ten. 1 ten remains.

Regroup the 1 ten as 10 ones. There are now 15 ones.

Divide 15 ones into 2 equal groups of ones. 1 one remains.

Regroup the 1 one into 10 tenths. There are now 14 tenths, which can be divided into 2 equal groups of tenths.

③—⑤ Students should be able to work these problems independently.

Exercise 6 • page 119

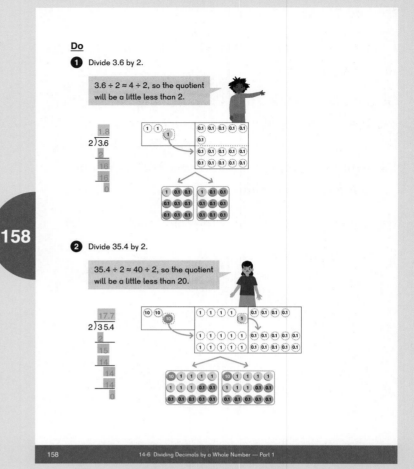

Do

① Divide 3.6 by 2.

3.6 ÷ 2 ≈ 4 ÷ 2, so the quotient will be a little less than 2.

2)3.6

② Divide 35.4 by 2.

35.4 ÷ 2 ≈ 40 ÷ 2, so the quotient will be a little less than 20.

2)35.4

③ Divide 23.4 by 3.

3)23.4

23.4 ÷ 3 ≈ 24 ÷ 3, so the quotient will be a little less than 8.

④ Estimate and then find the actual values.
Estimates may vary.
(a) 8.4 ÷ 2   4.2   (b) 4.8 ÷ 4   1.2

(c) 6.5 ÷ 5   1.3   (d) 7.8 ÷ 6   1.3

(e) 43.4 ÷ 7   6.2   (f) 83.2 ÷ 8   10.4

(g) 78.3 ÷ 9   8.7   (h) 136.5 ÷ 5   27.3

⑤ Dion ran 10.8 miles this week. He ran 3 times as far this week as he did last week. How many miles did he run last week?

10.8 miles

This week

Last week

?

10.8 ÷ 3 = 3.6
3.6 miles

Lesson 7 Dividing Decimals by a Whole Number — Part 2

Objective

- Divide a two-place decimal by a one-digit whole number.

Lesson Materials

- Place-value discs: ones, tenths, and hundredths

Think

Provide students with place-value discs and pose the **Think** problem. Have students try to solve the problem independently.

Discuss Alex's estimate. Ask students if the quotient will be closer to 1 or 2 and why.

Learn

Have students compare their solutions from **Think** with the ones shown in the textbook.

Have students work along with place-value discs as the steps are modeled.

Students should see that the steps in the algorithm for two-place decimals are the same as with one-place decimals. Just as we regroup from ones to tenths, we can regroup from tenths to hundredths.

Emma prompts students to check their answers.

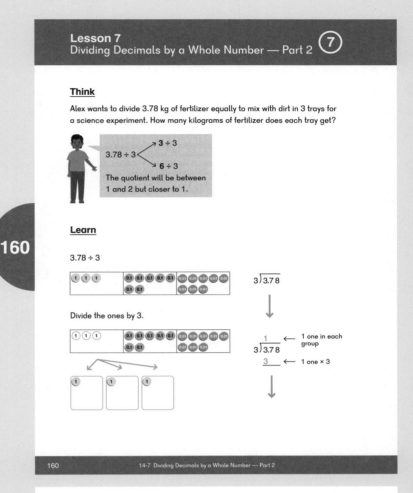

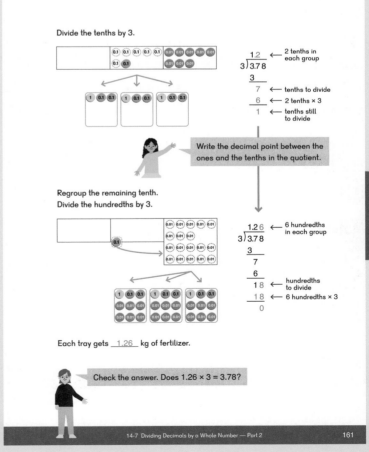

Do

Discuss the problems with students.

1 Ask students why Emma uses 0.4 and 0.8 to estimate. The multiples of 4 are 4, 8, etc. so the quotient will be between 4 tenths ÷ 4 and 8 tenths ÷ 4.

2 Divide the 6 ones into 3 equal groups of ones.

Record 2 ones in the quotient.

Divide the tenths.

2 tenths cannot be divided into 3 equal groups of tenths. Regroup the 2 tenths into 20 hundredths. There are now 24 hundredths.

Since the two tenths have been regrouped into hundredths, there are no tenths left to be divided. We write a "0" in the tenths place in the quotient to show that no tenths are divided.

Divide the hundredths.

24 hundredths ÷ 3 = 8 hundredths

Record an 8 in the hundredths place in the quotient.

3—**5** Throughout these problems, students should see that the quotients will be in hundredths, so there will be two decimal places in their answers. Students should be able to solve these problems independently.

Activity

▲ Grocery Shopping

Materials: Grocery Shopping (BLM)

Have students find the cost to buy different amounts of produce. They will need to find the cost per item or pound first.

Exercise 7 • page 122

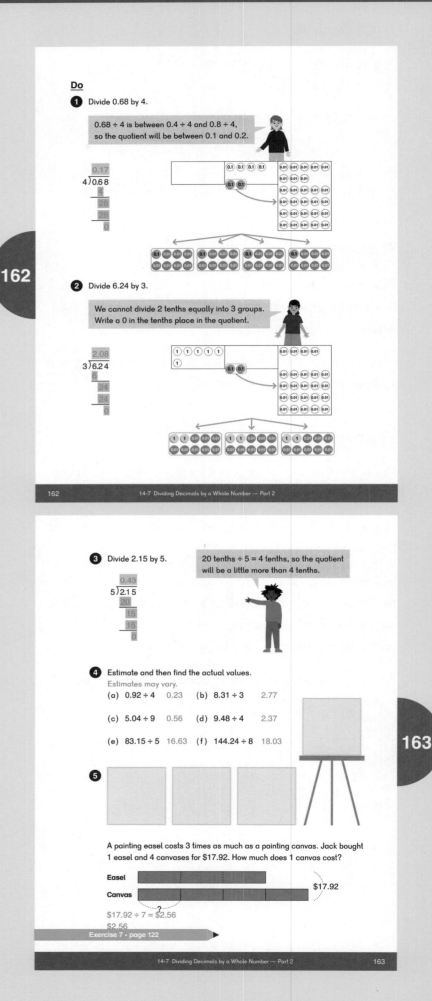

178   Teacher's Guide 4B Chapter 14   © 2019 Singapore Math Inc.

Objective

- Divide decimals to hundredths in cases where the quotient has a different number of decimal places than the dividend.

Lesson Materials

- Place-value discs: ones, tenths, and hundredths

Think

Provide students with place-value discs and pose the **Think** problem. Have students try to solve the problem independently.

Discuss Emma's estimate.

Learn

Have students compare their solutions from **Think** with the ones shown in the textbook. Discuss the examples shown.

Have students work along with place-value discs as the steps are modeled.

In this problem and lesson, we are regrouping to smaller place values, and then dividing. Rather than have a remainder, we can always regroup into a lesser decimal place value. We show this by writing zeros to keep track of the place in the quotient. This is students' first exposure to appending zeros to dividends when dividing. Up until now, students have been dividing and stating the remainder after the quotient. For example, 5 ÷ 4 = 1 R1.

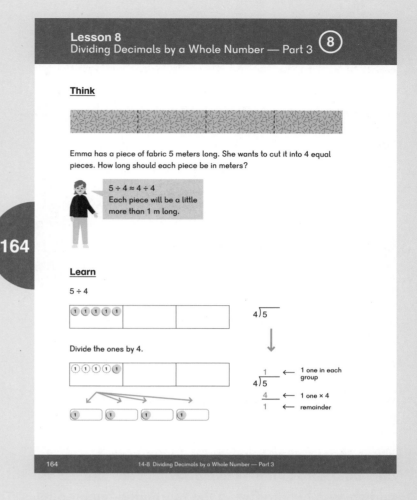

After dividing 5 ones into 4 equal groups, we have 1 one remaining. In previous problems, there have been tenths in the tenths place to begin with and students add together regrouped and existing tenths before dividing the tenths.

When there are no existing tenths, students are adding regrouped tenths to zero tenths to arrive at the total tenths to divide.

We know we can regroup the 1 one into 10 tenths. To do so, we put a decimal point between the ones and tenths, and append a zero (in the tenths place) to the dividend.

Divide the tenths. We can see that there are 2 tenths in each group, with 2 tenths remaining to be divided. In the quotient, write decimal point 2 for 2 tenths.

Continue to regroup the tenths and divide the hundredths.

When there are no hundredths to begin with, we append a zero to the dividend, to indicate that we are adding zero hundredths to the regrouped hundredths.

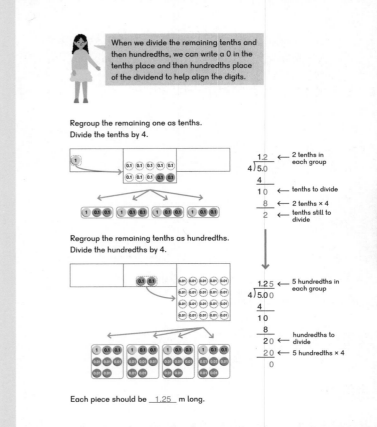

165

Do

1 — **3** Discuss the problems with students. They can use place-value discs to work through the problems as needed.

Point out to students that **1** — **3** involve adding zeros to the tenths and/or hundredths places in the algorithms when we need to regroup numbers into lesser place values to divide.

4 — **6** Students should be able to solve the problems independently.

Exercise 8 • page 125

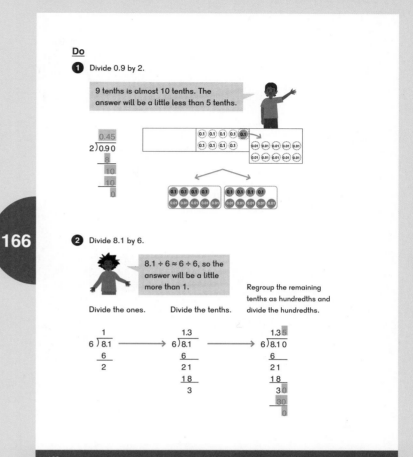

166

Do

1 Divide 0.9 by 2.

9 tenths is almost 10 tenths. The answer will be a little less than 5 tenths.

```
  0.45
2)0.90
    8
    10
    10
     0
```

2 Divide 8.1 by 6.

$8.1 ÷ 6 ≈ 6 ÷ 6$, so the answer will be a little more than 1.

Divide the ones.   Divide the tenths.   Regroup the remaining tenths as hundredths and divide the hundredths.

```
   1                      1.3                     1.35
6)8.1        →        6)8.1        →        6)8.10
  6                      6                       6
  2                      21                      21
                         18                      18
                          3                       30
                                                  30
                                                   0
```

166   14-8 Dividing Decimals by a Whole Number — Part 3

3 Divide 22 by 8.

```
          2.75
8)22  →  8)22.00
          16
          60
          56
          40
          40
           0
```

$22 ÷ 8 ≈ 24 ÷ 8$, so the quotient will be a little less than...

4 Estimate and then find the actual values.
Estimates may vary.
(a) 10 ÷ 4   (b) 4.3 ÷ 2   (c) 25.5 ÷ 6
     2.5   2.15   4.25
(d) 46 ÷ 4   (e) 30.4 ÷ 5   (f) 100 ÷ 8
     11.5   6.08   12.5

167

5 Five friends shared the cost of a meal equally. The meal cost $113. How much did each friend spend?
$113 ÷ 5 = $22.60
$22.60

6
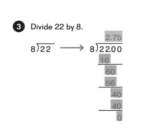

A laboratory technician is putting 70 g of sodium chloride equally into 4 test tubes. How many grams of sodium chloride need to be put into each test tube?
70 ÷ 4 = 17.5
17.5 g

Exercise 8 • page 125

14-8 Dividing Decimals by a Whole Number — Part 3   167

Lesson 9 Practice B

Objective

- Practice division with decimals to hundredths.

After students complete the **Practice** in the textbook, have them continue to practice multiplying and dividing decimals with activities from the chapter.

Encourage students to draw bar models if they need help understanding the problems.

7

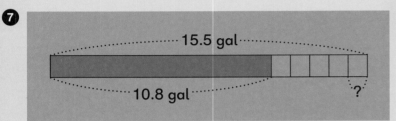

15.5 gal

10.8 gal   ?

---

1 Find the quotient. Express the answers as decimals.

(a) 1.8 ÷ 3   0.6   (b) 0.36 ÷ 9   0.04   (c) 5.6 ÷ 8   0.7

(d) 1 ÷ 2   0.5   (e) 3 ÷ 5   0.6   (f) 0.4 ÷ 8   0.05

2 Estimate and then find the actual values. Express the answers as decimals.
Estimates may vary.

(a) 4.8 ÷ 2   2.4   (b) 8.7 ÷ 3   2.9   (c) 41.6 ÷ 8   5.2

(d) 5 ÷ 2   2.5   (e) 7.8 ÷ 4   1.95   (f) 17 ÷ 5   3.4

(g) 41.6 ÷ 8   5.2   (h) 36.48 ÷ 8   4.56   (i) 14.2 ÷ 4   3.55

(j) 136.8 ÷ 6   22.8   (k) 15.05 ÷ 7   2.15   (l) 568.2 ÷ 5   113.64

168

3

Alex bought two puzzles that cost the same amount of money. He paid $7.70. How much did each puzzle cost?
$7.70 ÷ 2 = $3.85
$3.85

---

4 An employee put 6 lb of coffee equally into 4 bags. How much coffee is in each bag?
6 ÷ 4 = 1.5
1.5 lb

5 In a walkathon, 5 students walked a combined distance of 34 miles. If they each walked the same distance, how far did each student walk?
34 ÷ 5 = 6.8
6.8 miles

6

169

Store A sells 5 bottles of juice for $11.75. Store B sells 6 bottles of the same juice for $15.12.

(a) Estimate to determine which store has a better deal.
Estimates may vary.

(b) How much does one bottle of juice cost at each store?
$11.75 ÷ 5 = $2.35; $15.12 ÷ 6 = $2.52
Store A: $2.35; Store B: $2.52

7 Harrison added some plant food to water. He has 15.5 gal of this mixture. He used 10.8 gal to water his plants and poured the rest equally into 5 bottles. How much mixture is in each bottle?
15.5 − 10.8 = 4.7
4.7 ÷ 5 = 0.94; 0.94 gal

8 The perimeter of a square garden is 33.2 m. How many meters long is each side of the garden?
33.2 ÷ 4 = 8.3
8.3 m

11

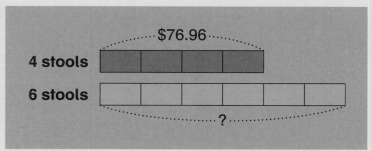

$76.96

4 stools

6 stools

?

13

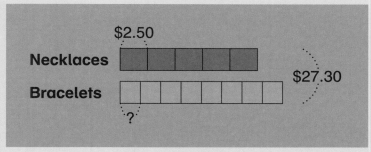

$2.50

Necklaces

Bracelets

$27.30

?

Necklaces:

1 unit ⟶ $2.50

5 units ⟶ 5 × $2.50 = $12.50

Bracelets:

8 units ⟶ $27.30 − $12.50 = $14.80

1 unit ⟶ $14.80 ÷ 8 = $1.85

Brain Works

★ Treats for Spot

Dion is buying treats for his dog from the pet store bulk bins.

$30.72 buys 8 lb of dog chewies.

$26.95 buys 7 lb of dog snaps.

$21.00 buys 6 lb of dog cruncheroos.

He wants to buy 5 lb of each type of treat. How much will he spend?

Hint: Find the cost of 1 lb of each type of treat first.

---

9 The area of a rectangle is 65.7 cm². The length of the rectangle is 9 cm. What is the perimeter of the rectangle?
65.7 ÷ 9 = 7.3; 9 + 9 + 7.3 + 7.3 = 32.6
32.6 cm

10 Aisha raised $25.50 a week for 3 weeks for charity. She gave the money equally to 5 animal shelters. How much money did each shelter receive?
$25.50 × 3 = $76.50; $76.50 ÷ 5 = $15.30
$15.30

11

4 stools cost $76.96. How much do 6 stools cost?
$76.96 ÷ 4 = $19.24
$19.24 × 6 = $115.44; $115.44

12 Jerry worked for 4 hours. He then spent $12.50 of the money he earned and had $50.90 left. How much was he paid per hour?
$12.50 + $50.90 = $63.40; $63.40 ÷ 4 = $15.85
$15.85

13

Sharon sells necklaces for $2.50 each. She sold 5 necklaces. She also sold 8 bracelets. Each bracelet had the same price. She received $27.30. How much did she sell each bracelet for?
$2.50 × 5 = $12.50
$27.30 − $12.50 = $14.80
$14.8 ÷ 8 = $1.85
$1.85

Exercise 9 • page 127

170

14-9 Practice B

170

Dog chewies:

30.72 ÷ 8 = 3.84

5 × 3.84 = 19.20

$19.20

Dog snaps:

26.95 ÷ 7 = 3.85

5 × 3.85 = 19.25

$19.25

Dog cruncheroos:

21 ÷ 6 = $3.50

5 × 3.50 = 17.50

$17.50

He will spend $55.95.

Exercise 9 • page 127

Chapter 14 Multiplication and Division of Decimals

Exercise 1

Basics

1 (a) 7 ones × 4 = [28] ones

7 × 4 = [28]

(b) 7 tenths × 4 = [28] tenths

0.7 × 4 = [2.8]

(c) 7 hundredths × 4 = [28] hundredths

0.07 × 4 = [0.28]

2 (a) 8 ones × 5 = [40] ones = [4] tens

8 × 5 = [40]

(b) 8 tenths × 5 = [40] tenths = [4] ones

0.8 × 5 = [4]

(c) 8 hundredths × 5 = [40] hundredths = [4] tenths

0.08 × 5 = [0.4]

Practice

3 (a) 90 × 8 = [720]

9 × 8 = [72]

0.9 × 8 = [7.2]

0.09 × 8 = [0.72]

(b) 50 × 6 = [300]

5 × 6 = [30]

0.5 × 6 = [3]

0.05 × 6 = [0.3]

4 Complete the number patterns.

(a) | **0.7** | **1.4** | **2.1** | 2.8 | 3.5 | 4.2 | 4.9 |
| --- | --- | --- | --- | --- | --- | --- |

(b) | **0.3** | **0.36** | **0.42** | 0.48 | 0.54 | 0.6 | 0.66 |

(c) | **0.45** | **0.54** | **0.63** | 0.72 | 0.81 | 0.9 | 0.99 |

5 (a) 0.3 × 4 = [1.2]   (b) 0.4 × 3 = [1.2]

(c) 0.07 × 8 = [0.56]   (d) 0.05 × 4 = [0.2]

(e) 0.06 × 7 = [0.42]   (f) 0.04 × 2 = [0.08]

6 A square is 0.8 m on one side. What is its perimeter?
0.8 × 4 = 3.2
3.2 m

Exercise 2

Basics

1 (a) Estimate the product of 6.7 and 8.

$6.7 \times 8 \approx 7 \times 8 =$ 56

(b) Multiply 6.7 by 8.

First multiply the tenths.

$0.7 \times 8 =$ 5.6

```
      5
    6.7
  ×   8
     .6
```

Then multiply the ones and add in any renamed tenths.

$(6 \times 8) + 5 =$ 53

$6.7 \times 8 =$ 5 3 .6

```
      5
    6.7
  ×   8
   53.6
```

2 (a) Estimate the product of 56.5 and 6.

$56.5 \times 6 \approx 60 \times 6 =$ 360

(b) Multiply 56.5 by 6.

```
   3 3
   5 6.5
 ×     6
   339.0
```

$56.5 \times 6 =$ 3 3 9 .0 = 3 3 9

Practice

3 (a) Alex estimated the product of 26.9 and 4 to be 120. With what number did he replace 26.9?

30

(b) Sofia estimated the product of 26.9 and 4 to be 100. With what number did she replace 26.9?

25

(c) Whose estimate will be closer to the actual product? Why?

Sofia's, because 25 is closer to 26.9 than 30 is.

(d) Find the product of 26.9 and 4.

```
      2 6.9
 ×        4
    1 0 7.6
```

4 Estimate and then find the actual product.
Estimates may vary.

(a) $8.3 \times 4 \approx$ [ ]

(b) $348.2 \times 5 \approx$ [ ]

```
      8.3
 ×      4
     33.2
```

```
    3 4 8.2
 ×        5
  1 7 4 1.0
```

$8.3 \times 4 =$ 33.2

$348.2 \times 5 =$ 1,741

5 Multiply. Remember to estimate first.

(a) 7.8×6
46.8

(b) 9.2×5
46

(c) 14.8×9
133.2

(d) 702.5×8
5,620

6 A brick weighs 3.5 kg. A concrete block weighs 5 times as much as the brick. How much does the concrete block weigh?

$3.5 \times 5 = 17.5$

17.5 kg

7 There are 7 fence posts in a row. The distance between the middle of each post is 34.5 cm. How far is it from the middle of the first post to the middle of the last post? Express the answer in meters and centimeters.

There are 6 intervals between 7 fence posts.

$34.5 \times 6 = 207$

207 cm = 2 m 7 cm

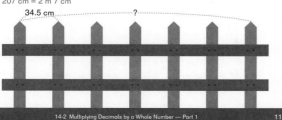

Exercise 3

Basics

1 (a) Estimate the product of 0.78 and 6.

$0.78 \times 6 \approx 0.8 \times 6 =$ | 4.8

(b) Multiply 0.78 by 6.

First multiply the hundredths.

$0.08 \times 6 =$ | 0.48

```
        4
      0 . 7 8
    ×       6
            8
```

Then, multiply the tenths and add any renamed hundredths.

$(0.7 \times 6) + 0.4 =$ | 4.6

$0.78 \times 6 =$ | 4 | 6 | 8

```
        4
      0 . 7 8
    ×       6
      4 | 6 8
```

2 (a) Estimate the product of 4.78 and 5.

$4.78 \times 5 \approx 5 \times 5 =$ | 25

(b) Multiply 4.78 by 5.

```
      3 | 4
      4 . 7 8
    ×       5
      2 | 3 | 9 | 0
```

$4.78 \times 5 =$ | 2 | 3 | 9 | 0 = | 2 | 3 | 9

Practice

3 0.72×5 is closest to which of the following?

| 5 | **3.5** | 50 | 35 |

4 9.72×3 is closest to which of the following?

| 2.7 | 27 | **29** | 32 |

5 Write > or < in each ◯. Use estimation.

(a) $0.89 \times 7 \;(>)\; 1.5 \times 3$

(b) $4.1 \times 8 \;(>)\; 6.29 \times 4$

6 Estimate and then find the actual product.
Estimates may vary.

(a) $0.56 \times 7 \approx$ [ ]   (b) $45.72 \times 5 \approx$ [ ]

```
        0 | 5 6
    ×         7
        3 | 9 2
```

```
      4 5 | 7 2
    ×         5
    2 2 8 | 6 0
```

$0.56 \times 7 =$ | 3.92 $45.72 \times 5 =$ | 228.6

7 Multiply. Remember to estimate first.

(a) 7.18×6
43.08

(b) 0.82×3
2.46

(c) 4.18×9
37.62

(d) 74.71×8
597.68

8 Renata has $20. She wants to buy 8 gel pens that cost $2.99 each.
Does she have enough money?
$\$2.99 \times 8 \approx \$3 \times 8 = \$24$
No

9 One t-shirt costs $8.99. A package of 5 t-shirts costs $43. Is it more or less
expensive to buy 5 individual t-shirts and by how much?
$\$8.99 \times 5 = \$44.95$
$44.95 > 43$
It is more expensive to buy 5 individual t-shirts by $1.95.

Exercise 4

Check

1. (a) $0.6 \times 4 =$ `2.4`   (b) $0.08 \times 3 =$ `0.24`

   (c) $0.07 \times 9 =$ `0.63`   (d) $0.05 \times 2 =$ `0.1`

   (e) $0.05 \times 5 =$ `0.25`   (f) $0.8 \times 4 =$ `3.2`

2. Estimate to arrange the expressions in order from least to greatest.

0.68×9	1.4×3	12.3×2	0.34×8
A	**B**	**C**	**D**

   D, B, A, C

3. Multiply.

   (a) 2.82×6
   16.92

   (b) 12.2×5
   61

   (c) 0.95×5
   4.75

   (d) 7.12×3
   21.36

   (e) 23.27×7
   162.89

   (f) 444.4×8
   3,555.2

4. A 2-inch ball bearing costs $9.45 and a 1-inch ball bearing costs $0.77. Mr. Jung bought eight 1-inch ball bearings and two 2-inch ball bearings. How much did he spend?
   2-inch ball bearings: $9.45 \times 2 = 18.90
   1-inch ball bearings: $0.77 \times 8 = 6.16
   $18.90 + $6.16 = 25.06
   $25.06

5. A rectangular field is 0.26 km long and 0.08 km wide. What is the perimeter of the field?
   $0.26 \times 2 = 0.52$
   $0.08 \times 2 = 0.16$
   $0.52 + 0.16 = 0.68$
   0.68 km

Challenge

6. Julian has $14.85. Hudson has 4 times as much money as Julian. Simone has $5.60 less than twice as much money as Julian. How much money do they have altogether?

   7 units ⟶ $14.85 \times 7 = 103.95
   $103.95 - $5.60 = 98.35
   $98.35

Exercise 5

Basics

1. (a) 24 ones ÷ 8 = `3` ones

   $24 \div 8 =$ `3`

   (b) 24 tenths ÷ 8 = `3` tenths

   $2.4 \div 8 =$ `0.3`

   (c) 24 hundredths ÷ 8 = `3` hundredths

   $0.24 \div 8 =$ `0.03`

2. (a) $56 \div 8 =$ `56` ones ÷ 8 = `7` ones = `7`

   (b) $5.6 \div 8 =$ `56` tenths ÷ 8 = `7` tenths = `0.7`

   (c) $0.56 \div 8 =$ `56` hundredths ÷ 8 = `7` hundredths = `0.07`

3. (a) $720 \div 8 =$ `90`

   $72 \div 8 =$ `9`

   $7.2 \div 8 =$ `0.9`

   $0.72 \div 8 =$ `0.09`

   (b) $300 \div 5 =$ `60`

   $30 \div 5 =$ `6`

   $3 \div 5 =$ `0.6`

   $0.3 \div 5 =$ `0.06`

Practice

4. (a) $0.4 \div 2 =$ `0.2`   (b) $0.2 \div 4 =$ `0.05`

   (c) $0.09 \div 3 =$ `0.03`   (d) $3.6 \div 9 =$ `0.4`

   (e) $0.36 \div 6 =$ `0.06`   (f) $4.2 \div 7 =$ `0.6`

   (g) $8.1 \div 9 =$ `0.9`   (h) $0.3 \div 6 =$ `0.05`

5. The perimeter of a square tile is 3.6 ft. How long is one side? Express the answer as a decimal.
   $3.6 \div 4 = 0.9$
   0.9 ft

6. A package of 6 plates costs $3. What is the cost of 1 plate?
   $3 \div 6 = 0.50
   $0.50

Exercise 6

Basics

1 (a) Complete the following estimations for 93.6 ÷ 4.

$80 \div 4 =$ 20

$100 \div 4 =$ 25

The quotient will be between __20__ and __25__.

(b) Divide 93.6 by 4.

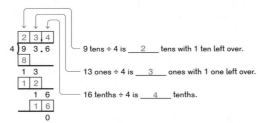

9 tens ÷ 4 is __2__ tens with 1 ten left over.

13 ones ÷ 4 is __3__ ones with 1 one left over.

16 tenths ÷ 4 is __4__ tenths.

(c) Compare the estimates to the actual product.

Which estimate is lower?
$80 \div 4 = 20$
Which estimate is higher?
$100 \div 4 = 25$
Which estimate is closest?
$100 \div 4 = 25$

(d) Check: 23.4 × 4 = 93.6

Practice

2 (a) Sofia estimated 52.2 ÷ 6 by dividing 60 by 6.
Mei estimated 52.2 ÷ 6 by dividing 54 by 6. Find their estimates.
Sofia: 10
Mei: 9

(b) Which estimate will be closer to the actual answer? Why?
Mei's, because 54 is closer to 52.2 than 60 is.

(c) Divide 52.2 by 6.

```
      8 7
  6 ) 5 2 . 2
      4 8
        4 2
        4 2
           0
```

3 Estimate and then find the quotient.   Estimates may vary.

(a) $7.8 \div 3 \approx$ ☐

```
      2 6
  3 ) 7 8
      6
      1 8
      1 8
         0
```

$7.8 \div 3 =$ 2.6

(b) $67.2 \div 7 \approx$ ☐

```
      9 6
  7 ) 6 7 2
      6 3
        4 2
        4 2
           0
```

$67.2 \div 7 =$ 9.6

4 Divide. Remember to estimate mentally first.

(a) $7.6 \div 4$
1.9

(b) $9.5 \div 5$
1.9

(c) $71.6 \div 2$
35.8

(d) $702.4 \div 8$
87.8

5 The capacity of a pail is 7 times as much as the capacity of a bottle. If the capacity of the pail is 9.1 L, what is the capacity of the bottle?
$9.1 \div 7 = 1.3$
1.3 L

6 6 lampposts are equally spaced in a row. The total distance between the first post and the last post is 75.5 m. What is the distance between each lamppost?
There are 5 intervals between 6 lampposts.
$75.5 \div 5 = 15.1$
15.1 m

Teacher's Guide 4B Chapter 14

Exercise 7

Basics

1 (a) Complete the following estimations for 8.28 ÷ 6.

$$6 \div 6 = \boxed{1} \qquad 12 \div 6 = \boxed{2}$$

The quotient will be between __1__ and __2__.

(b) Divide 8.28 by 6.

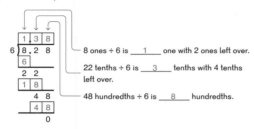

8 ones ÷ 6 is __1__ one with 2 ones left over.

22 tenths ÷ 6 is __3__ tenths with 4 tenths left over.

48 hundredths ÷ 6 is __8__ hundredths.

(c) Check: $\boxed{1.38} \times 6 = 8.28$

2 Which of the following have a quotient greater than 1 but less than 10? Use estimation.

| 0.72 ÷ 9 | **4.62 ÷ 2** | 3.76 ÷ 8 | **51.17 ÷ 7** | 52.64 ÷ 4 |

Practice

3 1.76 ÷ 6 is closest to which number below?

| 0.1 | 0.2 | **0.3** | 0.4 |

4 6.64 ÷ 8 is greater than which numbers below?

| **0.7** | **0.8** | 0.9 | 1 |

5 Estimate and then find the exact quotient.

(a) $51.17 \div 7 \approx \boxed{7}$ (b) $69.45 \div 5 \approx \boxed{14}$

$51.17 \div 7 = \boxed{7.31}$ $69.45 \div 5 = \boxed{13.89}$

6 Divide. Remember to estimate mentally first.

(a) 0.85 ÷ 5
0.17

(b) 9.54 ÷ 6
1.59

(c) 28.98 ÷ 3
9.66

(d) 702.44 ÷ 4
175.61

8 A package of five 1-inch steel ball bearings costs $7.95. What is the cost of one ball bearing?
$7.95 ÷ 5 = $1.59
$1.59

9 A bottle of perfume costs 4 times as much as 3 tubes of toothpaste. The bottle of perfume costs $35.16. What is the cost of one tube of toothpaste?
$35.16 ÷ 4 = $8.79
3 tubes of toothpaste is $8.79.
$8.79 ÷ 3 = $2.93
$2.93

Exercise 8

Basics

1 (a) Estimate 26 ÷ 8.

$26 \div 8 \approx 24 \div 8 =$ [3]

(b) Divide 26 by 8.

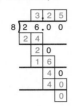

```
        3 . 2 5
  8 ) 2 6 . 0 0
      2 4
        2 0
        1 6
          4 0
          4 0
            0
```

2 (a) Estimate 9.6 ÷ 5.

$9.6 \div 5 \approx$ [2]

(b) Divide 9.6 by 5.

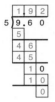

```
      1 . 9 2
  5 ) 9 . 6 0
      5
      4 6
      4 5
        1 0
        1 0
          0
```

Practice

3 Divide. Remember to estimate first.

(a) 45 ÷ 6
7.5

(b) 81 ÷ 4
20.25

(c) 80.8 ÷ 5
16.16

(d) 56.4 ÷ 6
9.4

(e) 452 ÷ 5
90.4

(f) 91.1 ÷ 2
45.55

4 A package of 4 pens cost $19. What is the cost of 1 pen?
$19 ÷ 4 = $4.75
$4.75

14-8 Dividing Decimals by a Whole Number — Part 3   125

126   14-8 Dividing Decimals by a Whole Number — Part 3

Exercise 9

Check

1 (a) $2.4 \div 3 = \boxed{0.8}$ (b) $0.08 \div 4 = \boxed{0.02}$

(c) $1 \div 5 = \boxed{0.2}$ (d) $4.9 \div 7 = \boxed{0.7}$

(e) $0.4 \div 8 = \boxed{0.05}$ (f) $0.54 \div 9 = \boxed{0.06}$

2 Divide.

(a) $8.7 \div 3$
2.9

(b) $9.48 \div 6$
1.58

(c) $2.94 \div 7$
0.42

(d) $13 \div 4$
3.25

(e) $62.2 \div 5$
12.44

(f) $8.1 \div 6$
1.35

3 Three children shared the cost of a birthday present equally. The present cost $29.40. How much did each child contribute?
$29.40 ÷ 3 = $9.80
$9.80

4 Lisa bought 3 boxes of tissues and 1 package of paper towels for $16.93. The paper towels cost $10.99. What is the price of one box of tissues?
$16.93 − $10.99 = $5.94
$5.94 ÷ 3 = $1.98
$1.98.

5 Melvin had 12 bags of topsoil. Each bag of topsoil weighed 30.8 pounds. He divided the topsoil equally among 8 plots in his garden. How many pounds of topsoil did he put in each plot?
30.8 × 12 = 369.6
369.6 ÷ 8 = 46.2
46.2 lb

6 Rope A is 4 times as long as Rope B. Rope B is 14.3 m shorter than Rope C. The total length of the three ropes is 71.9 m. How long is Rope C?

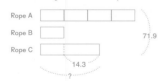

6 units ⟶ 71.9 − 14.3 = 57.6
1 unit ⟶ 57.6 ÷ 6 = 9.6
9.6 + 14.3 = 23.9
23.9 m

7 4 bowls and 4 plates cost $94.32 altogether. Each plate costs $4.50 more than each bowl. What is the cost of the 4 bowls?

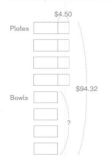

$4.50 × 4 = $18
$94.32 − $18 = $76.32
8 units ⟶ $76.32
4 units ⟶ $76.32 ÷ 2 = $38.16
$38.16

Challenge

8 2 plates and 2 bowls cost $22.20. 4 plates and 1 bowl cost $30. How much does 1 bowl cost?
If 2 plates and 1 bowl cost $22.20, then 4 plates and 4 bowls cost twice that:
$22.20 × 2 = $44.40

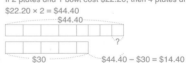

$44.40 − $30 = $14.40

1 bowl: $14.40 ÷ 3 = $4.80
$4.80

9 Katie has $40.85 more than Eliza. After Katie spent $12.25, she had 3 times as much money as Eliza. How much money did Katie have at first?

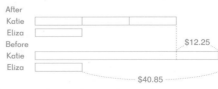

2 units ⟶ $40.85 − $12.25 = $28.60
1 unit ⟶ $28.60 ÷ 2 = $14.30
$40.85 + $14.30 = $55.15
$55.15

Notes

Suggested number of class periods: 6–7

	Lesson	Page	Resources		Objectives
	Chapter Opener	p. 197	TB:	p. 171	Investigate angles and turns.
1	The Size of Angles	p. 198	TB: WB:	p. 172 p. 131	Express $\frac{1}{4}$ turns, $\frac{1}{2}$ turns, $\frac{3}{4}$ turns, and complete turns in degrees. Find the measure in degrees of the angles of set squares.
2	Measuring Angles	p. 201	TB: WB:	p. 177 p. 135	Measure angles between 0° and 180° with a protractor.
3	Drawing Angles	p. 204	TB: WB:	p. 182 p. 139	Draw angles between 0° and 180°.
4	Adding and Subtracting Angles	p. 206	TB: WB:	p. 186 p. 144	Combine two or more angles to make another angle. Add and subtract angle measurements in figures with compound angles.
5	Reflex Angles	p. 208	TB: WB:	p. 190 p. 147	Recognize, measure, and draw angles between 180° and 360°.
6	Practice	p. 211	TB: WB:	p. 195 p. 151	Practice skills from the chapter.
	Workbook Solutions	p. 213			

In Dimensions Math 3B, students:

- learned the parts of circles (center, radius, and diameter) and their relationships.
- learned that the size of angles depends on the rotation around a circle of one side with respect to another with the vertex of the angle at the center of a circle.
- compared the size of angles to a right angle.
- classified triangles and quadrilaterals by their angles and side lengths.

In this chapter, students will measure angles in degrees, draw angles with a given measurement, and see that angle measures can be added and subtracted.

Angles

An angle is formed when two lines intersect. The vertex of the angle is the point of intersection. The sides of the angle are the boundaries.

The size of an angle is a measure of the amount of rotation of one side relative to the other about the vertex.

The length of the sides does not change the angle measure. Angles can also be thought of as portions of circles.

Throughout the chapter, students use set squares, which are a pair of right-angled triangle-shaped rulers commonly used for drawing angles of 90°, 45°, 60°, or 30°.

The size of an angle depends on the degree of a turn of one side relative to the other.

Changing the size of an angle can be modeled in various ways, including:

- two cardboard strips connected at the vertex by a brad.
- arms, with the elbow as a vertex.
- scissors opening and closing.

In drawings, angles are often marked with an arc. They can be named by labeling a point on each side and the point of intersection.

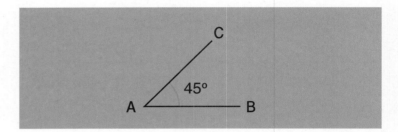

The above angle is referred to as ∠BAC or ∠CAB.

They can also be named by labeling the arc or the angle itself with a lowercase letter.

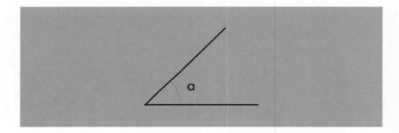

The above angle is referred to as ∠a.

Measuring Angles

Angles are measured in degrees. The degree is derived from ancient peoples such as the Babylonians, who used a base sixty system where a complete revolution about a vertex is 360°. They may have assigned 360° to a circle because they saw that it takes approximately 360 days for the sun to complete a circuit across the sky.

The number 360 is divisible by 1, 2, 3, 4, 5, 6, 8, 9, 10, 12, 15, 18, 20, 24, 30, 36, 40, 45, 60, 72, 90, 120, 180, and 360 making the degree a useful unit for dividing a circle into an equal number of parts.

Students will learn that there are 360° around a circle and 180° around a half circle. A quarter turn is $\frac{1}{4}$ of 360° (90°) and a three quarter turn is $\frac{3}{4}$ of 360° (270°).

Students will learn the definition of acute, obtuse, and reflex angles.

An acute angle measures between 0° and 90°.	
A right angle measures exactly 90°.	
An obtuse angle measures between 90° and 180°.	
A straight line is an angle that measures 180°.	
A reflex angle measures between 180° and 360°.	

They will then determine the measure of the angles of a set square by finding what fraction each set square angle is of a half turn or a quarter turn. This will help them to estimate the size of angles and read the measurements on a protractor.

Next, students will learn to measure angles up to 180° using a protractor, as well as draw angles of specified sizes, including reflex angles.

It is suggested that teachers use a large demonstration protractor if not projecting protractors on a document camera.

Adding and Subtracting Angles

Students will add and subtract angle measures. Students will find unknown angles without using a protractor, given the measurement of other angles.

Examples:

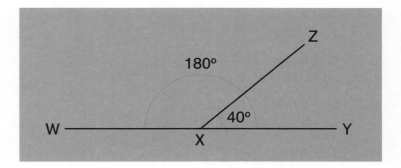

To find ∠WXZ:

180° − 40° = 140°

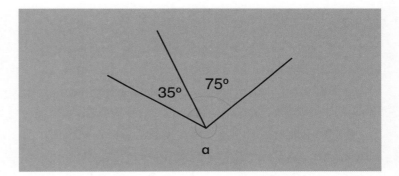

To find ∠a:

35° + 75° = 110°
360° − 110° = 250°

The idea that angles can be added and subtracted is used to measure and draw reflex angles (angles greater than 180°).

Materials

- Chalk
- Demonstration protractor
- Dry erase markers, 2 colors
- Dry erase sleeves
- Hula hoops
- Paper
- Set squares
- Straightedges or rulers
- Student protractors
- Whiteboards

Blackline Masters

- Measuring Angles (BLM)
- Paper Circles (BLM)
- Sim Game Board (BLM)
- Tangram Pieces (BLM)

Note on protractors: Student protractors come in various sizes. Most should be sized so that the angle sides as shown in the textbook extend beyond the protractor. If students have difficulty measuring angles on the textbook pages, a Blackline Master: Measuring Angles (BLM) is included. All angles to be measured with a protractor in this chapter are included on the BLM.

Activities

Fewer games and activities are included in this chapter as students will be measuring and drawing angles. The included activities can be used after students complete the **Do** questions, or anytime additional practice is needed.

Chapter Opener

Objective

- Investigate angles and turns.

Lesson Materials

- Chalk
- Hula hoops

Have students read Alex's directions and discuss Sofia's question.

Students can play the same compass game as Alex and Sofia.

Take hula hoops outside and use chalk to draw lines for the 8 directions. Have students stand in the middle and play the compass game by having them turn using the same directions given to Alex and Sofia.

Continue to Lesson 1.

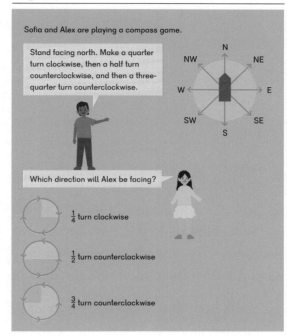

Lesson 1 The Size of Angles

Objectives

- Express $\frac{1}{4}$ turns, $\frac{1}{2}$ turns, $\frac{3}{4}$ turns, and complete turns in degrees.
- Find the measure in degrees of the angles of set squares.

Lesson Materials

- Paper Circles (BLM)
- Set squares

Think

Provide students with Paper Circles (BLM) and set squares. Ask students to find the right angles on the set squares. Ask them to recall what they have learned about a circle (center, radius, and diameter).

Have students build the angle circles as directed in **Think**, and complete the **Think** questions.

Learn

Discuss the different examples in **Learn**. Help students see how the turns are related to the number of degrees in a circle and the number of right angles.

Students can see that a $\frac{1}{2}$ turn, or 180° turn, makes a straight line, which is the diameter of a circle.

Introduce the terms in bold in **Learn**, as well as the degree symbol.

Students should see that the size of the angle depends on how big a turn or rotation is from one side to the other. Have students show different angles with their angle circles and say whether they are acute, obtuse, or reflex angles.

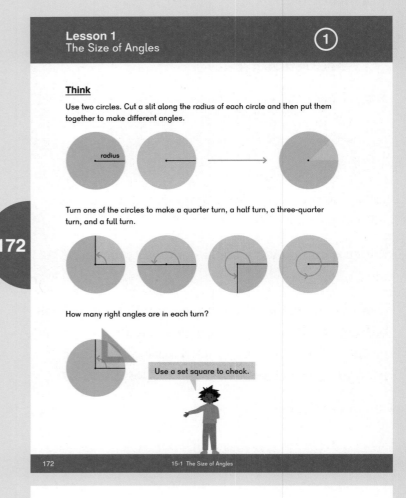

Lesson 1
The Size of Angles ①

Think

Use two circles. Cut a slit along the radius of each circle and then put them together to make different angles.

Turn one of the circles to make a quarter turn, a half turn, a three-quarter turn, and a full turn.

How many right angles are in each turn?

Use a set square to check.

172 15-1 The Size of Angles

Learn

We measure angles in degrees. When a circle is divided into 360 equal size angles, the size of one angle is 1 degree. We write 1 degree as 1°.

A quarter turn is 90°. A 90° angle is a right angle. Angles that measure between 0° and 90° are called **acute angles**.

A half turn is 2 × 90° = 180°. A 180° angle makes a straight line. Angles that measure between 90° and 180° are called **obtuse angles**. A 180° angle is called a **straight angle**.

A three-quarter turn is 3 × 90° = 270°. Angles that measure between 180° and 360° are called **reflex angles**.

A full turn is 4 × 90° = 360°.

15-1 The Size of Angles 173

Do

① – **③** Discuss the problems with students.

① Have students use the set squares to find angles in the classroom and classify them as acute, right, or obtuse. Have them compare the right angles on the set square the way Mei suggests.

③ (b) Alex points out that if two similar angles from two set squares form a right angle, then each of these angles is 90° ÷ 2 = 45°.

(c) Students will need to work in groups or with partners.

If three similar angles form a right angle, then each of these angles is 90° ÷ 3 or 30°.

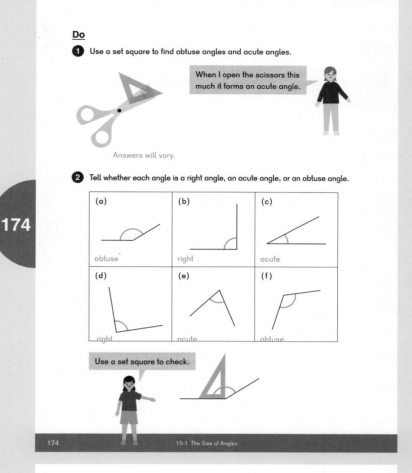

Do

① Use a set square to find obtuse angles and acute angles.

When I open the scissors this much it forms an acute angle.

Answers will vary.

② Tell whether each angle is a right angle, an acute angle, or an obtuse angle.

(a)	(b)	(c)
obtuse	right	acute
(d)	(e)	(f)
right	acute	obtuse

Use a set square to check.

174

174   15-1 The Size of Angles

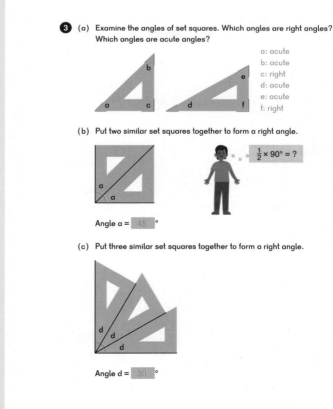

③ (a) Examine the angles of set squares. Which angles are right angles? Which angles are acute angles?

a: acute
b: acute
c: right
d: acute
e: acute
f: right

(b) Put two similar set squares together to form a right angle.

$\frac{1}{2} \times 90° = ?$

Angle a = 45 °

(c) Put three similar set squares together to form a right angle.

Angle d = 30 °

175

15-1 The Size of Angles   175

(d) If three similar angles form a straight line, or a straight angle, then each of these angles is 180° ÷ 3 or 60°.

4 — **5** Students should be able to solve the problems independently.

4 If students have trouble remembering the number of degrees the set squares measure on each angle, have them write the number on the angle with a dry erase marker. Alternatively, they could trace the two set squares onto cardstock, cut them out, and label the measures of the angles.

5 Students may solve this problem in different ways.

They may see that if there are 90° in each quarter turn then there are 45° in each eighth turn. From there, they could calculate 5 one-eighth turns.

5 × 45° = 225°

They could also see that there are 3 one-eighth turns more to make a full turn of 360°.

3 × 45° = 135°

360° − 135° = 225°

Activity

▲ Compass Game

Materials: Chalk, hula hoops

Replay the game from the Chapter Opener. Change the turns to degrees and have students turn:

90° clockwise
180° counterclockwise
270° counterclockwise, etc.

Exercise 1 · page 131

(d) Put three similar set squares together to form a straight line.

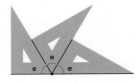

Angle e = [60] °

4 Use the set squares to find the measure of each angle.

30°   60°   90°   45°

5 The compass shows a circle divided into 8 equal sized angles. Dion is facing east. He makes a 5/8 turn counterclockwise. How many degrees did he turn?

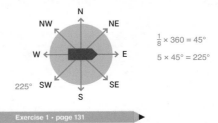

$\frac{1}{8} \times 360 = 45°$

$5 \times 45° = 225°$

Exercise 1 · page 131

176   15-1 The Size of Angles

Lesson 2 Measuring Angles

Objective

- Measure angles between 0° and 180° with a protractor.

Lesson Materials

- Protractors
- Set squares

Think

Provide students with protractors.

(a) Discuss what they notice about the protractor.

Students may see:

- There are two scales.
- Large tick marks show 10° intervals to 180°.
- Each smaller tick mark is for intervals of 1°.

(b) Have them experiment and see if they can figure out how to use the protractor to measure angles.

Discuss Sofia's questions. Ask students if knowing whether an angle is acute or obtuse can help them estimate the measure of an angle.

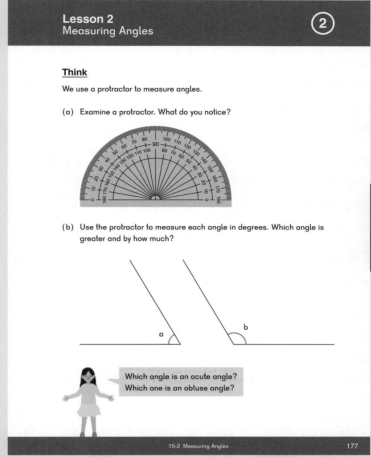

Learn

Discuss the concepts in the textbook regarding how to read and use a protractor. Have students identify the center and base line. Show them how to line the center up to the vertex and the base line with one side of the angle.

Emma asks what scale was used. To help students make sure they read the correct scale after positioning the protractor, they can first determine whether the angle is obtuse or acute.

For example, ∠a cannot be 140°, since it is an acute angle, it must be less than 90°.

Students can use their circles from Lesson 1 or their arms to make angles. Lead them to see that their arms always start at an angle of 0° regardless of which arm they open to form the angle.

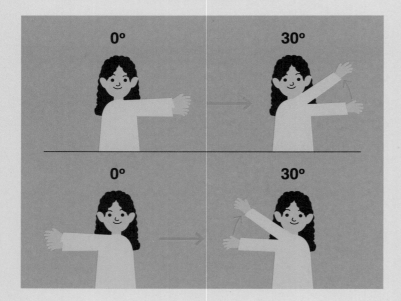

Do

❶ — ❸ Discuss the examples with students.

❶ Students practice reading the correct scale on the protractors in the textbook before using protractors to measure angles.

Ask students why Mei suggests they think about whether the angle is acute or obtuse first. (Doing so will help know which scale to read.)

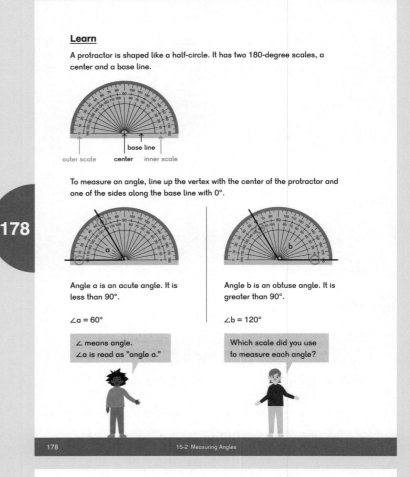

2 — **4** Ensure students are lining up the center of the protractor with the vertex and one side of the angle with the base line.

Alex points out that the base line of the protractor can be lined up with either side of the angle. We still measure by lining up the vertex and one side on the base line of the protractor. The side of the angle that is aligned with the base line on the protractor determines which scale is read.

3 Sofia shares another way to name angles. Remind students they can name this angle ∠ABC or ∠CBA, but the letter labeling the vertex must be in the middle letter. Students should be able to complete the problem independently.

4 Dion provides guidance on how to estimate the measurement of angles. Students may see (a) as "about 45°." As they gain more experience measuring angles with a set square, their estimates will become more accurate.

(c)—(d) These angles do not have a horizontal side (parallel to the edge of the textbook). Emma reminds students to line up the base line of the protractor along an angle side to ensure they are reading the correct scale.

Exercise 2 • page 135

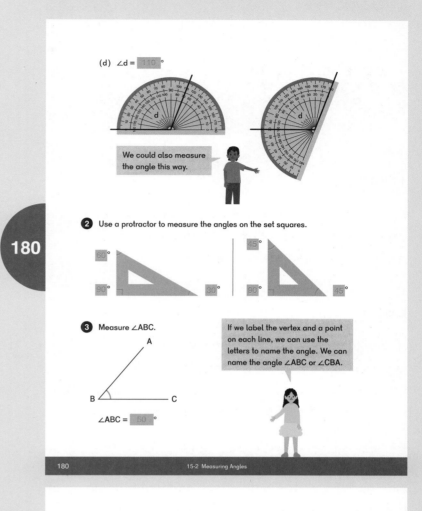

180

181

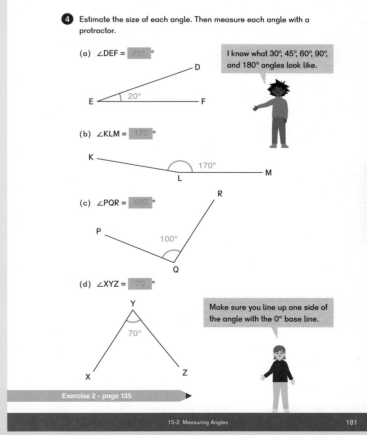

Lesson 3 Drawing Angles

Objective

- Draw angles between 0° and 180°.

Lesson Materials

- Protractors

Think

Provide students with protractors and have them experiment to see if they can figure out how the protractor is used to draw angles.

Learn

Have students follow the directions in the textbook regarding how to draw an angle accurately using the protractor. They can use the straight edge of the protractor to draw lines to or from the vertex.

Have students draw different angles and mark the angle with an arc. They should label a point on each side and the vertex with letters and write the name of the angle. They will draw angles of a specified size in **Do**.

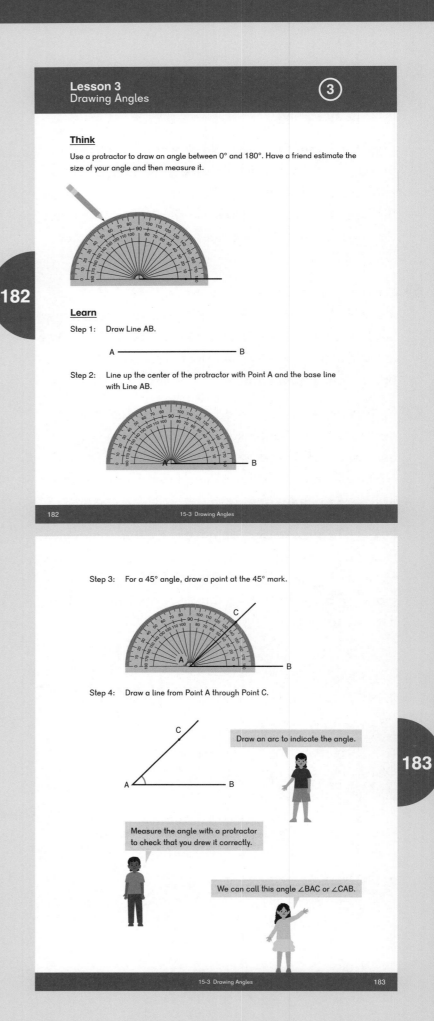

Do

①—④ Discuss the problems with students.

⑤—⑥ Students should be able to do these problems independently.

Activity

▲ **How Close?**

Materials: Protractors, straightedges or rulers, paper

Play with 3–5 players. On each round, one player is the Caller and holds the protractor. He chooses an angle measurement between 1° and 180°. The remaining players use a straightedge to draw an angle as close to the given angle as possible. The Caller uses the protractor to measure each player's angle.

The player whose angle measures closest to the amount called wins the round and earns a point.

The first player with five points is the winner.

Exercise 3 • page 139

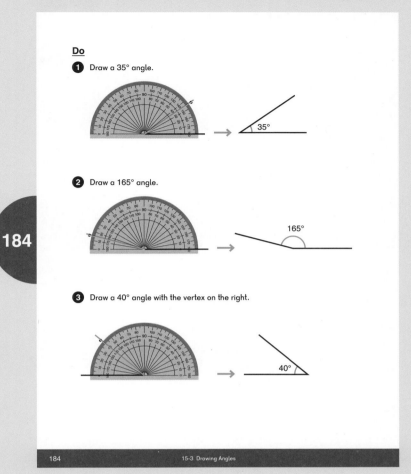

Do

① Draw a 35° angle.

35°

② Draw a 165° angle.

165°

③ Draw a 40° angle with the vertex on the right.

40°

184

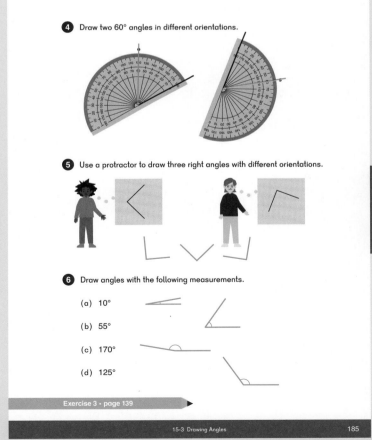

④ Draw two 60° angles in different orientations.

⑤ Use a protractor to draw three right angles with different orientations.

⑥ Draw angles with the following measurements.

(a) 10°

(b) 55°

(c) 170°

(d) 125°

185

Exercise 3 • page 139

Lesson 4 Adding and Subtracting Angles

Objectives

- Combine two or more angles to make another angle.
- Add and subtract angle measurements in figures with compound angles.

Lesson Materials

- Set squares

Think

Provide students with set squares and have them complete the **Think** tasks.

Discuss and compare the angle Mei drew with the ones students drew with their set squares.

Learn

Ask students how they found the measurement of the angles they drew. They should see that we can add the angle measurements on the set squares to get the size of the drawn angle without using a protractor.

Alex challenges them to find angles of other sizes using the set squares.

Have students write equations for the angles they make.

Some possible angles:

$30° + 30° = 60°$
$90° + 90° = 180°$
$90° − 30° = 60°$
$45° − 30° = 15°$
$30° + 30° + 30° = 90°$
$90° + 45° = 135°$

Students might notice that they can make every angle in increments of 15° up to 180° using set squares. Although they will not work with reflex angles until the next lesson, this is also true up to 360°.

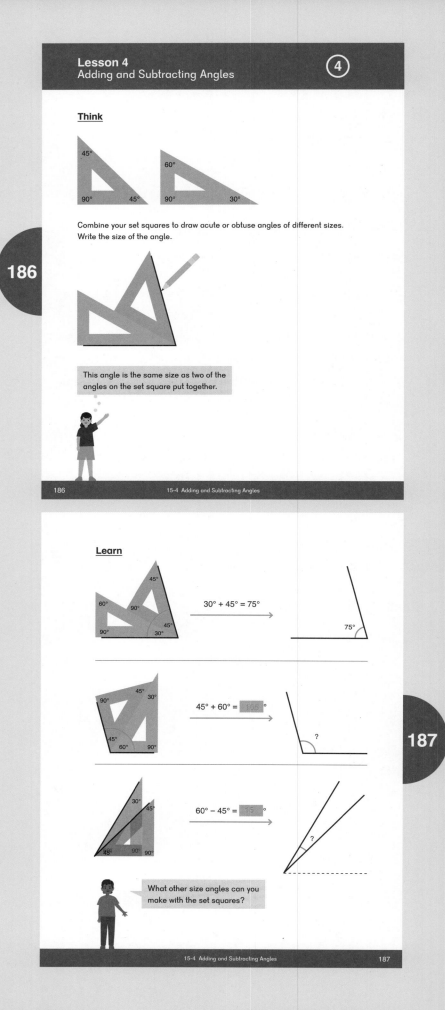

Do

❶—❷ Discuss the problems with students.

❸—❹ Students should be able to complete the problems independently.

❸ If students need additional help, have them recall what they know about addition and subtraction and parts and wholes. If we know the measure of two parts of an angle, we can add them to find the measure of the whole angle. If we know the measure of the whole angle and the measure of one part of the angle, we can subtract to find the measure of the unknown part of the angle.

Exercise 4 • page 144

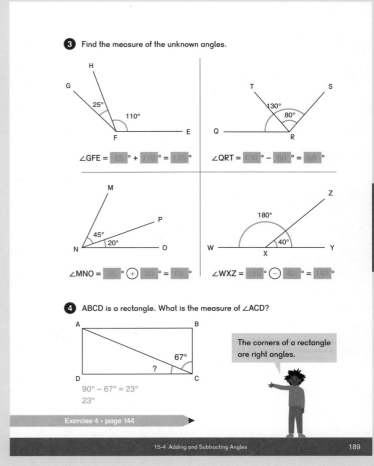

Lesson 5 Reflex Angles

Objective

- Recognize, measure, and draw angles between 180° and 360°.

Lesson Materials

- Protractors
- Set squares

Think

Provide students with set squares and have them complete the **Think** tasks. Since several set squares are needed, have students work with partners or in small groups. Students should put the set squares together as shown and draw the angle.

Ask students:

- "How many angles are created?"
- "How many degrees are created by the two angles?"
- "Why are Emma and Mei comparing the angle to 180°?"

Learn

Have students compare their solutions from **Think** with the ones shown in the textbook.

They should see that where the two line segments intersect there are two angles, formed at the vertex, one of which is a reflex angle. The sum of the measure of both angles is 360°.

(a) Students add the angle measurements of the set squares together to find the measure of the reflex angle.

(b) Alex reminds students that there are 360° in a full turn, or circle. They can subtract the reflex angle from 360° to find the measure of the angle labeled with a question mark in (b).

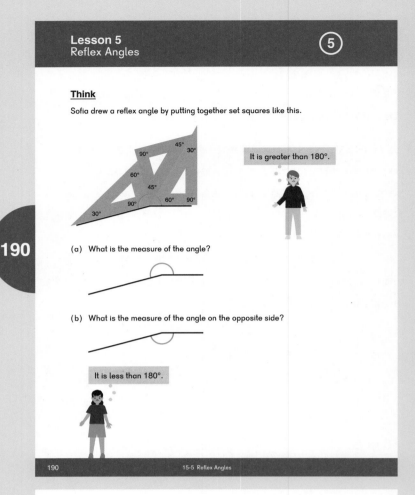

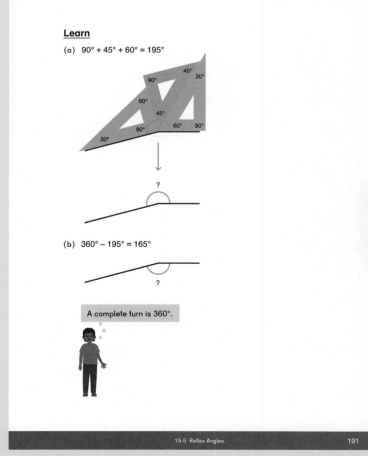

Do

1—**3** Discuss the problems with students.

2 (a) We can find the measure of the reflex angle by measuring the acute angle and subtracting from 360°.

(b) We can extend one side of the angle to make a straight angle, which we know is 180°. We then measure ∠c and add the measurement to 180° to find ∠a.

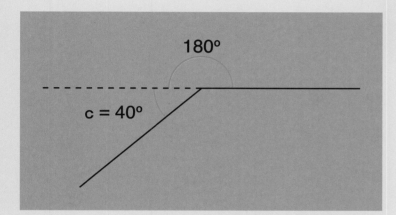

This method works well when extending one side divides the angle to be measured into a straight angle and an acute angle.

4—**7** Students should be able to complete the problems independently.

4 Students can use either method from **2** to solve the problems.

Do

1 Put set squares together to make angles that are greater than 180°. Write the measure of the angle you made.

90° + 90° + 45° = 225°

90° 90° 45°

225°

Angles will vary, but should all be greater than 180°.

2 How can we measure ∠a using a protractor?

a

(a)

a

∠b = 140 °

∠a = 360° − ∠b = 220 °

192

(b)

a

∠c = 40 °

∠a = ∠c + 180° = 220 °

3 What is the measure of Angle f?
360° − 30° = 330°

f

f

193

4 What is the measure of each angle?

255°

a

290°

b

230°

c

5 Dion subtracts the given angle, 300°, from 360° to find an angle he can draw with the protractor. He knows if he draws a 60° angle, the reflex angle will be 300°.

Activity

▲ It Figures

Materials: Protractors, straightedges

Have students draw four-sided closed figures, which include the following:

- 1 angle that measures 80°
- 1 angle that measures 60°
- 1 angle that measures 140°
- A line to create the fourth side

Have them measure the fourth angle. Ask them what they notice about the measure of the fourth angle. (It is an acute angle.)

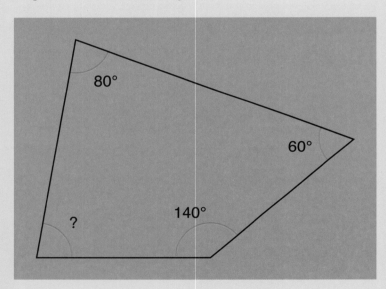

If time permits, have students draw another four-sided closed figure and measure all of the interior angles. Then have them compare their figures with those of other students. What is the sum of the interior angles in their drawings? (360°)

Exercise 5 • page 147

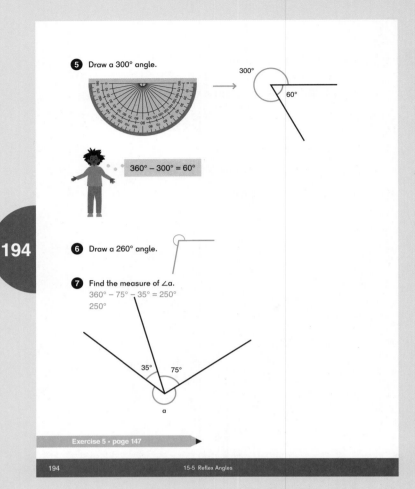

5 Draw a 300° angle.

300°

60°

360° − 300° = 60°

194

6 Draw a 260° angle.

7 Find the measure of ∠a.
360° − 75° − 35° = 250°
250°

35° 75°

a

Exercise 5 · page 147

194   15-5 Reflex Angles

Lesson 6 Practice

Objective

- Practice skills from the chapter.

Lesson Materials

- Protractors
- Straightedges of rulers

After students complete the **Practice** in the textbook, have them continue to practice measuring angles with activities from the chapter.

Activity

▲ Tangrams

Materials: Tangram Pieces (BLM)

Provide students with tangrams. Challenge them to create an animal and then measure the angles in the shape.

They can do this by first measuring the angles on the tangrams, then adding them to find the angles on their figures.

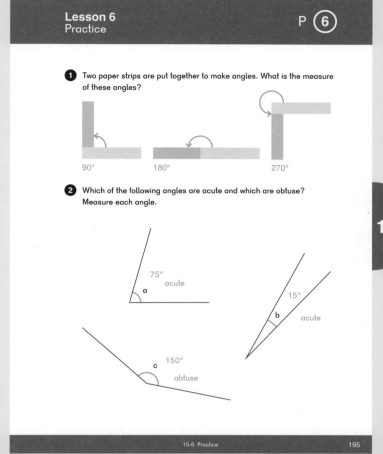

Brain Works

★ Sim

Materials: Sim Game Board (BLM) in a dry erase sleeve, two different colored dry erase markers

The players take turns tracing along an uncolored line between two points (intersections).

The first player forced to complete a triangle in her own color loses the game.

The game cannot end in a tie because there is no way to color all the lines without creating at least one triangle.

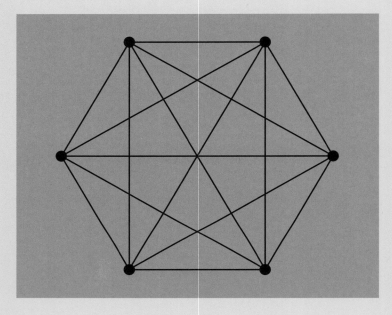

Exercise 6 · page 151

---

3 Measure each reflex angle.

295°
b

a
190°

4 Draw angles with the following measurements.

(a) 65° (b) 140°

(c) 92° (d) 128°

(e) 245° (f) 310°

5 ABCD is a rectangle. Find the measure of ∠ADB and ∠DCE.

A   B

32°   C   133°
D   E

∠ADB: 90° − 32° = 58°
∠DCE: 270° − 133° = 137°

Exercise 6 · page 151

196   15-6 Practice

196

Chapter 15 Angles

Exercise 1

Basics

1 A complete turn is 360 degrees.

1 turn = 360°

$\frac{1}{4}$ turn = $\frac{1}{4}$ × 360° = $\boxed{90}$ °

$\frac{1}{2}$ turn = $\frac{1}{2}$ × 360° = $\boxed{180}$ °

$\frac{3}{4}$ turn = $\frac{3}{4}$ × 360° = $\boxed{270}$ °

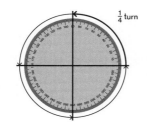
$\frac{1}{4}$ turn

2 Write 0°, 90°, 180°, or 360° in each blank to complete the table.

∠	acute angle	less than __90°__
⌐	right angle	equal to __90°__
⌐	obtuse angle	between __90°__ and __180°__
—	straight angle	equal to __180°__
⌐	reflex angle	between __180°__ and __360°__
⊙	full turn	equal to __360°__

Practice

3 Use the right angle on a set square or the corner of an index card to identify each angle as an acute angle, a right angle, or an obtuse angle.

(a) acute	(b) obtuse	(c) right
(d) obtuse	(e) right	(f) acute

4 (a) A right angle is divided into 3 equal angles. What is the measure of each smaller angle in degrees?

$\frac{1}{3}$ × 90° = 30°
30°

(b) A straight line is divided into 5 equal angles. What is the measure of each smaller angle in degrees?

$\frac{1}{5}$ × 180° = 36°
36°

5 The fraction of a whole turn is given for each of these angles. Give the measure of each in degrees.

(a) $\frac{1}{12}$ turn = $\frac{1}{12}$ × 360° = $\boxed{30}$ °

(b) $\frac{1}{8}$ turn = $\frac{1}{8}$ × 360° = $\boxed{45}$ °

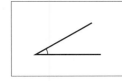
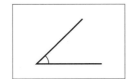

(c) $\frac{1}{6}$ turn = $\boxed{60}$ °

(d) $\frac{1}{5}$ turn = $\boxed{72}$ °

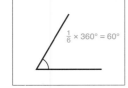
$\frac{1}{6}$ × 360° = 60°

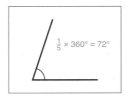
$\frac{1}{5}$ × 360° = 72°

(e) $\frac{2}{3}$ turn = $\boxed{240}$ °

(f) $\frac{4}{5}$ turn = $\boxed{288}$ °

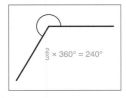
$\frac{2}{3}$ × 360° = 240°

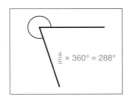
$\frac{4}{5}$ × 360° = 288°

Challenge

6 The compass divides a circle into 8 equal angles. The directions on a compass going clockwise from the north (N) are, northeast (NE), east (E), southeast (SE), south (S), southwest (SW), west (W), and northwest (NW).

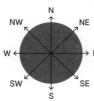

(a) Connor is facing south. If he turns 225° counterclockwise, what direction will he face?

225° − 180° = 45°
$\frac{1}{8}$ of a turn is = 45°
He will turn half way and another eighth; NW

(b) Rodrigo is facing northeast. If he turns 135° clockwise, what direction will he face?

180° − 135° = 45°
He will turn one eighth less than half way.
S

(c) Ximena is facing southwest. If she makes a $\frac{1}{4}$ turn to her right and then a $\frac{3}{4}$ turn to her left, what direction will she be facing?

To her right is clockwise, to her left is counterclockwise.
A quarter turn is two points on the above compass.
She will turn half way counterclockwise; NE

(d) Sara is facing southeast. If she turns 45° clockwise and then 315° counterclockwise, what direction will she be facing?

360° − 315° = 45°
She will turn one eighth turn clockwise, and then one eighth less than a full turn counterclockwise.
SW

Exercise 2

Basics

1 What is the size of each angle in degrees?

(a) ∠a = [25]°

(b) ∠b = [80]°

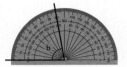

(c) ∠c = [135]°

(d) ∠d = [150]°

2 Match, without measuring.

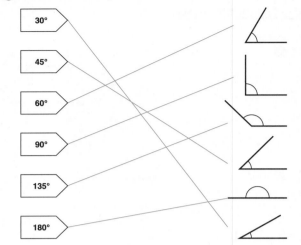

30°

45°

60°

90°

135°

180°

3 In the diagrams below, name the marked angles using the given letters.

(a) ∠ [   ] ABC or CBA   (b) ∠ [   ] FED or DEF

Practice

4 Circle the angle that is 75°. Use estimation.

75° is close to but less than 90°

5 Estimate the size of each angle. Then measure each angle with a protractor.   Estimates may vary but should be reasonable. See comments.

∠ABC ≈	∠DEF ≈
∠ABC = 35°	∠DEF = 145°

This is almost a quarter turn, or half of a right angle, so the angle is a bit less than 45°.

Measurements may vary by a few degrees, since measuring accurately with a protractor is challenging.

This is about quarter turn (45°) past 90°, so the angle is about 135°.

Estimates may vary but should be reasonable.

∠GHI ≈	∠JKL ≈	∠MNO ≈	∠PQR ≈
∠GHI = 152°	∠JKL = 85°	∠MNO = 17°	∠PQR = 5°

Measurements may vary by a few degrees.

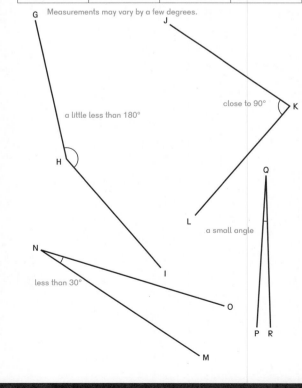

close to 90°

a little less than 180°

a small angle

less than 30°

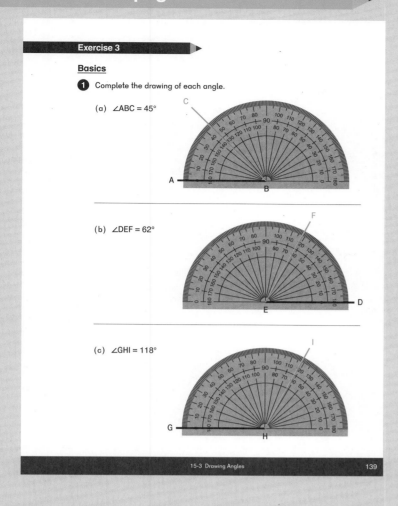

Exercise 3

Basics

1. Complete the drawing of each angle.

(a) ∠ABC = 45°

(b) ∠DEF = 62°

(c) ∠GHI = 118°

15-3 Drawing Angles   139

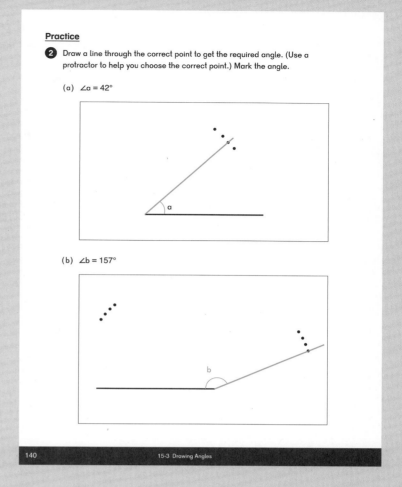

Practice

2. Draw a line through the correct point to get the required angle. (Use a protractor to help you choose the correct point.) Mark the angle.

(a) ∠a = 42°

(b) ∠b = 157°

140   15-3 Drawing Angles

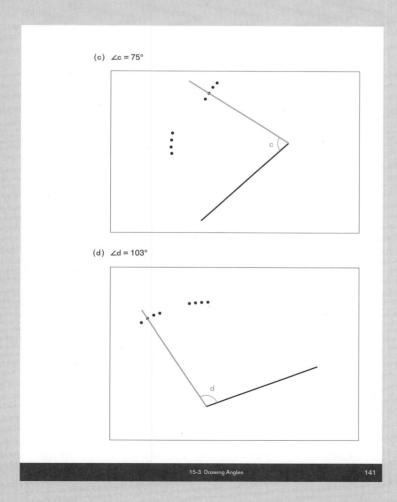

(c) ∠c = 75°

(d) ∠d = 103°

15-3 Drawing Angles   141

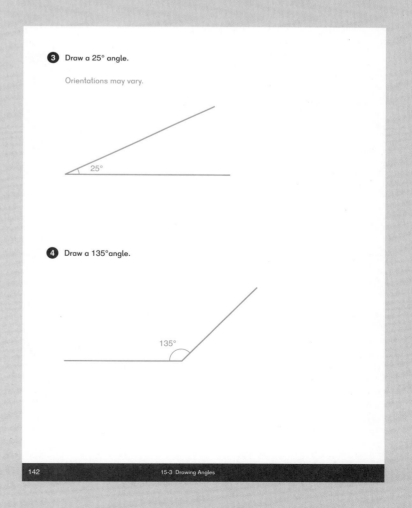

3. Draw a 25° angle.

Orientations may vary.

25°

4. Draw a 135° angle.

135°

142   15-3 Drawing Angles

5 Draw a quadrilateral with 4 angles that are each 90°.

Drawings will vary. They should be rectangles.

Challenge

6 Draw a quadrilateral with 3 angles the same size, but not 90°. All the inside angles should be less than 180°.

Drawings will vary. Students might do a rough sketch first and realize the three angles should be greater than 90°.

Exercise 4

Basics

1 ∠ABC = 35° and ∠CBD = 45°. What is the measure of ∠ABD?

∠ABC + ∠CBD = [35]° + [45]°

= [80]°

∠ABD = [80]°

2 ∠EFG is a right angle. Find the measure of the unknown angle.

90° − 33° = [57]°

∠a = [57]°

Practice

3 JK is a straight line. Find the measure of the unknown angle.

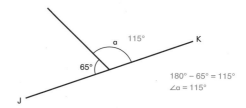

180° − 65° = 115°
∠a = 115°

4 Calculate to find the measure of the unknown marked angles in each rectangle.

∠a = 45°	∠b = 26°	∠c = 58°	∠d = 46°

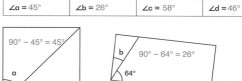

90° − 45° = 45°

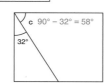

b 90° − 64° = 26°

c 90° − 32° = 58°

90° − 22° − 22° = 46°

Challenge

5 AC is a straight line. Find the measure of ∠BED.

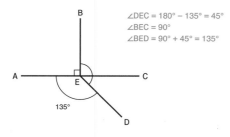

∠DEC = 180° − 135° = 45°
∠BEC = 90°
∠BED = 90° + 45° = 135°

6 AB is a straight line. ∠f is 4 times as large as ∠g. Find the measure of ∠f.

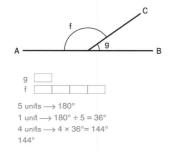

g [ ]
f [ ][ ][ ][ ]

5 units ⟶ 180°
1 unit ⟶ 180° ÷ 5 = 36°
4 units ⟶ 4 × 36° = 144°
144°

Teacher's Guide 4B Chapter 15

Exercise 5

Basics

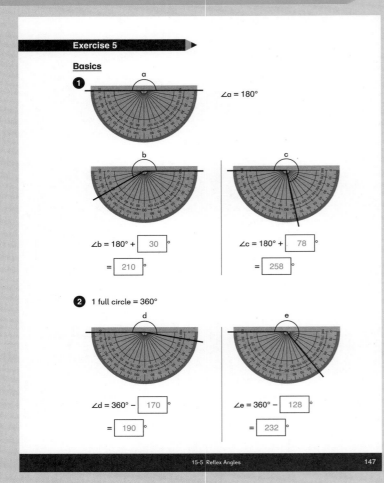

1. ∠a = 180°

∠b = 180° + 30 °

= 210 °

∠c = 180° + 78 °

= 258 °

2. 1 full circle = 360°

∠d = 360° − 170 °

= 190 °

∠e = 360° − 128 °

= 232 °

Practice

3. Estimate the size of each reflex angle. Then measure each angle with a protractor.

Estimates may vary but should be reasonable.

∠a ≈	∠b ≈	∠c ≈
∠a = 190°	∠b = 265°	∠c = 332°

Measurements may vary by a few degrees.

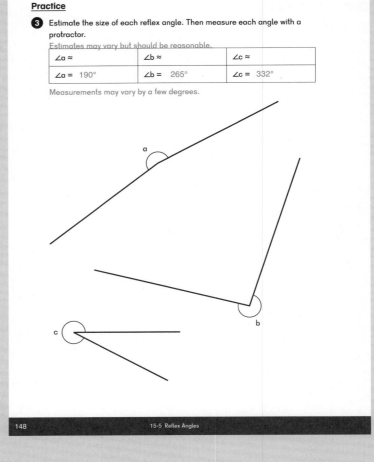

4. Draw a 200° angle.   Orientations may vary.

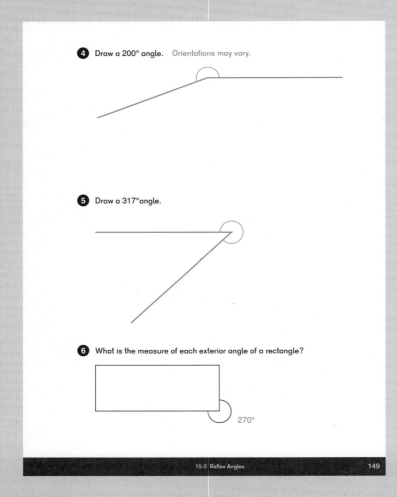

5. Draw a 317° angle.

6. What is the measure of each exterior angle of a rectangle?

270°

Challenge

7. Find the measure of ∠a.

67°

a

∠a = 360° − 90° − 67° = 203°

8. ∠b is three times as large as ∠a. ∠c is twice as large as ∠b. What is the measure of ∠c?

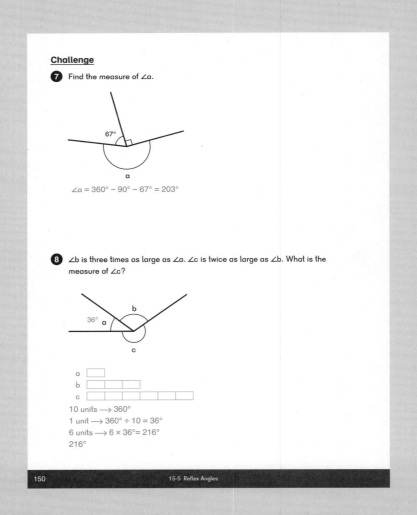

a ▭
b ▭▭▭
c ▭▭▭▭▭▭

10 units ⟶ 360°

1 unit ⟶ 360° ÷ 10 = 36°

6 units ⟶ 6 × 36° = 216°

216°

Exercise 6

Check

1. Write the type of angle for each internal angle in the shapes below (acute, right, obtuse, reflex). Then measure each labeled angle. Write each measure.
Measurements may vary by a few degrees.

(a)
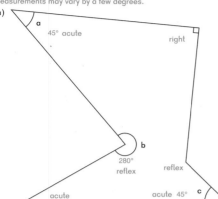

a 45° acute
right
b 280° reflex
reflex
acute
acute 45° c

(b)
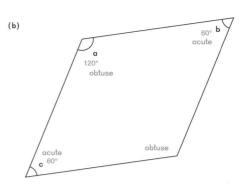

60° b acute
a 120° obtuse
acute c 60°
obtuse

2. (a) Draw an angle that measures 74°.
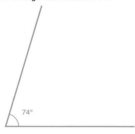
74°

(b) Calculate the measure of the reflex angle that was formed in your drawing for (a).
360° − 74° = 286°

3. (a) Draw an angle that measures 346°.

346°

(b) Calculate the measure of the acute angle that was formed in your drawing for (a).
360° − 346° = 14°

4. ABCD is a rectangle. Find the measure of the Angles ADE and DEC.
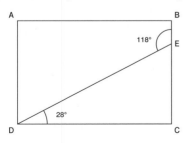

A   B
118° E
28°
D   C

∠ADE = 90° − 28° = 62°

∠DEC = 180° − 118° = 62°

5. WX and YZ are straight lines. Find the measure of Angles WPZ, WPY, and YPX.

∠WPZ = 132°	∠WPY = 48°	∠YPX = 132°
180° − 48° = 132°	180° − 132° = 48°	180° − 48° = 132°

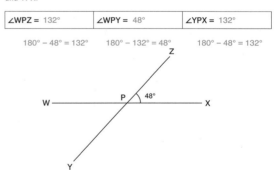

W —————— P 48° —————— X
Z
Y

6.
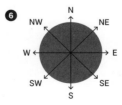

N
NW   NE
W   E
SW   SE
S

Sara is facing west. She turns 270° counterclockwise. What direction is she now facing?
N

Challenge

7 How many right angles does the minute hand move through between 12:00 a.m. and 3:00 a.m.?   12 right angles

8 (a) How many degrees does the hour hand turn each hour?

$\frac{1}{12} \times 360° = 30°$

(b) How many degrees does the minute hand turn each minute?

$\frac{1}{60} \times 360° = 6°$

9 What is the measure of the obtuse angle between the hands at 4:00 p.m.?

$4 \times 30° = 120°$

10 What is the measure of the reflex angle between the hands at 10:30 p.m.?

$180° + 30° = 210°$
$\frac{1}{2} \times 30° = 15°$
$210° + 15° = 225°$

Teacher's Guide 4B Chapter 15   © 2019 Singapore Math Inc.

Suggested number of class periods: 7–8

	Lesson	Page	Resources		Objectives
	Chapter Opener	p. 227	TB:	p. 197	Review quadrilaterals.
1	Perpendicular Lines	p. 228	TB: WB:	p. 198 p. 157	Recognize perpendicular lines in figures and the environment and verify that they intersect at right angles.
2	Parallel Lines	p. 230	TB: WB:	p. 202 p. 160	Recognize parallel lines in figures and in the environment and verify that they are parallel by determining if they both are perpendicular to a third line. Recognize that the distance between two parallel lines is a constant.
3	Drawing Perpendicular and Parallel Lines	p. 233	TB: WB:	p. 206 p. 162	Draw perpendicular and parallel lines.
4	Quadrilaterals	p. 235	TB: WB:	p. 210 p. 166	Classify quadrilaterals based on the number of parallel sides.
5	Lines of Symmetry	p. 238	TB: WB:	p. 215 p. 170	Identify figures that have line symmetry. Identify lines of symmetry in symmetrical figures.
6	Symmetrical Figures and Patterns	p. 240	TB: WB:	p. 219 p. 174	Complete the drawings of symmetrical figures. Identify characteristics of symmetrical figures.
7	Practice	p. 242	TB: WB:	p. 222 p. 177	Practice skills from the chapter.
	Workbook Solutions	p. 244			

In Dimensions Math 3B, students classified triangles and quadrilaterals by the number of equal sides, equal angles, and the presence of right angles.

In this chapter, students build on concepts learned in Chapter 15 to identify and draw parallel and perpendicular lines. They will use that knowledge to classify quadrilaterals based on the number of parallel sides, as well as the number of equal sides and right angles.

Finally, students will identify and draw lines of symmetry in a figure. Geometry in Dimensions Math 4B moves beyond classification of shapes to introducing abstract ideas about relationships and logical reasoning that will be important in future grades.

Dimensions Math does not formally teach how to identify and draw points, lines, line segments, and rays, nor distinguish between lines and line segments. If that topic does need to be taught for state standards, use the table below. For more detail, refer to Lines (BLM). A practice lesson for students is also included in Lines (BLM).

A point is a position in space. It has no size.	• P
A line is a set of points along a straight path that extends infinitely in both directions.	←•————————•→ N O
A line segment is a part of a line that has two endpoints.	•————————• E F
A ray is a part of a line that has one end point and extends infinitely in one direction.	•————————→ Q R

Concepts included on Lines (BLM) can be taught as an extension with formal geometry terms if needed. As you proceed through the lessons, occasionally redraw some of the figures, such as parallel lines, to look like the accepted method of representing lines as figures on paper. Note that points occur at intersections of lines and do not always have to be drawn with a dot.

Perpendicular and Parallel Lines

Perpendicular lines are straight lines that intersect at right angles. In this series, the right angle will be marked with a small square to show that the lines are perpendicular to each other. All four angles formed at the intersection are right angles, but only one is marked.

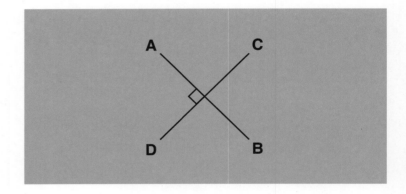

The symbol for "is perpendicular to" is ⊥. We can write AB is perpendicular to CD using this symbol: AB ⊥ CD.

Because lines extend indefinitely, their intersections may not be shown, but they do intersect somewhere. For example, if we extend RS it will intersect TU at a right angle, thus RS is perpendicular to TU.

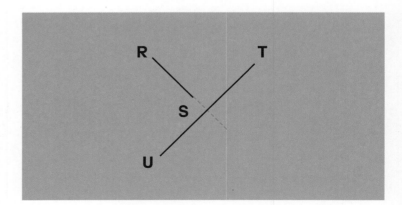

Two lines are parallel to each other if they do not intersect. One way to determine if they are parallel is to find out if they are both perpendicular to a third line. This idea is also used to draw a line that is parallel to a given line. In Dimensions Math, students will learn that perpendicular lines are used to determine parallel lines: two lines that are both perpendicular to the same line are parallel lines.

Parallel lines are marked by arrowheads to show which pairs of lines are parallel. Each set of parallel lines has the same number of arrowheads.

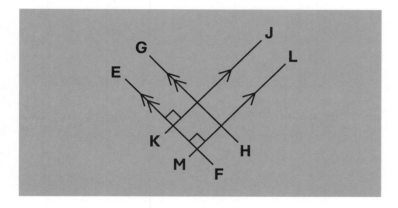

The symbol for "is parallel to" is ||. EF || GH means that Line EF is parallel to Line GH.

If two lines are perpendicular to the same line, then we know the two lines are parallel to each other. JK ⊥ EF and LM ⊥ EF, so JK || LM.

Students will be using set squares and rulers to help them identify and draw parallel and perpendicular lines for much of the chapter. Students can use a compass to determine whether lines are parallel. Because parallel lines are always the same distance from each other, students can measure the perpendicular distance between the two lines at two different sets of points. If the two different sets of points are the same distance apart, the two lines are parallel.

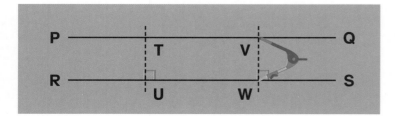

Quadrilaterals

Students will classify quadrilaterals by the number of parallel sides and right angles.

Just as students have learned that squares are special cases of rectangles, in this chapter students will again see how shapes can be defined as special cases of other shapes. For example, parallelograms are special cases of trapezoids, which are special cases of quadrilaterals.

Students will begin to understand the hierarchical relationships in terms of properties of angles and sides.

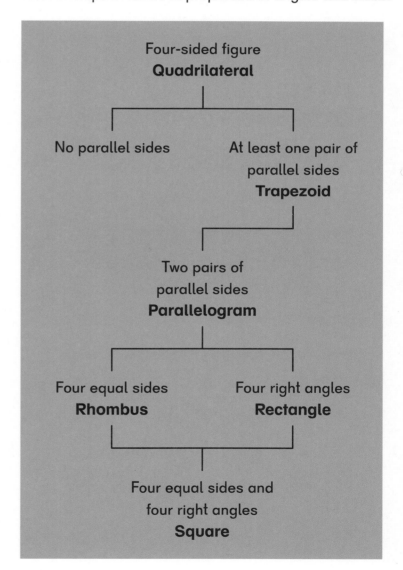

Symmetrical Figures

Recognizing symmetry in elementary grades will help students in middle school as they learn to make more formal geometric arguments and proofs.

Figures that can be divided into 2 identical halves that reflect each other are symmetrical figures.

Imagine holding a mirror along the dotted line. What you see reflected is identical to the other half of the figure.

Some figures have multiple lines of symmetry:

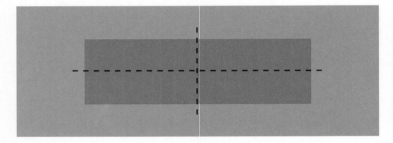

Students will fold paper shapes to identify lines of symmetry.

Students will also be investigating lines of symmetry of quadrilaterals and of equilateral and isosceles triangles.

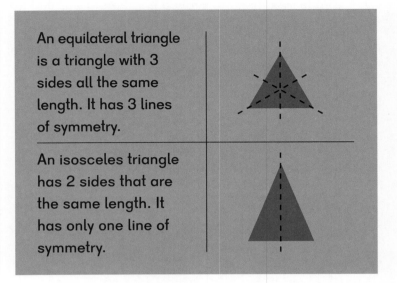

An equilateral triangle is a triangle with 3 sides all the same length. It has 3 lines of symmetry.

An isosceles triangle has 2 sides that are the same length. It has only one line of symmetry.

Students will complete drawings or patterns on grid paper given one half of the figure and the line of symmetry.

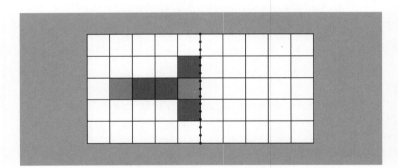

Materials

- Colored pencils
- Compass
- Grid paper
- Paper
- Protractors
- Rulers
- Scissors
- Set Squares
- Whiteboards

Blackline Masters

- Drawing Perpendicular and Parallel Lines (BLM)
- Lines (BLM)
- Quadrilaterals (BLM)
- Shapes (BLM)
- Symmetrical Figures (BLM)
- Tangram Pieces (BLM)

Activities

Fewer games and activities are included in this chapter, as students will be using set squares and other tools to identify and draw lines and figures. The included activities can be used after students complete the **Do** questions, or anytime additional practice is needed.

Notes

Chapter Opener

Objective

- Review quadrilaterals.

Have students discuss Emma's question.

They should look for shapes that they see formed by the streets, such as the rectangle created by Romero Rd, Salerno St, Thomas Blvd, and Curran Ave.

They may see parallelograms and trapezoids as well, although the formal names for these shapes have not yet been introduced in Dimensions Math.

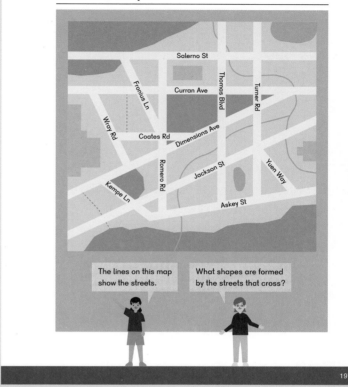

Chapter 16

Lines and Shapes

The lines on this map show the streets.

What shapes are formed by the streets that cross?

197

Lesson 1 Perpendicular Lines

Objective

- Recognize perpendicular lines in figures and the environment and verify that they intersect at right angles.

Lesson Materials

- Paper
- Set squares

Think

Provide students with set squares and have them complete the **Think** tasks.

Ask students:

- "If one line meets another at a right angle, are the other angles created also right angles?" (Yes.)

Discuss Dion's question.

Learn

Discuss the concepts introduced in the textbook. We can name any two points on a line and use those to name the line. In this case, the letters are naming the two points that form a segment of the line.

Discuss the definition of perpendicular lines and the symbol for "is perpendicular to."

Students should see that two lines can be perpendicular even if the drawing does not show them intersecting. We can extend the lines to see how they intersect.

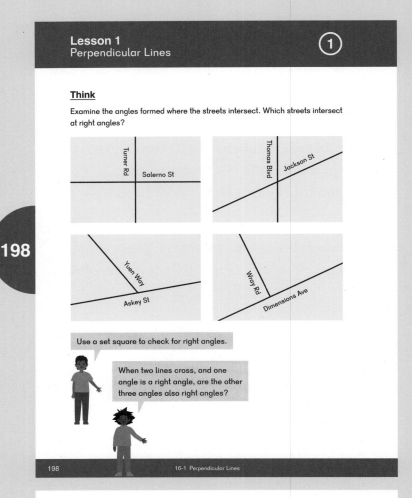

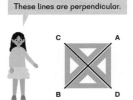

Do

1 Students should fold their paper as shown in the textbook, on a skew, so that they can see the perpendicular lines in a different orientation other than lines that are horizontal or vertical to the edges of the paper. When making the second fold, students must align the edges of the first fold.

2 — **4** Students should recall that the small squares indicate that the corners are right angles. They will then conclude that the sides that meet at the corners are perpendicular to each other.

5 Students can slide one side of the set square along line QX to determine which of the other lines intersect QX at a right angle.

Exercise 1 • page 157

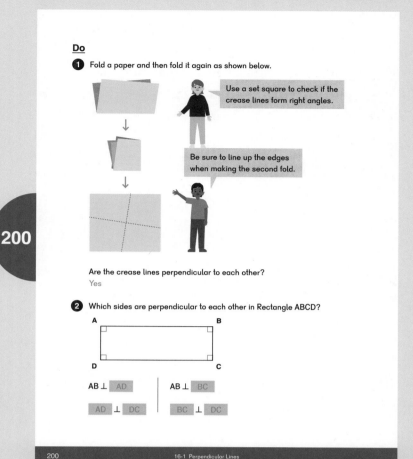

200

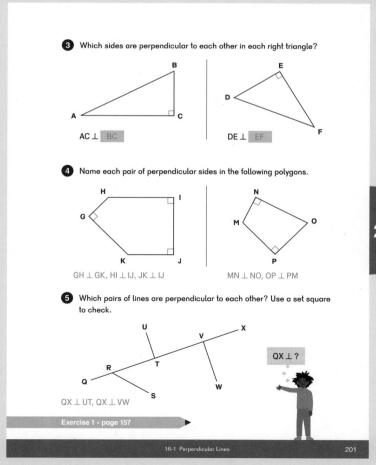

201

Lesson 2 Parallel Lines

Objectives

- Recognize parallel lines in figures and in the environment and verify that they are parallel by determining if they both are perpendicular to a third line.
- Recognize that the distance between two parallel lines is a constant.

Lesson Materials

- Compasses
- Paper
- Rulers
- Set squares

Think

Provide students with set squares and have them complete the **Think** tasks.

Learn

Discuss the concepts introduced in the textbook, including the definition of parallel lines and the symbol for "is parallel to." Students should understand that because both AB and CD are perpendicular to EF, then AB and CD are parallel to each other. In other words, AB and CD will never intersect.

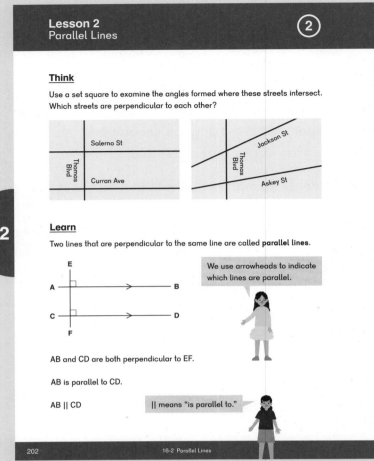

202

Lesson 2
Parallel Lines ②

Think

Use a set square to examine the angles formed where these streets intersect. Which streets are perpendicular to each other?

Salerno St · Thomas Blvd · Curran Ave

Jackson St · Thomas Blvd · Askey St

Learn

Two lines that are perpendicular to the same line are called **parallel lines**.

We use arrowheads to indicate which lines are parallel.

AB and CD are both perpendicular to EF.

AB is parallel to CD.

AB || CD

|| means "is parallel to."

202   16-2 Parallel Lines

Do

1 Students should fold their paper as shown in the textbook. The edges of the paper form right angles with the creases from the fold, so the lines formed by the creases are parallel to each other.

2 Alex shows how we can indicate which two lines in a drawing are parallel to each other using arrow heads.

The lines with the single arrowheads are parallel to each other and the lines with the double arrowheads are parallel to each other.

3 Students can use a compass to compare and contrast the lines PR and QS as well as AB and CD. Discuss Dion's and Sofia's comments.

4 Discuss Mei's question. Even though a perpendicular line is not shown, using a set square, we can see that a line drawn from Point E to Point H is perpendicular to both lines.

If we draw lines from Point E to all points on Line RS, the shortest line, Line EH, marks the line that is perpendicular to Line RS.

The shortest line between any two points on a pair of parallel lines always creates a line that is perpendicular to the two parallel lines.

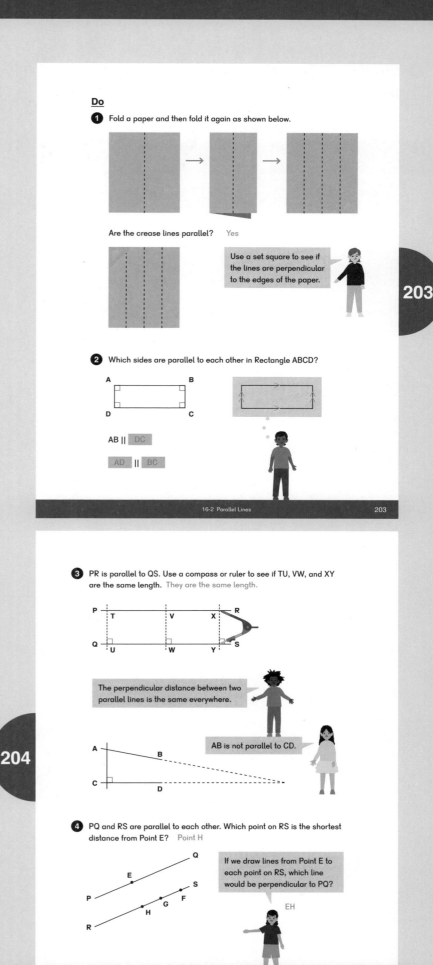

6 Provide students with set squares to determine if two lines are perpendicular to a third line.

Exercise 2 • page 160

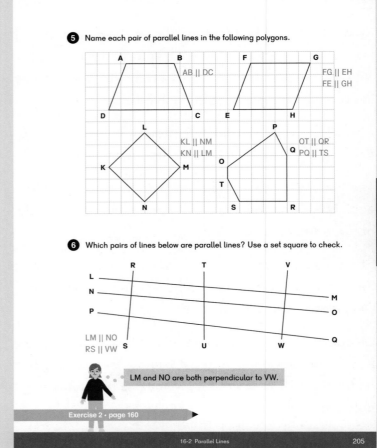

5 Name each pair of parallel lines in the following polygons.

AB ∥ DC

FG ∥ EH
FE ∥ GH

KL ∥ NM
KN ∥ LM

OT ∥ QR
PQ ∥ TS

205

6 Which pairs of lines below are parallel lines? Use a set square to check.

LM ∥ NO
RS ∥ VW

LM and NO are both perpendicular to VW.

Exercise 2 • page 160

16-2 Parallel Lines   205

Lesson 3 Drawing Perpendicular and Parallel Lines

Objective

- Draw perpendicular and parallel lines.

Lesson Materials

- Drawing Perpendicular and Parallel Lines (BLM)
- Grid paper
- Rulers
- Set squares

Think

Provide students with Drawing Perpendicular and Parallel Lines (BLM) and set squares and have them experiment to see if they can figure out that the set squares and ruler can be used to draw perpendicular and parallel lines.

Learn

Have students compare their methods for drawing perpendicular and parallel lines from **Think** with the ones shown in the textbook.

(a) Demonstrate how to draw a line perpendicular to AB.

Students should use the right angle on the set square. One side of the set square is lined up along the given line, Line AB. Students can slide the set square along the line until they can see Point C on the other side of the set square. They draw a line starting at a point on Line AB continuing through Point C.

(b) Demonstrate how to draw a line parallel to Line PQ.

Students will need a ruler and a set square. They lay the set square along Line PQ and place the ruler along the side of the set square that is perpendicular to Line PQ. They then slide the set square along the ruler until the side of the set square is at Point R. Drawing a line along the side of the set square through Point R will make a line parallel to Line PQ.

(c) Demonstrate how to draw parallel lines that are 8 cm apart based on the image in the textbook.

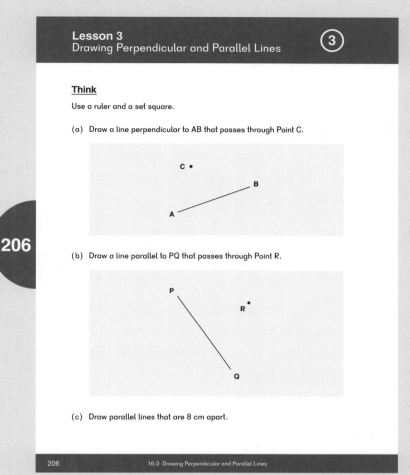

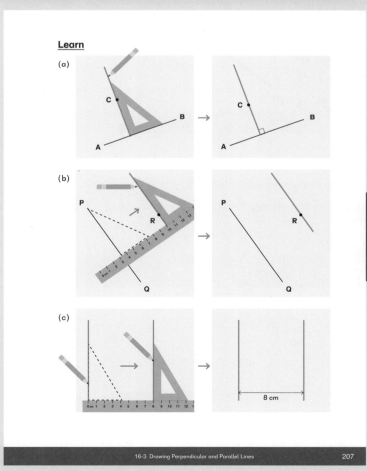

Do

1 Students should draw a line at an angle and label the points with A and B, similar to the answer shown in the textbook.

3 It can be difficult to identify the parallel lines just by looking at them. Students should use a set square and a ruler, as Emma suggests, to verify which set of lines are parallel to each other.

4 — 5 Students should look at the lines on the grid paper and see if they can determine a way to use the grid to verify if lines are parallel to each other.

Students may see that by using the grid and counting the squares, they can determine that the orange, purple, and green sets of lines are always the same distance from each other.

Example:

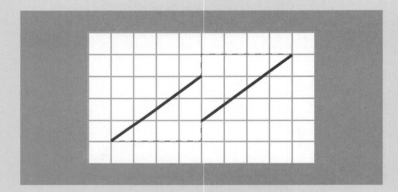

If students count the number of squares over and down, they will see that they are the same distance apart. Therefore, the lines must be parallel.

Exercise 3 • page 162

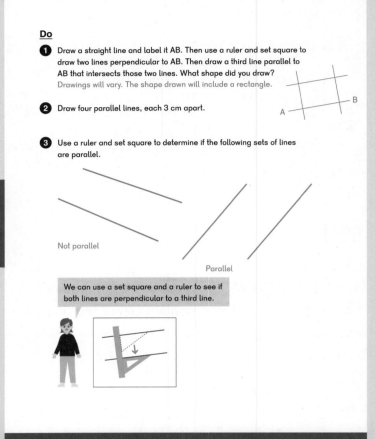

Do

1 Draw a straight line and label it AB. Then use a ruler and set square to draw two lines perpendicular to AB. Then draw a third line parallel to AB that intersects those two lines. What shape did you draw?
Drawings will vary. The shape drawn will include a rectangle.

2 Draw four parallel lines, each 3 cm apart.

3 Use a ruler and set square to determine if the following sets of lines are parallel.

Not parallel

Parallel

We can use a set square and a ruler to see if both lines are perpendicular to a third line.

4 Use a ruler and set square to draw perpendicular and parallel lines on grid paper. Have the lines end at an intersection of the graph lines. Some examples are shown below.
Drawings will vary.

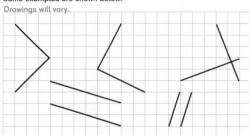

5 Which pairs of lines below are parallel lines? How can you tell?

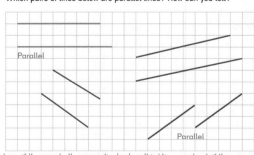

Parallel

Parallel

Students could see if they are both perpendicular to a third line, or check if they are always the same distance apart. They could also count squares over and up to see if they are the same.

Exercise 3 • page 162

Lesson 4 Quadrilaterals

Objective

- Classify quadrilaterals based on the number of parallel sides.

Lesson Materials

- Compasses or rulers
- Paper
- Quadrilaterals (BLM)
- Set squares

Think

Provide students with set squares and have them complete the **Think** tasks. They can use a set square and a ruler to prove which sides of the figures have parallel lines, and which form right angles.

The shapes are included in Quadrilaterals (BLM) for students to cut out and sort or classify in different ways. Examples: quadrilaterals with parallel sides, quadrilaterals with perpendicular sides, quadrilaterals with right angles, quadrilaterals without right angles, etc.

Learn

Discuss the concepts in the textbook.

Ask students:

- "Can you make a parallelogram with only three right angles? Two?" (No. A parallelogram will have either 0 or 4 right angles.)
- "Is a square a trapezoid? Why or why not?" (Since a square is a parallelogram, it is a trapezoid.)
- "Are all parallelograms trapezoids?" (Yes.)
- "Are all trapezoids parallelograms?" (No.)

Ensure students understand that a square is also a rectangle because it has four right angles. It is also a rhombus because it has four equal sides and opposite sides are parallel.

Lesson 4
Quadrilaterals

Think

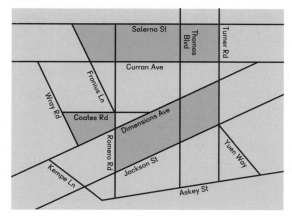

Look at the four-sided figures formed by the intersections of the streets.

(a) Which figure has no parallel sides?

(b) Which figures have at least one pair of parallel sides?

(c) Which figures have two pairs of parallel sides?

(d) Which figures have right angles?

Learn

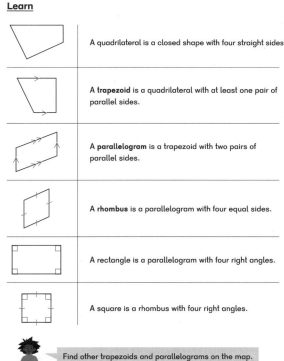

Find other trapezoids and parallelograms on the map.

Do

1 Students should fold and cut their paper as shown in the textbook.

2—**3** Provide students with compasses or rulers to verify if the sides are the same length.

4 Since it is given that these are parallelograms, and, by definition, parallelograms have two pairs of parallel sides, students can deduce that:

AB || DC and BC || AD
EF || HG and EH || FG

212

Do

1 Draw a diagonal on a rectangular sheet of paper. Cut the paper along the diagonal.

Put the two right triangles together to make a different parallelogram.

We can also make a parallelogram like this

2 Which parallelograms below are rhombuses?

Rhombus   Rhombus

You can use a compass to see if the sides are the same length.

---

3 Compare the lengths of the sides of this parallelogram.

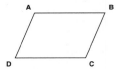

(a) Which sides have the same length?
AB and DC, AD and BC

(b) What can you say about the lengths of the opposite sides of a parallelogram?
They are the same length.

Are opposite sides the same length for all trapezoids?

No, for example the trapezoid in Learn.

213

4 Identify and name the parallel sides of the parallelograms below.

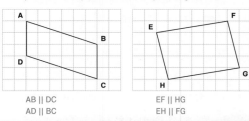

AB || DC   EF || HG
AD || BC   EH || FG

---

5 Since it is given that these are trapezoids, and trapezoids have at least one pair of parallel sides, then KL || NM and PS || QR.

6 Provide students with compasses. They can use the compass to check the distance between the lines to determine which lines are parallel to each other, and thus, which lines form trapezoids and parallelograms.

Activity

▲ Mapmaking

Materials: Rulers, set squares, paper, protractors

On a full-sized sheet of paper, have students create their own maps similar to the one in the textbook. They should make enough roads or paths that intersect so that they end up with several quadrilaterals. They should also make some of the roads parallel to each other and identify different types of trapezoids.

They can shade in the different quadrilaterals they find. To practice measuring angles, have them measure and label the angles created by the roads or paths they have drawn.

Exercise 4 • page 166

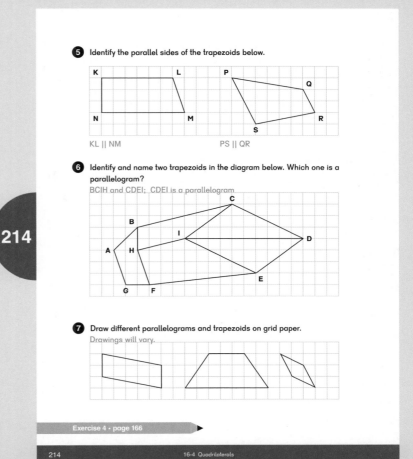

5 Identify the parallel sides of the trapezoids below.

KL || NM   PS || QR

6 Identify and name two trapezoids in the diagram below. Which one is a parallelogram?
BCIH and CDEI; CDEI is a parallelogram

7 Draw different parallelograms and trapezoids on grid paper.
Drawings will vary.

Exercise 4 • page 166

214   16-4 Quadrilaterals

214

Lesson 5 Lines of Symmetry

Objectives

- Identify figures that have line symmetry.
- Identify lines of symmetry in symmetrical figures.

Lesson Materials

- Paper
- Scissors
- Shapes (BLM)

Think

Provide students with paper and scissors and have them complete the **Think** tasks. The figures can be simpler than the one in the textbook.

Learn

Discuss the concepts and terms in the textbook.

Introduce the terms "symmetrical" and "line of symmetry."

Ensure students understand why the vertical line on the butterfly is a line of symmetry, while the horizontal line is not.

Have students draw a line of symmetry on their cutouts.

Do

1 — **6** Discuss these problems with students.

1 Students should fold their paper as shown in the textbook.

2 — **6** and **8** The shapes are included as Shapes (BLM) for students to cut and fold as needed.

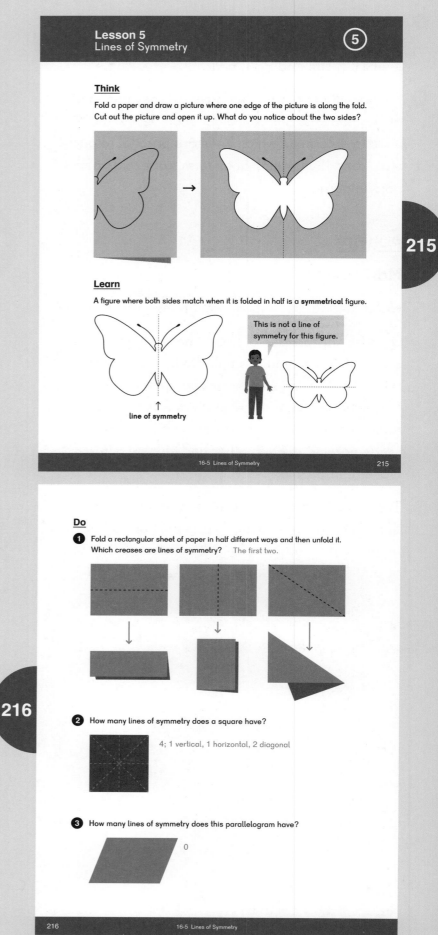

5 — **6** The terms "equilateral triangle" and "isosceles triangle" are introduced.

An isosceles triangle can always be folded in half between the two equal length sides so it has one line of symmetry.

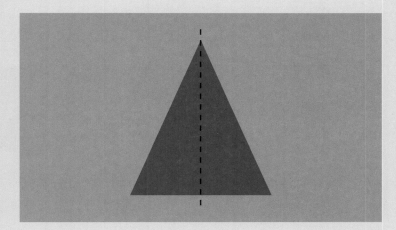

An equilateral triangle is a special case of isosceles triangle because it has three equal length sides. Since we can draw a line of symmetry between any two equal sides, it has three lines of symmetry.

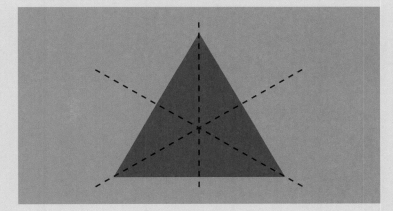

7 — **10** Students should be able to solve the problems independently.

Exercise 5 • page 170

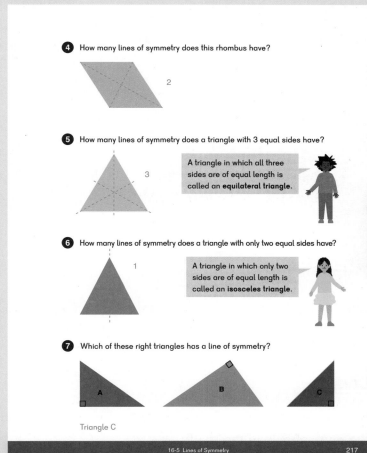

4 How many lines of symmetry does this rhombus have?

2

5 How many lines of symmetry does a triangle with 3 equal sides have?

3

A triangle in which all three sides are of equal length is called an **equilateral triangle**.

6 How many lines of symmetry does a triangle with only two equal sides have?

1

A triangle in which only two sides are of equal length is called an **isosceles triangle**.

7 Which of these right triangles has a line of symmetry?

A   B   C

Triangle C

217

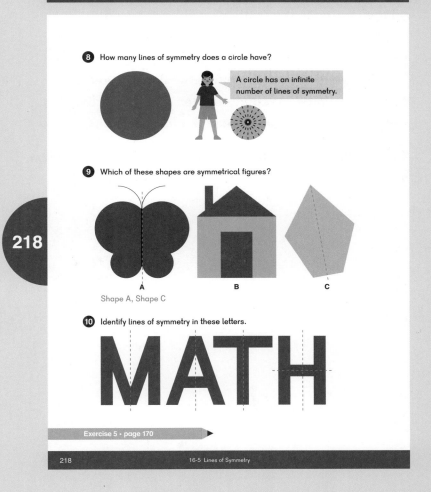

8 How many lines of symmetry does a circle have?

A circle has an infinite number of lines of symmetry.

9 Which of these shapes are symmetrical figures?

A   B   C

Shape A, Shape C

10 Identify lines of symmetry in these letters.

MATH

Exercise 5 • page 170

218

Lesson 6 Symmetrical Figures and Patterns

Objectives

- Complete the drawings of symmetrical figures.
- Identify characteristics of symmetrical figures.

Lesson Materials

- Grid paper
- Rulers
- Symmetrical Figures (BLM)

Think

Provide students with Symmetrical Figures (BLM) and rulers and have them complete the **Think** tasks.

Learn

Have students compare their drawings from **Think** with the ones shown in the textbook.

All the figures in the textbook will have corners, (vertices), and will be on the intersection of a grid line. To find the symmetric point, students can draw a line from the point of intersection to the line of symmetry, count the number of squares, then extend the line the same number of squares past the line of symmetry.

If students do these steps for all the points of intersection, they will be able to draw the entire other half.

Lesson 6
Symmetrical Figures and Patterns ⑥

Think

Two symmetrical figures are partially drawn on grid paper. The dotted lines are lines of symmetry. Copy and complete the drawing.

Learn

To create a symmetrical figure we can first draw points on the other side of the line of symmetry that are the same perpendicular distance from the line of symmetry.

Do

1 and **3** — **4** Provide students with grid paper to complete the problems.

To create symmetrical figures, students can think of the line of symmetry as a folding line and plot points that mirror the ones they already have.

Activity

▲ **Finish It**

Materials: Grid paper, colored pencils

Have students fold the grid paper in half and create a drawing on half of the paper. The drawing should touch the folded edge of the paper. Students then unfold the paper and trade it with a classmate. Classmates complete the drawing by making symmetrical sides.

Exercise 6 • page 174

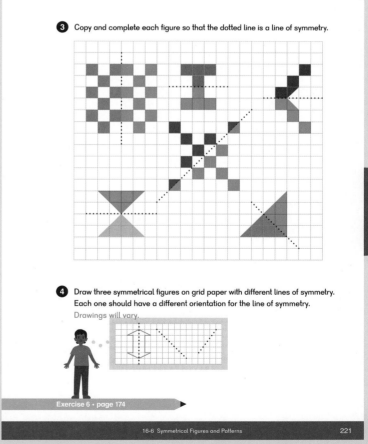

Lesson 7 Practice

Objective

- Practice skills from the chapter.

Lesson Materials

- Compasses or rulers
- Grid paper
- Set squares

After students complete the **Practice** in the textbook, have them continue to practice concepts with activities from the chapter.

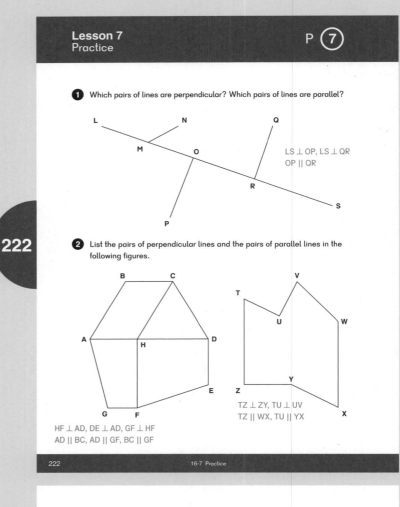

1 Which pairs of lines are perpendicular? Which pairs of lines are parallel?

LS ⊥ OP, LS ⊥ QR
OP || QR

222

2 List the pairs of perpendicular lines and the pairs of parallel lines in the following figures.

HF ⊥ AD, DE ⊥ AD, GF ⊥ HF
AD || BC, AD || GF, BC || GF

TZ ⊥ ZY, TU ⊥ UV
TZ || WX, TU || YX

222   16-7 Practice

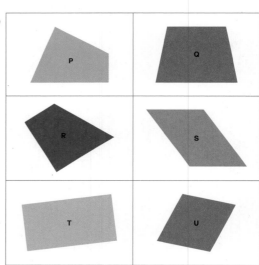

3

223

(a) How many pairs of perpendicular lines are in each shape?
    Shape P: 1; Shape Q: 0; Shape R: 2; Shape S: 0; Shape T: 4; Shape U: 0
(b) How many pairs of parallel lines are in each shape?
    Shape P: 0; Shape Q: 1; Shape R: 1; Shape S: 2; Shape T: 2; Shape U: 2
(c) Which of the shapes are trapezoids?
    Shapes Q, R, S, T, U
(d) Which of the shapes are parallelograms?
    Shapes S, T, U
(e) Which of the shapes have a line of symmetry?
    Shapes Q, T, U

16-7 Practice   223

Brain Works

★ Tangram Shapes

Materials: Tangram Pieces (BLM)

Using two pieces of the tangram set, make a:

- triangle
- square
- parallelogram that is not a square or a rectangle
- trapezoid that is not a parallelogram

Using only three pieces of the tangram set, make a:

- triangle
- square
- rectangle that is not a square
- parallelogram that is not a square or a rectangle

Using only four pieces of the tangram set, make a:

- triangle
- square
- rectangle that is not a square

Using all seven pieces of the tangram set, make a:

- triangle
- square
- parallelogram that is not a square or a rectangle

Exercise 7 · page 177

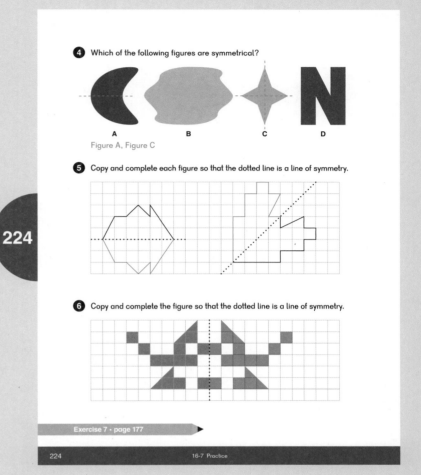

224

4 Which of the following figures are symmetrical?

A   B   C   D

Figure A, Figure C

5 Copy and complete each figure so that the dotted line is a line of symmetry.

6 Copy and complete the figure so that the dotted line is a line of symmetry.

Exercise 7 · page 177

224   16-7 Practice

Chapter 16 Lines and Shapes

Exercise 1

Basics

1 The two lines are perpendicular to each other because they intersect at __right__ angles.

AB ⊥ CD

2 Write a check mark in the box if the lines are perpendicular to each other. Extend the lines to intersect if needed. Use a set square to identify right angles.

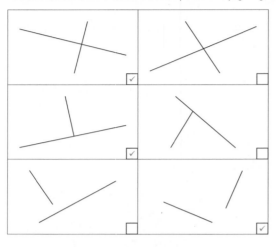

Practice

Order of letters and names may vary throughout.

3 Name the pairs of perpendicular sides in Rectangle ABCD. The first has been done for you.

AB ⊥ AD
AB ⊥ BC
CD ⊥ BC
CD ⊥ AD

4 For each of the following figures, name each pair of perpendicular lines. Use a set square to identify right angles.

(a) AF ⊥ CH

DG ⊥ AF

(b) IL ⊥ JN
OK ⊥ PM

(c) QR ⊥ RS

(d) VW ⊥ WX
WX ⊥ XT
VU ⊥ UT

(e) YD ⊥ DB
ZC ⊥ DB
YZ ⊥ ZA
YA ⊥ AB

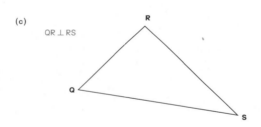

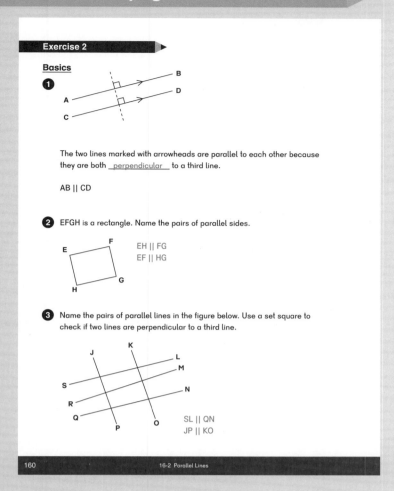

Exercise 2

Basics

1

The two lines marked with arrowheads are parallel to each other because they are both __perpendicular__ to a third line.

AB || CD

2 EFGH is a rectangle. Name the pairs of parallel sides.

EH || FG
EF || HG

3 Name the pairs of parallel lines in the figure below. Use a set square to check if two lines are perpendicular to a third line.

SL || QN
JP || KO

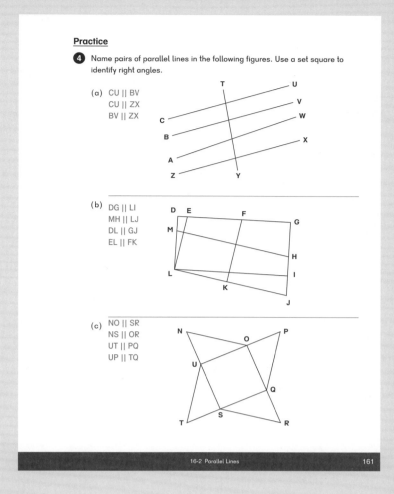

Practice

4 Name pairs of parallel lines in the following figures. Use a set square to identify right angles.

(a) CU || BV
CU || ZX
BV || ZX

(b) DG || LI
MH || LJ
DL || GJ
EL || FK

(c) NO || SR
NS || OR
UT || PQ
UP || TQ

Exercise 3

Basics

1 (a) Use a set square. Draw a line through C perpendicular to AB. Draw a line through D perpendicular to AB.

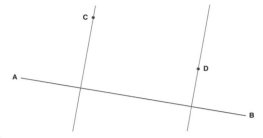

(b) Are the two lines you drew parallel to each other?   Yes

2 Use a ruler and a set square to draw a line through G that is parallel to EF.

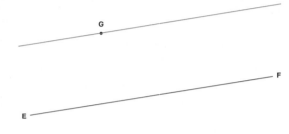

Practice

3 Use a ruler and a set square to draw one line perpendicular and one line parallel to the given lines through the given points.

(a) 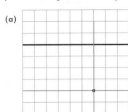   (b)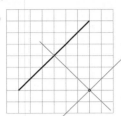

(c) 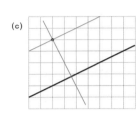   (d)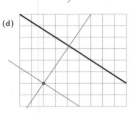

(e) 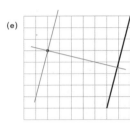   (f)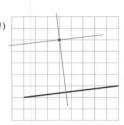

4 Use a ruler and set square to identify parallel lines. Name all pairs of parallel lines.

GH || QR
IJ || MN
KL || ST

5 Use a ruler and a set square to draw a rectangle with a length of 8 cm and a width of 3 cm. Use the given line for one side.

Challenge

Students may see that parallel lines have the same slope (number of squares in each direction) and perpendicular lines have an opposite slope.

6 Draw a line parallel and a line perpendicular to the given lines through the points. To draw the lines without a set square, count the number of squares horizontally and vertically from one intersection to another on the grid.

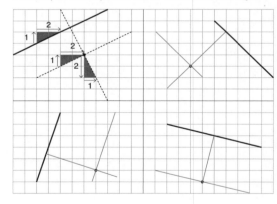

7 Draw a rectangle using the given line as one side. One side must pass through the given point.

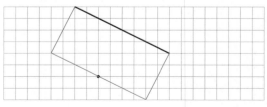

Exercise 4

Basics

1 Write a check mark below each name for each quadrilateral. Use the definitions below.

	Trapezoid	Parallelogram	Rhombus	Rectangle	Square
	✓				
	✓	✓			
	✓	✓	✓		
	✓	✓		✓	
	✓	✓	✓	✓	✓

Trapezoid	Quadrilateral with at least one pair of parallel sides.
Parallelogram	Trapezoid with two pairs of parallel sides.
Rhombus	Parallelogram with four equal sides.
Rectangle	Parallelogram with four right angles.
Square	Rhombus with four right angles.

Practice

2 Complete the table. Use a set square if needed to check right angles and parallel sides, and a ruler or compass to compare lengths.

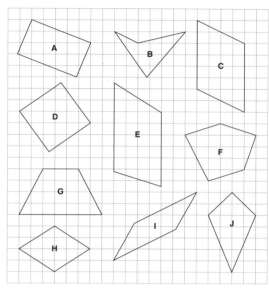

Quadrilateral	Trapezoid	Parallelogram	Rhombus	Rectangle	Square
A, B, C, D, E, G, H, I, J	A, C, D, E, G, H, I	A, C, D, H, I	D, H	A, D	D

3 Draw two different trapezoids that are not parallelograms, and two different parallelograms that are not rectangles.   Drawings will vary.

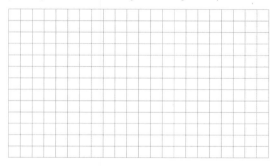

4 Name all the trapezoids in the figure below. Which of them are parallelograms? Which one is a rhombus?

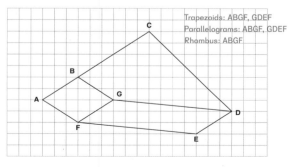

Trapezoids: ABGF, GDEF
Parallelograms: ABGF, GDEF
Rhombus: ABGF

Challenge

5 AC and BD are diagonals of Quadrilateral ABCD. They intersect at Point E. Use a compass or ruler to compare the lengths of AE to EC and DE to EB. What do you notice? This is a property of all parallelograms.

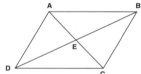

DE = EB
AE = EC

6 These two perpendicular lines intersect at their midpoint. Use them to draw a parallelogram. What kind of parallelogram is it?

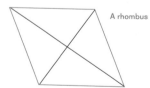

A rhombus

7 Use a ruler to draw a parallelogram by drawing the diagonals first. Drawings will vary. Start by drawing two lines that intersect at their midpoint, the diagonals. Then connect the endpoints as done above.

Teacher's Guide 4B   Chapter 16

Exercise 5

Basics

1 On which of these identical figures is the dotted line a line of symmetry? You can trace, cut out, and fold one to check.

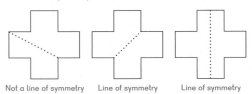

Not a line of symmetry   Line of symmetry   Line of symmetry

2 Check (✓) the box if the dotted line is a line of symmetry.

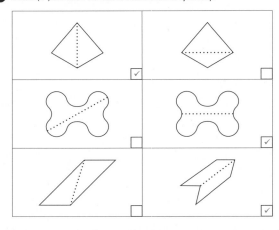

3 How many lines of symmetry do the equilateral triangle and the square each have? Draw them.

(a)      3

(b)   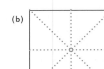   4

Practice

4 All the sides of the pentagon and the hexagon below are equal. How many lines of symmetry does each shape have? Draw them.

(a)   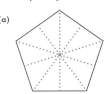   5

(b)   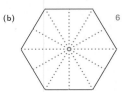   6

5 Find all the lines of symmetry in the following figures.

(a) 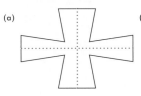   (b)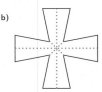

Students only need to draw one line of symmetry.

6 For each figure, if it is symmetrical, draw a line of symmetry.

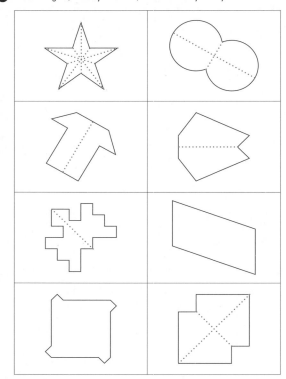

Challenge

7 The dotted line is a line of symmetry for the entire figure.

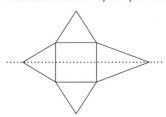

Draw a line of symmetry for the following figures.

(a)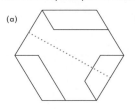

(b) Answers may vary. This figure has more than one line of symmetry.
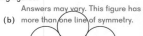
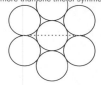

(c)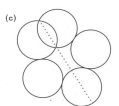

(d)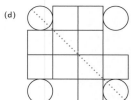

Exercise 6

Basics

1 Use the dots and a ruler to complete the symmetrical figures. Each dot is the same perpendicular distance from the line of symmetry as a vertex on the other side of the line of symmetry.

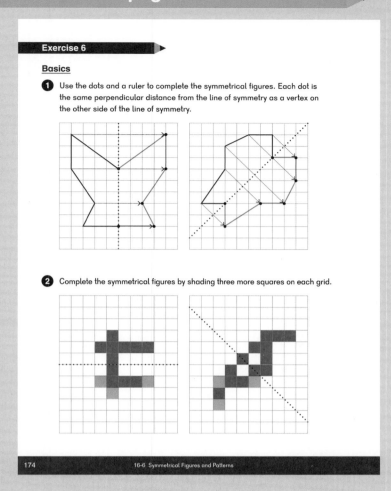

2 Complete the symmetrical figures by shading three more squares on each grid.

Practice

3 Complete each figure so that the dotted line is a line of symmetry.

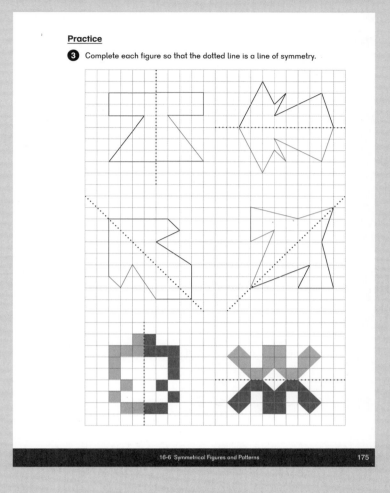

Challenge

4

© 2019 Singapore Math Inc.   Teacher's Guide 4B Chapter 16   249

From earlier lessons, students should realize they can use a set square to check for right angles and parallel lines, and a ruler or compass to compare lengths.

Exercise 7

Check

❶ In this figure, "S" is written inside a square.

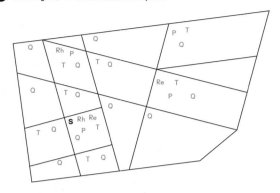

(a) Write "Rh" inside the rhombuses.

(b) Write "Re" inside the rectangles.

(c) Write "P" inside the parallelograms.

(d) Write "T" inside the trapezoids.

(e) Write "Q" inside the quadrilaterals.

❷ Use a ruler and a set square to draw one line perpendicular and one line parallel to the given line through each of the given points.

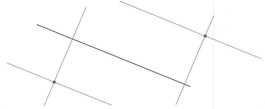

❸ Use a ruler and set square to draw a parallelogram that is not a rectangle.
Drawings will vary.

❹ Use a ruler and set square to draw a trapezoid that is not a parallelogram.
Drawings will vary.

❺ (a) What type of quadrilateral is the symmetrical figure below?
Trapezoid
(b) Draw a line of symmetry and write the measure of ∠a.

❻ Draw the lines of symmetry on the equilateral triangle below. Write the measure of the other two angles. (Use symmetry.)

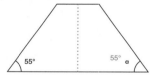

❼ Draw a line of symmetry on the isosceles triangle below. Write the measure of ∠a.

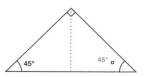

❽ Complete each figure so that the dotted line is a line of symmetry.

(a)
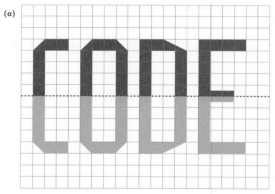

(b)
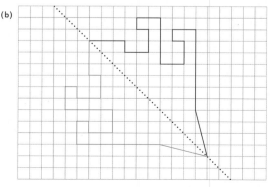

Challenge

9 What word will be formed if the figure below is completed so that the dotted line is a line of symmetry?   BOX

BOX

10 Shade one more square in the entire figure to make it symmetrical.

(a)

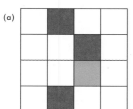

(b)

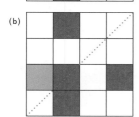

11 Complete the figure so that it has two lines of symmetry.

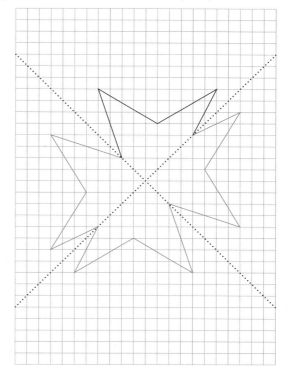

Notes

Suggested number of class periods: 6–7

	Lesson	Page	Resources		Objectives
	Chapter Opener	p. 257	TB:	p. 225	Investigate cuboids.
1	Cuboids	p. 258	TB: WB:	p. 226 p. 183	Investigate the lengths of the edges and the dimensions of the faces of cuboids.
2	Nets of Cuboids	p. 260	TB: WB:	p. 230 p. 186	Construct cubes and cuboids using a net. Identify matching edges and vertices. Distinguish between nets that will and will not make a cuboid.
3	Faces and Edges of Cuboids	p. 262	TB: WB:	p. 234 p. 190	Investigate and identify parallel edges and faces of cubes and cuboids.
4	Practice	p. 264	TB: WB:	p. 238 p. 194	Practice concepts from the chapter.
	Review 4	p. 266	TB: WB:	p. 241 p. 198	Review concepts from Chapter 1 through Chapter 17.
	Review 5	p. 268	TB: WB:	p. 245 p. 204	Review concepts from Chapter 1 through Chapter 17.
	Workbook Solutions	p. 270			

In Dimensions Math 2B, students identified faces, corners, and edges of three-dimensional solids.

In Dimensions Math 3B students learned the term vertex as a point where two lines meet. They also learned to find the area of a rectangle, and applied right angle concepts to understanding rectangles.

In Dimensions Math 4B Chapter 11, students mastered those concepts with composite rectangles.

In this chapter, students will apply knowledge from Chapter 15 and Chapter 16, to identify faces (planes), edges (lines), and vertices (points) on cuboids, or rectangular prisms.

They will see the parallel and perpendicular relationships between edges and faces through examining, composing, and decomposing shapes.

Cuboid is another term for rectangular prism. A cuboid is a closed, solid shape that has 6 faces, 8 vertices, and 12 edges. On a cuboid, all cross sections are rectangles and all faces are rectangles. A cube is a cuboid in which all faces are the same size and shape and all edges are the same length.

After identifying the two-dimensional surfaces of cuboids, students will learn to represent cuboids as nets. A net is a single flat shape that can be folded into a solid. Nets help students visualize and make connections between how edges and faces connect to form three-dimensional solids. In future grades, nets help students with the concepts of surface area and volume.

Students will fold, cut, and build cuboids from nets. It is important for students to understand that cuboids can have more than one net. This helps them to visualize and understand how edges and faces connect, and how their spatial relationships work.

Finally, students will identify parallel and perpendicular lines on cuboids. They will see that all of the pairs of faces that share a common edge meet at right angles.

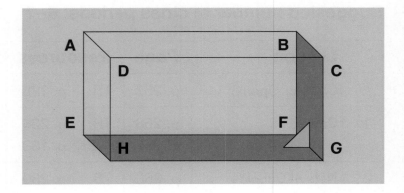

Just as lines can be perpendicular to each other, faces can be perpendicular to each other. Lines intersect at a point. Faces intersect at a line.

Perpendicular faces always define three dimensions (length, height, and width).

Students will also see that opposite faces on a cuboid are parallel:

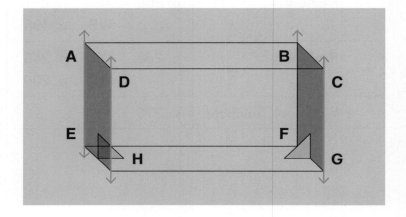

Materials

- Colored markers
- Cubes
- Cuboids (rectangular prisms)
- Grid paper
- Protractors
- Rulers
- Scissors
- Set Squares
- Shipping boxes with lids/tops
- Square Cards
- Tape
- Whiteboards

Blackline Masters

- Large Cuboid Net (BLM)
- Net of a Cuboid (BLM)
- Nets of Cubes (BLM)

Activities

Limited additional games and activities are included in this chapter, as students will be cutting, folding, and drawing cuboids and their nets. Use activities from prior chapters after students complete the **Do** questions, or anytime additional practice is needed.

Notes

Chapter Opener

Objective

- Investigate cuboids.

Lesson Materials

- Cubes
- Cuboids (rectangular prisms)
- Shipping boxes with lids/tops

Have students examine different boxes and discuss Dion's question.

Possible students answers:

- "The sides are flat, which makes them easy to stack on top of each other and next to each other."
- "The boxes have right angles. They aren't round."
- "The sides are all rectangles."

This introduction can be a short discussion before beginning Lesson 1.

Chapter 17

Properties of Cuboids

Dion and Sofia are packing and stacking boxes.

Why are boxes so easy to stack?

I wonder if it has something to do with the angles of the sides and the edges.

225

225

Lesson 1 Cuboids

Objective

- Investigate the lengths of the edges and the dimensions of the faces of cuboids.

Lesson Materials

- Colored markers
- Cuboids (rectangular prisms)
- Cubes
- Shipping boxes with the tops taped closed

Think

Discuss the **Think** problem and provide groups of students with shipping boxes. Have them label the faces that are the same size and shape. They can use markers to match and color edges that are the same length.

At the end of the lesson, keep the boxes for use in Lesson 2.

Learn

Have students compare their answers from **Think** with the ones shown in the textbook.

Faces are named by their vertices, i.e. Face BCGF.

If boxes used for **Think** are cubes, have students compare and contrast the lengths of their edges and sizes of their faces with those of the other cuboids. Students should see that all edges are the same length, and all faces are the same size and shape. Just as squares are special rectangles, cubes are special cuboids.

In addition to the faces and edges identified in **Learn**, have students discuss the edges that are parallel or perpendicular to one another on the faces.

For example,

- Edge DC and Edge HG are parallel to each other.
- Edge DH is perpendicular to Edge HG.

Think

Examine the faces, edges, and vertices of a cuboid.

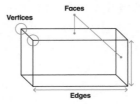

The top and bottom faces are the same size and shape.

(a) How many vertices, faces, and edges are there?

(b) Which faces are the same size and shape?

(c) Which edges are the same length?

Learn

A cuboid is a solid figure. A cuboid is also called a **right rectangular prism**.

(a) A cuboid has 6 faces, 8 vertices, and 12 edges.

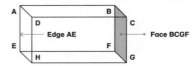

Edge AE   Face BCGF

(b) Opposite faces are the same size and shape.

Face ABFE is the same size and shape as Face DCGH.

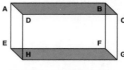

Face ABCD is the same size and shape as Face EFGH.

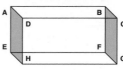

Face ADHE is the same size and shape as Face BCGF.

(c) Opposite pairs of edges are the same length.

AB and DC are the same length as EF and HG.

AD and EH are the same length as BC and FG.

AE and DH are the same length as BF and CG.

Do

① Students may have completed this task in **Think**. Provide students with cubes for them to examine.

Ask students, "What is alike and what is different between a cube and a cuboid?"

② Have students identify opposite pairs of edges on the cuboid.

③ Although the cuboid shown looks almost like a cube, students should see that some edges are different lengths.

Alex points out that opposite faces are the same size and shape. Students can find the area of one face and use that information to determine the area of the opposite face. Ensure they list all six faces.

Exercise 1 • page 183

Do

① Examine the faces, edges, and vertices of a cube.

(a) How many faces, edges, and vertices does a cube have?
   6 faces, 12 edges, 8 vertices
(b) How many edges are the same length?
   All 12 edges
(c) How many faces are the same size and shape?
   All 6 faces

228

② Examine the edges of the cuboid.

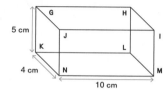

(a) List all the edges that measure 5 cm.
   GK, JN, HL, IM
(b) List all the edges that measure 10 cm.
   GH, JI, KL, NM
(c) List all the edges that measure 4 cm.
   KN, GJ, HI, LM

---

③ Name the faces of the cuboid shown below, then find the area of each face.

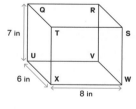

Opposite faces have the same size and shape, so we don't need to find the area of every face.

QRST: 48 in²
UVWX: 48 in²
QRVU: 56 in²
TSWX: 56 in²
QTXU: 42 in²
RSWV: 42 in²

229

④ This figure is a cuboid.

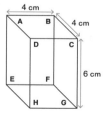

(a) List all the edges that measure 6 cm.
   AE, BF, CG, DH
(b) List all the edges that measure 4 cm.
   AB, BC, CD, DA, EF, FG, GH, HE
(c) Which face has the same area as Face ABCD?
   EFGH
(d) Which faces have an area of 24 cm²?
   ABFE, BCGF, DCGH, ADHE

Exercise 1 • page 183

Lesson 2 Nets of Cuboids

Objectives

- Construct cubes and cuboids using a net.
- Identify matching edges and vertices.
- Distinguish between nets that will and will not make a cuboid.

Lesson Materials

- Nets of Cubes (BLM)
- Net of a Cuboid (BLM)
- Square cards
- Tape

Think

Provide students with the Nets of Cubes (BLM) for **Think** and have them cut around the shapes. They should fold along the dotted lines and answer both the **Think** and Mei's question.

Note: The bulk of this lesson will involve cutting, folding, and taping to complete the **Think** task as well as problems ❶ – ❷.

Learn

Have students compare their cubes from **Think** with the ones shown in the textbook. They should try to fold their nets as shown.

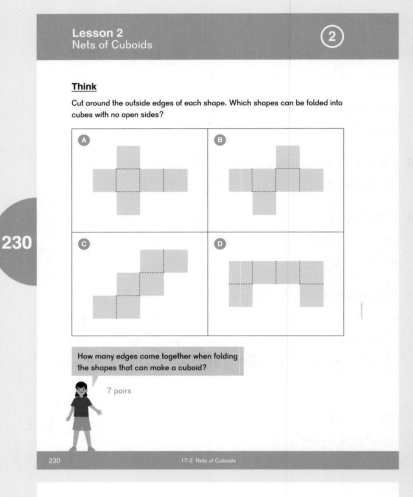

Think

Cut around the outside edges of each shape. Which shapes can be folded into cubes with no open sides?

A   B

C   D

How many edges come together when folding the shapes that can make a cuboid?

7 pairs

230   17-2 Nets of Cuboids

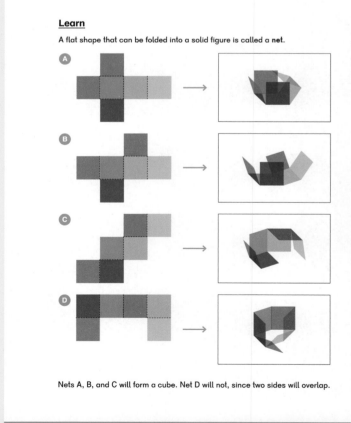

Learn

A flat shape that can be folded into a solid figure is called a **net**.

A
B
C
D

Nets A, B, and C will form a cube. Net D will not, since two sides will overlap.

17-2 Nets of Cuboids   231

Do

1 The Net of a Cuboid (BLM) is provided so that students can complete **1** (f).

2 The squares can be taped together on a flat surface then folded to make sure they will make a closed cube.

Sofia shows one net that forms a cube, and one that does not.

Activity

▲ Making Nets from Cuboids

Materials: Shipping boxes from Lesson 1, scissors

Have students cut the boxes open in different ways to make nets from the three-dimensional solids.

Exercise 2 • page 186

Do

1 The net of a cuboid is shown below.

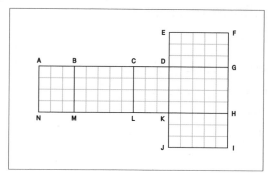

When the net is folded:

(a) Which vertices will touch?
E and C, F and B, A and G, L and J, M and I, N and H

(b) Which edges will touch?
CD and DE, BC and EF, AB and FG, LK and KJ, ML and JI, NM and HI, AN and GH

(c) Which faces will be opposite each other?
ABMN and CDKL, BCLM and DGHK, EFGD and KHIJ

(d) Which faces have the same shape and size?
ABMN and CDKL, BCLM and DGHK, EFGD and KHIJ

(e) How many pairs of edges will match up as it is folded?
7 pairs

(f) Cut out and fold a copy of the net and make the cuboid to verify your answers.

---

2 Use 6 square cards. Tape some of the edges together to form a net. Fold to see if it will form a cube.

Try to find a net that will form a cube that is different than Nets A, B, and C on page 230.

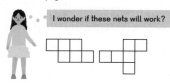

I wonder if these nets will work?

Compare your net with your classmates' nets. How many different nets of a cube were found?   There are 11 possible nets of a cube:

3 Look at the net of this die.

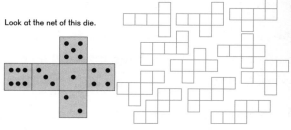

(a) When the net is folded, what numbers of dots will be on the faces that are opposite each other?
6 and 1, 3 and 4, 2 and 5

(b) What is the sum of the numbers that are on opposite sides of the die?
7

Exercise 2 • page 186

Lesson 3 Faces and Edges of Cuboids

Objective

- Investigate and identify parallel edges and faces of cubes and cuboids.

Lesson Materials

- Grid paper
- Large Cuboid Net (BLM)
- Nets of Cubes (BLM)
- Rulers
- Set squares

Think

Provide students with the Large Cuboid Net (BLM) and have them fold the net to make the cuboid. They should answer both the **Think** questions and Dion's question.

Discuss Emma's comment. Have students look at edges that might be parallel to each other.

Learn

Have students compare their answers from **Think** with the ones shown in the textbook.

Just as lines intersect to form a vertex, faces intersect to form an edge. Students can use a set square to see that all of the pairs of faces that share a common edge meet at right angles.

Faces can be perpendicular to each other just as lines can be perpendicular to each other.

Because Face ADHE and Face BCGF are both perpendicular to Face EFGH, they are parallel to each other.

Additionally, because the two opposite Faces ABFE and DCGH are perpendicular to Face EFGH, those faces are parallel to each other.

Think

Fold a net to make a cuboid. Use a set square to investigate the angles of the cuboid.

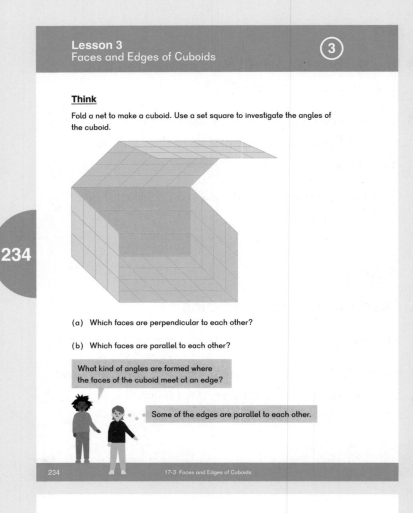

(a) Which faces are perpendicular to each other?

(b) Which faces are parallel to each other?

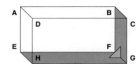
What kind of angles are formed where the faces of the cuboid meet at an edge?

Some of the edges are parallel to each other.

234   17-3 Faces and Edges of Cuboids

Learn

(a) For a cuboid, two faces that meet at a common edge are perpendicular to each other.

Faces EFGH and BCGF meet at edge FG.

Face BCGF is perpendicular to Face EFGH.

What other faces are perpendicular to Face EFGH?

ADHE, ABFE, DCGH

(b) For a cuboid, opposite faces are parallel to each other.

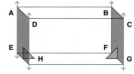

Faces ADHE and BCGF are both perpendicular to Face EFGH.

Face ADHE is parallel to Face BCGF.

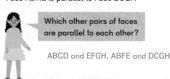
Which other pairs of faces are parallel to each other?

ABCD and EFGH, ABFE and DCGH.

17-3 Faces and Edges of Cuboids   235

Do

1 Students can line the right angle on a set square along the edges of a cube to find perpendicular faces. They can then determine which faces are parallel to each other.

3 Students can use Nets of Cubes (BLM), shape B from Lesson 2, if they need to cut and fold the shapes to solve the problem.

4 Provide students with grid paper and a ruler.

Exercise 3 · page 190

Do

1 Use a set square to investigate the angles formed by the faces of a cube.

(a) Which faces are perpendicular to each other?
Faces that share an edge are perpendicular to each other.

(b) Which faces are parallel to each other?
The faces on opposite sides.

2 The figure below is a cuboid.

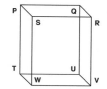

(a) Name two edges that are perpendicular to Edge WV.
Any two: TW, UV, SW, RV. Students may also name edges not touching WV: PT and QU.

(b) Which faces are perpendicular to Face TUVW?
SRVW, PSWT, QRVU, PQUT

(c) Name two edges that are parallel to Edge QR.
PS, UV. Students may also name edges not sharing a face with PQ: TW

(d) Which face is parallel to Face SRVW?
PQUT

---

3 This is a net of a cube.

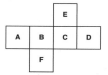

(a) When folded, which faces will be perpendicular to face E?
A, B, C, D

(b) Which face will be parallel to face E?
F

4 Use grid paper and a ruler to draw a cuboid.

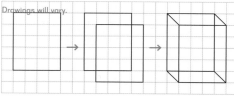

Drawings will vary.

Exercise 3 · page 190

236

237

Objective

- Practice concepts from the chapter.

After students complete the **Practice** in the textbook, have them move to Review 3, which reviews concepts from Dimensions Math 4B.

1 (h)

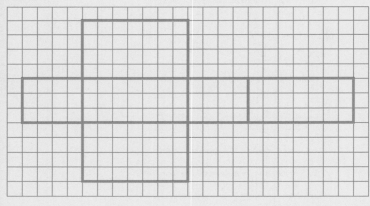

238

Lesson 4
Practice

P ④

1 This figure is a cuboid.

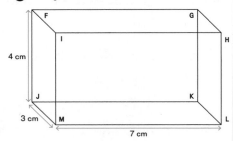

4 cm

3 cm

7 cm

(a) Which edges are the same length?
LM, JK, HI, and FG. JM, FI, GH, and KL. FJ, IM, GK, and HL.

(b) Which sides have the same size and shape?
FGHI and JKLM. GHLK and FIMJ. FGKJ and IHLM.

(c) What is the area of each face?
GHLK and FIMJ: 12 cm². FGHI and JKLM: 21 cm². FGKJ and IHLM: 28 cm².

(d) Name a pair of perpendicular edges.
Some possible answers: FI and IM. HI and IM. HL and LM. GK and KL.

(e) Which faces are perpendicular to each other?
Some possible answers: FGHI and IHLM. JKLM and IHLM. FIMJ and FGKJ.

(f) Name a pair of parallel edges.
Some possible answers: FG and HI. IM and HL. GK and FJ. JM and FI.

(g) Which faces are parallel to each other?
FGHI and JKLM. IHLM and FGKJ. FIMJ and GHLK.

(h) Draw a net of this cuboid on centimeter grid paper.
Nets may vary.

2 This is a net of a cube.

(a) When folded, which faces will be perpendicular to Face E?
A, C, D, F

(b) Which face will be parallel to Face E?
B

3 This is the net of a cuboid.

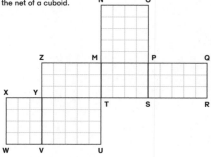

N   O

Z   M   P   Q

X   Y   T   S   R

W   V   U

239

(a) Which faces have the same size and shape?
XYVW and MPST, PQRS and ZMTY, YTUV and MNOP

(b) Which faces will be parallel to each other?
XYVW and MPST, PQRS and ZMTY, YTUV and MNOP

(c) When the net is folded which edges will touch?
XY and ZY, ZM and NM, OP and PQ, XW and NO, TS and TU, UV and SR, WV and QR

Brain Works

▲ Unique Cubes

Materials: Nets of Cubes (BLM) Shape A

How many possible ways are there to color the faces of a white cube red? Each colored cube will be unique. No two cubes will have the same faces no matter how the cubes are turned or placed.

Start with a net of a cube.

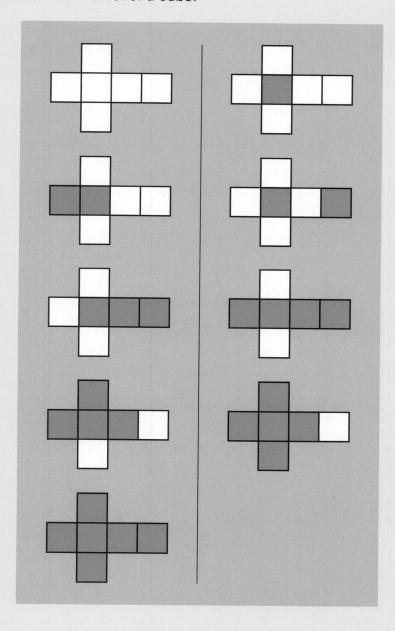

Exercise 4 • page 194

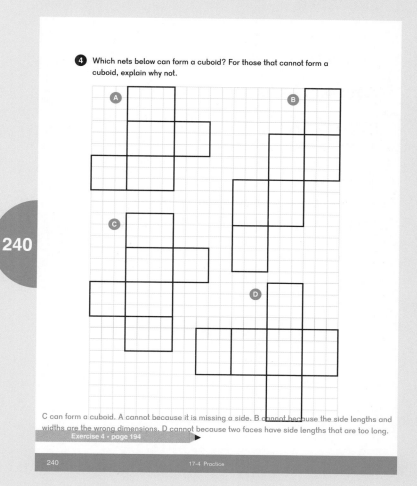

4 Which nets below can form a cuboid? For those that cannot form a cuboid, explain why not.

240

C can form a cuboid. A cannot because it is missing a side. B cannot because the side lengths and widths are the wrong dimensions. D cannot because two faces have side lengths that are too long.

Exercise 4 • page 194

240   17-4 Practice

Review 4

Objective

- Review concepts from Chapter 1 through Chapter 17.

Lesson Materials

- Protractors

Review 4 is an end of course review and covers content from Dimensions Math 4A and 4B.

1 Find the values. Express the answer as a quotient and remainder.

  (a) 8,987 ÷ 4
    2,246 R 3
  (b) 4,098 ÷ 6
    683
  (c) 9,999 ÷ 7
    1,428 R 3

2 Estimate and then find the values.
Estimates will vary

(a) 85,987 + 856	(b) 6,172 − 1,752	(c) 40,345 − 728
86,843	4,420	39,617
(d) 6,459 × 7	(e) 58 × 49	(f) 482 × 64
45,213	2,842	30,848
(g) 33.3 + 0.9	(h) 5.98 + 17.5	(i) 21 − 7.4
34.2	23.48	13.6
(j) 16.21 − 7.5	(k) 9.6 × 5	(l) 0.08 × 4
8.71	48	0.32
(m) 3.56 × 9	(n) 0.9 × 7	(o) 11.6 ÷ 4
32.04	6.3	2.9
(p) 7.68 ÷ 3	(q) 7.56 ÷ 7	(r) 4.08 ÷ 6
2.56	1.08	0.68

3 Express the values as a fraction or as a mixed number in simplest form.

  (a) 3 ÷ 5 $\frac{3}{5}$ (b) 6 ÷ 9 $\frac{2}{3}$ (c) 8 ÷ 3 $2\frac{2}{3}$

  (d) 14 ÷ 5 $2\frac{4}{5}$ (e) 56 ÷ 6 $9\frac{1}{3}$ (f) 42 ÷ 8 $5\frac{1}{4}$

4 Express the values as a fraction or mixed number in simplest form.

  (a) $\frac{3}{4} + \frac{3}{8}$ $1\frac{1}{8}$ (b) $1\frac{2}{3} - 1\frac{1}{12}$ $\frac{7}{12}$ (c) $7\frac{1}{10} - \frac{3}{5}$ $6\frac{1}{2}$

  (d) $7\frac{1}{2} - 2\frac{5}{8}$ $4\frac{7}{8}$ (e) $18 \times \frac{2}{3}$ 12   (f) $\frac{3}{4} \times 24$ 18

  (g) $\frac{4}{7} \times 14$ 8   (h) $3 \times \frac{2}{5}$ $1\frac{1}{5}$ (i) $\frac{7}{12} \times 8$ $4\frac{2}{3}$

5 The graph shows the number of tornadoes each month of 2018 in the U.S.

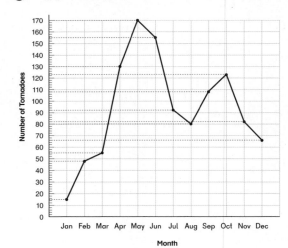

(a) Which month had the greatest number of tornadoes? How many?
May, 170

(b) Which month had the least number of tornadoes? How many?
January, 15

(c) Between which two months was there the sharpest rise in the number of tornadoes?
March and April

(d) Which two months had almost the same number of tornadoes?
August and November

(e) How many fewer tornadoes were there in October than in May?
47 tornadoes

(f) Which three-month period, Jan–Mar, Apr–Jun, Jul–Sep, or Oct–Dec, had the most tornadoes? How many tornadoes were there during that period?
Apr-Jun; 455 tornadoes

(g) How many tornadoes were recorded for 2018?
1,124

6 A number between 20 and 50 is a multiple of 8. When it is divided by 6, there is a remainder of 4. What is the number?
40

7 Which of the following numbers are composite numbers?

| 18 | 49 | 67 | 101 | 134 |

8 Which of the following numbers are common factors of 12 and 30?

| 2 | 4 | 6 | 12 | 30 |

243

9 Andrew has the same amount of money in pennies, in nickels, in dimes, and in quarters.

(a) What is the least number of each type of coin he could have?
Pennies: 50; Nickels: 10; Dimes: 5; Quarters: 2

(b) What is the total amount of money for all the coins in the answer for (a)? Express the answer in dollars.
$2.00

10 Measure each marked angle.

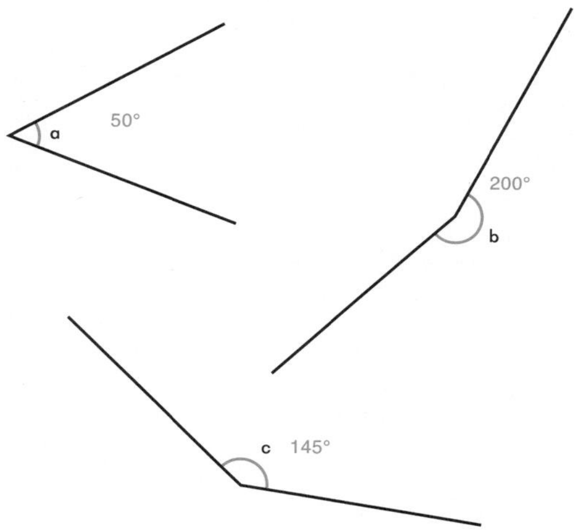

a   50°

200°   b

c   145°

244

Review 5

Objective

- Review concepts from Chapter 1 through Chapter 17.

Review 5 is an end of course review and covers content from Dimensions Math 4A and 4B.

1 The line plot shows the length of some rattlesnakes in a reptile exhibit, measured to the closest fourth of a foot.

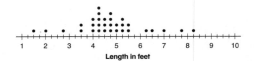

Length in feet

(a) How many rattlesnakes were measured?
32

(b) How many rattlesnakes were longer than 6 feet 4 inches?
6 ft 4 in = $6\frac{1}{3}$ ft; 4 are longer than $6\frac{1}{3}$ ft.

(c) What is the difference in length between the shortest and the longest rattlesnake? Express the answer in feet as a mixed number, in feet and inches, and in inches.
$8\frac{1}{4} - 1\frac{1}{2} = 6\frac{3}{4}$; $6\frac{3}{4}$ ft, 6 ft 9 in; 81 in

(d) What fraction of the total number of rattlesnakes were between 3 feet and 6 feet long? Express the answer in simplest form.
$\frac{24}{32} = \frac{3}{4}$; $\frac{3}{4}$

(e) One of the rattlesnakes weighs 5 lb 4 oz. Express this weight in ounces only, and in pounds as a mixed number.
84 oz; $5\frac{1}{4}$ lb

(f) Two other rattlesnakes weigh 4 lb 10 oz and 6 lb 2 oz. What is the sum of the weights of these two rattlesnakes? Express the answer in compound units.
4 lb 10 oz + 6 lb 2 oz = 10 lb 12 oz
10 lb 12 oz

245

2 Add or subtract. Express the answers using compound units where possible.

(a) 3 m 25 cm + 2 m 80 cm
6 m 5 cm

(b) 5 km 280 m – 2 km 700 m
2 km 580 m

(c) 6 L – 2 L 15 mL
3 L 985 mL

(d) 6 cm 9 mm + 3 cm 8 mm
10 cm 7 mm

(e) 4 lb 8 oz + 2 lb 9 oz
7 lb 1 oz

(f) 4 ft 7 in – 1 ft 10 in
2 ft 9 in

3 A baker uses 1.25 lb of flour to make a loaf of sourdough bread. How many pounds of flour does she need to make 8 loaves of this bread?
1.25 × 8 = 10
10 lb

4 Maya ran the same distance each day Monday through Friday. She ran a total of 17.5 km. How far did she run each day? Express the answer in kilometers as a mixed number.
17.5 ÷ 5 = 3.5
$3\frac{1}{2}$ km

5 A red ribbon is 4 times as long as a blue ribbon. The total length of both ribbons is $10\frac{4}{5}$ m. How long is each ribbon in meters? Express the answers as decimals.
Blue ribbon: $10\frac{4}{5}$ = 10.8; 10.8 ÷ 5 = 2.16; 2.16 m
Red ribbon: 2.16 × 4 = 8.64; 8.64 m

6 Jesse had $45. He spent $\frac{2}{3}$ of his money on a book, then $1.65 on a snack. How much money did he have left?
$\frac{2}{3}$ × $45 = $30; $30 + $1.65 = $31.65; $45 – $31.65 = $13.35
$13.35

7 What is the measure of Angle a?
360° – 79.5° = 280.5°

79.5°

a

246

⑨ (d)

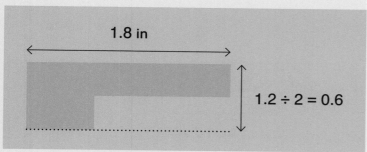

1.8 in

$1.2 \div 2 = 0.6$

Perimeter:

$1.8 + 1.8 + 0.6 + 0.6 = 4.8$

$4.8 = 4\frac{8}{10} = 4\frac{4}{5}$

Exercise 6 • page 204

---

⑧ The garden shown below has a rectangular pond in the center and a lawn around the pond. What is the area of the lawn?

$12.3 \times 6 = 73.8 \text{ m}^2$
$12.3 - 3.4 - 2.8 = 6.1 \text{ m}$
$6 - 1.5 - 1.5 = 3 \text{ m}$
$6.1 \times 3 = 18.3 \text{ m}^2$

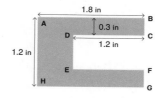

1.5 m

2.8 m   3.4 m

6 m

1.5 m

12.3 m

$73.8 - 18.3 = 55.5 \text{ m}^2$
Area: 55.5 m²

⑨ The figure below is symmetrical. All sides meet at right angles.

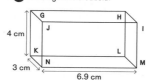

1.8 in

A   0.3 in   B

D   C

1.2 in

1.2 in

E   F

H

G

(a) Which sides are perpendicular to AH?
AB, HG

(b) Which sides are parallel to AH?
BC, DE, FG

(c) Express the perimeter in inches both as a decimal and as a mixed number in simplest form.
8.4 in; $8\frac{2}{5}$ in

(d) The shape is cut in half along a line of symmetry. Express the perimeter of each half both as a decimal and as a mixed number in simplest form.
4.8 in; $4\frac{4}{5}$ in

---

⑩ This figure is a cuboid.

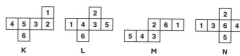

G   H

J   I

4 cm

K   L

3 cm   M

N

6.9 cm

(a) Which faces are parallel to each other?
GHIJ and KLMN, GJNK and HIML, GHLK and JIMN

(b) What is the area of each face?
GHIJ and KLMN: each 20.7 cm². GJNK and HIML: each 12 cm². GHLK and JIMN: each 27.6 cm².

(c) Which faces are perpendicular to each other?
Each face is perpendicular to all faces except the ones they are parallel to.

⑪ On a cube where the faces are numbered 1–6, the sum of the numbers on parallel faces is 7.

(a) Which of the following could be nets of the cube? K, N

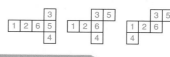

	1	
4	5	3	2
	6	

K

	2	
1	4	3	5
	6	

L

| | |2|6|1|
|5|4|3| |

M

		2	
1	3	6	4
		5	

N

(b) Copy the nets below and write 1–6 on the faces so that they could be a net of the cube. Answers may vary.

		3	
1	2	6	5
		4	

		3	5
1	2	6	
		4	

		3	5
1	2	6	
		4	

Exercise 6 • page 204

Chapter 17 Properties of Cuboids

Exercise 1

Basics

1 These are illustrations of the same cuboid.

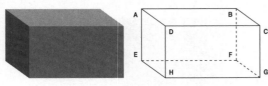

(a) A cuboid has __6__ faces, __8__ vertices, and __12__ edges.

(b) Face ABCD is the same size and shape as Face __EFGH__.

(c) Name two other pairs of faces that have the same size and shape.
ADHE and BCGF
ABFE and DCGH

(d) On Face ABCD, AD is the same length as __BC__.

(e) List the other edges that have the same length as AD.
EH and FG

(f) List all the edges with the same length as AB.
DC, EF, and HG

(g) List all the edges with the same length as AE.
DH, BF, and CG

Practice

2

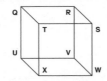

(a) Which edges have the same length as NO?
IL, JK, and MP
(b) Which edges have the same length as PO?
MN, LK, and IJ
(c) Which edges have the same length as JN?
KO, IM, and LP
(d) Find the area of each of the faces.
LKOP and IJNM: 29 × 32 = 928; 928 cm² IJKL and MNOP: 29 × 8 = 232; 232 cm²
JKON and ILPM: 32 × 8 = 256; 256 cm²

3 For this cube, the length of Edge RS is 9 cm.

(a) What is the length of Edge UV?
9 cm
(b) What is the area of Face QTXU?
81 cm²

4 For this cuboid the area of Face WZDA is 48 cm².

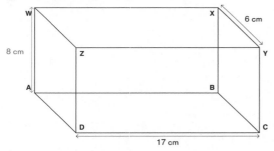

(a) What is the area of Face WXBA?
WZ = XY; WX = DC; WZ = 48 ÷ 6 = 8; 8 cm   17 × 8 = 136; 136 cm²
(b) What is the perimeter of Face WZDA?
8 + 8 + 6 + 6 = 28
28 cm

5 For this cuboid, the perimeter of Face EFGH is 98 cm.

HG: 98 ÷ 2 = 49; 49 − 15 = 34; 34 cm
(a) What is the area of Face HGKL?
34 × 11 = 374; 374 cm²
(b) What is the perimeter of Face IJKL?
34 + 34 + 15 + 15 = 98; 98 cm

Exercise 2

Basics

1 A and C are nets of this cuboid, but B and D are not. Explain why B and D cannot be nets of this cuboid.

4 cm
3 cm
8 cm

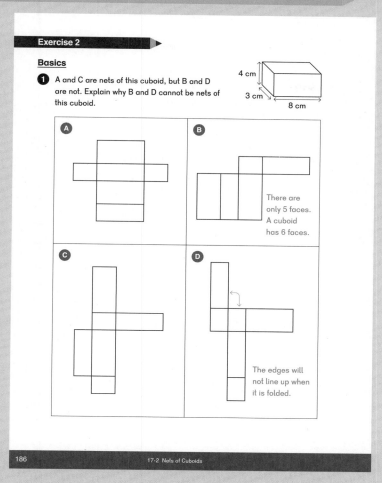

A

B

There are only 5 faces. A cuboid has 6 faces.

C

D

The edges will not line up when it is folded.

186   17-2 Nets of Cuboids

Practice

2 Label the rest of the vertices of the two nets of the cuboid to match the vertices of the cuboid. Some letters will be used more than once. (You can copy the nets onto graph paper and fold them if needed.)

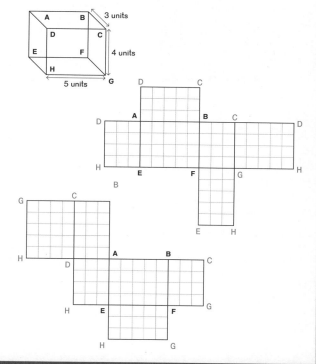

3 units
4 units
5 units

17-2 Nets of Cuboids   187

3 Draw more faces on each of the following nets so that they can be folded to form the given cube. Each net should be different.

Answers may vary. See next page to check.

2 units

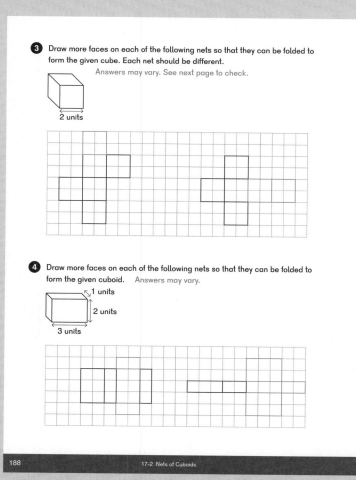

4 Draw more faces on each of the following nets so that they can be folded to form the given cuboid.   Answers may vary.

1 units
2 units
3 units

188   17-2 Nets of Cuboids

Challenge

5 The faces of this cube are numbered 1 through 6 so that the sum of the numbers on opposite sides is always 7.

Answers may vary with exactly which side of the 1 the 5 and 4 will be. Students do not need to be concerned about orientation of numbers. If students need help, tell them to determine the position of 6 first, then place 5 so it shares an edge with 1.

Number the rest of the faces of each of these nets so that when they are folded into a cube, the sum of the numbers on opposite sides will be 7.

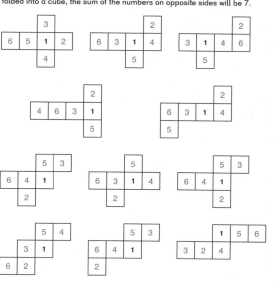

17-2 Nets of Cuboids   189

© 2019 Singapore Math Inc.   Teacher's Guide 4B Chapter 17   271

Exercise 3

Basics

1 These are illustrations of the same cuboid.

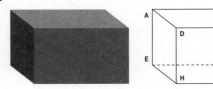

(a) Face ABCD is parallel to Face __EFGH__.

(b) Name two other pairs of faces that are parallel to each other.
ADHE and BCGF; ABFE and DCGH.

(c) Face ABCD and Face __DCGH__ are perpendicular to each other at Edge DC.

(d) Name three other faces that are perpendicular to Face ABCD.
ABFE, ADHE, BCGF

(e) Name all the faces that are perpendicular to Face ADHE.
ABFE, ABCD, DCGH, EFGH

(f) On Face ABCD, Edge AD is parallel to Edge __BC__.

(g) On Face ADHE, Edge AD is parallel to Edge __EH__.

(h) Name another edge that is parallel to Edge AD.
FG

(i) Name three edges that are parallel to Edge AE.
DH, BF, CG

(j) Name two edges that are perpendicular to Edge AD.
Possible answers: DC, DH, AE, AB

(k) Name four edges perpendicular to Edge HG.
HE, HD, GF, GC

(l) Name three edges that are not perpendicular to Edge FG.
BC, AD, EH

Practice

2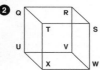

(a) Name two edges that are parallel to Edge XW.
Two of the following: TS, UV, QR

(b) Name two edges that are perpendicular to Edge QR.
Two of the following: QT, QU, RV, RS, UX, VW

(c) Which face is parallel to Face RSWV?
QTXU

(d) Which faces are perpendicular to Face RSWV?
QRVU, QRST, TSWX, UVWX

3 Draw two more cuboids below. Each cuboid should be different.
Drawings may vary.

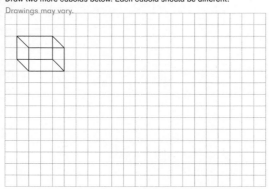

4 A cuboid is formed from this net.

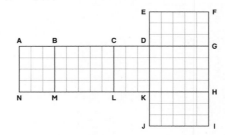

(a) List all pairs of faces that will be parallel to each other.
DGHK and BCLM, EFGD and KHIJ, ABMN and CDKL

(b) Name the faces that will be perpendicular to Face BCLM.
ABMN, CDKL, EFGD, KHIJ

Challenge

5 For each of these nets, shade the four faces that will be perpendicular to the shaded face when the net is folded.

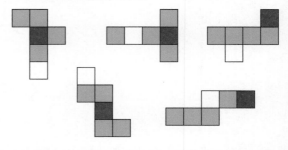

Exercise 4

Check

1

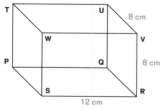

3 units

7 units

5 units

(a) Find the area of the face that is parallel to Face ABCD.
$5 \times 3 = 15$; 15 square units

(b) Find the area of two faces that are perpendicular to Face EFGH and have D as one vertex.
$7 \times 3 = 21$; 21 square units
$7 \times 5 = 35$; 35 square units

(c) If another identical cuboid was glued to Face DCGH to make a larger cuboid, what would be the area of the top face of the new cuboid?
The length of 3 units doubles to 6 units.
$6 \times 5 = 30$; 30 square units

(d) On the next page, two different nets of the cuboid have been started. Complete each net and find the perimeter of each.

Drawings may vary. Perimeters given for ones shown here.

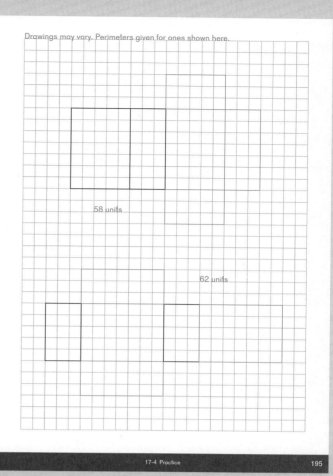

58 units

62 units

---

2 On this cuboid, Face TWSP is a square and has a perimeter of 32 cm. PQ is 12 cm long.

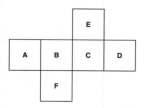

8 cm

8 cm

12 cm

(a) Which other face is also a square?
UVRQ

(b) What is the length of Edge VR?
Each edge of Face UVRQ: $32 \div 4 = 8$; 8 cm

(c) What is the area of each face that is perpendicular to Face TWSP?
All of the faces perpendicular to TWSP have the same dimensions.
$12 \times 8 = 96$; 96 cm   QR = PS = 8 cm

3 This is a net of a cube.

		E	
A	B	C	D
	F		

(a) When folded, which faces will be perpendicular to Face A?
B, E, F, D

(b) Which face will be parallel to Face B?
D

Challenge

4 Five white cubes are stacked as shown to form a cuboid. The surface of the cuboid is painted and then the cuboid is separated into cubes. How many faces are unpainted in all?   8 faces

5 64 white cubes are stacked as shown to form a large cube. The surface of the cuboid is painted and then the cuboid is separated into cubes.

(a) How many cubes have exactly 3 faces painted?
8 cubes (the ones at each vertex of the cube)

(b) How many cubes have only 2 faces painted?
The two middle ones along each edge will have only 2 faces painted. There are 12 edges.
$12 \times 2 = 24$
24 cubes

Teacher's Guide 4B Chapter 17

Exercise 5

Check

1 | 36.6 | 6.53 | 56.36 | 345.05 | 3.65 |

(a) What does the digit 3 stand for in each number?
36.6: 3 tens; 6.53: 3 hundredths; 56.36: 3 tenths;
345.05: 3 hundreds; 3.65: 3 ones

(b) Arrange the numbers in order from least to greatest.
3.65, 6.53, 36.6, 56.36, 345.05

(c) Write the greatest number in expanded notation.
345.05 = 300 + 40 + 5 + 0.05

(d) Multiply the number with the digit 5 in the first decimal place by 6.
6.53 × 6 = 39.18

(e) Divide the difference between the least number and the greatest number by 5.
345.05 − 3.65 = 341.4
341.4 ÷ 5 = 68.28

(f) Find the sum of the 3 least numbers.
3.65 + 6.53 + 36.6 = 46.78

2

(a) Express the difference in length between the two lines as a decimal.
3.9 − 0.2 = 3.7; 8.7 − 2.3 = 6.4
6.4 − 3.7 = 2.7
2.7 cm

(b) Express the difference in length between the two lines in compound units of centimeters and millimeters.
2 cm 7 mm

(c) Express the sum of the lengths of the two lines as a mixed number in simplest form.
$3.7 + 6.4 = 10.1 = 10\frac{1}{10}$
$10\frac{1}{10}$ cm

3 What is the difference in perimeter of these two figures?

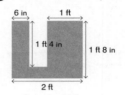
Perimeter: 10 ft

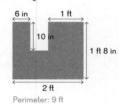
Perimeter: 9 ft

10 − 9 = 1
1 ft

Or, 1 ft 4 in = 16 in, one of the cut out sides is 6 in longer, so difference is 2 × 6 in or 1 ft.

---

4 Martin has a rectangular garden that measures 6 ft by 12 ft.

(a) What is the area of his garden in square feet?
6 × 12 = 72
72 ft²

(b) What is the area of his garden in square yards?
2 × 4 = 8
8 yd²

(c) There is a 3-foot wide path all the way around Martin's garden. What is the total area of both the garden and the path in square feet?
6 + 6 = 12; 12 + 6 = 18, 12 × 18 = 216
216 ft²

5 (a) The table below shows the amount of water Martin used each month to water his garden from April to September. Complete the line graph to show this data.

Month	Apr	May	Jun	Jul	Aug	Sep
Gallons	145	130	170	180	195	140

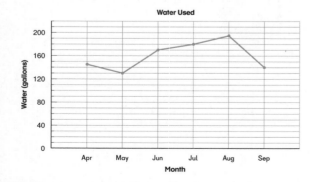

Water Used

(b) What is the total amount of water he used over the 6 months?
960 gallons

(c) What fraction of the months did he use more than 140 gallons? Express the answer in simplest form.

$\frac{4}{6} = \frac{2}{3}$

6 Ani baked some cookies. After giving 25 of the cookies to Fuyu and $\frac{2}{5}$ of the remaining cookies to Kawai, she had 48 cookies left. How many cookies did she bake?

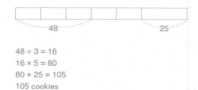

48 ÷ 3 = 16
16 × 5 = 80
80 + 25 = 105
105 cookies

7 1 sheet of paper is 27 cm 8 mm long. How long are 5 sheets of paper laid end to end? Express the answer in meters and centimeters.

5 × 278 mm = 1,390 mm

1,390 mm = 139 cm

1 m 39 cm

8 Nathan had $14.35 less than Parker. Nathan saved another $6.40 and Parker spent $4.65. How much less money does Nathan now have than Parker?

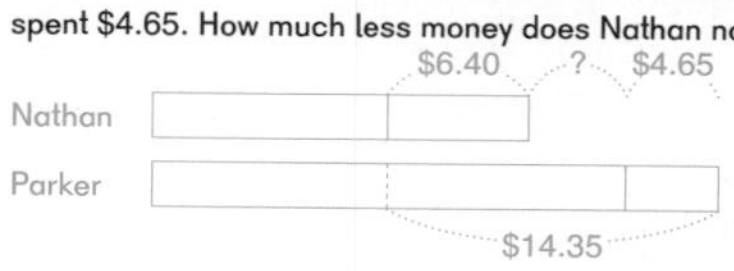

Nathan ┌─────────┬─────────┐ $6.40 ··· ? ··· $4.65

Parker ┌──────────────────┬──────┐

$14.35

$14.35 − $6.40 − $4.65 = $3.30

$3.30 less

Challenge

9 ABCD is a rectangle. Find the measure of the angles ADE, DEC, and FAB.

∠ADE = 42°	∠DEC = 107°	∠FAB = 132°
90° − 48° = 42°	180° − 73° = 107°	90° + 42° = 132°

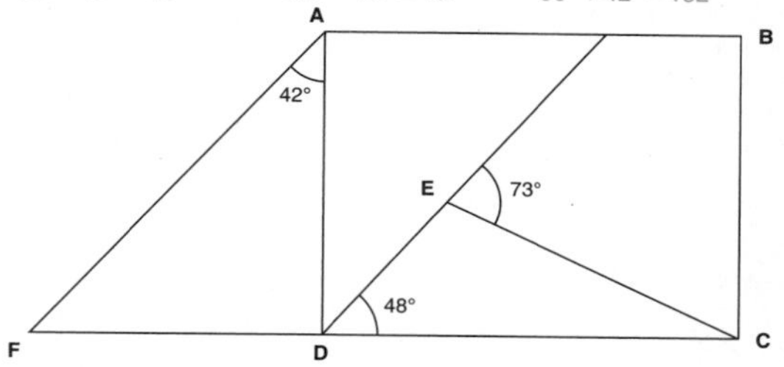

Exercise 6

Check

1 Find the difference between the sum of the first two multiples of 8 and the third multiple of 5.

24 − 15 = 9

9

2 What is the greatest prime number less than 100?

99 is divisible by 9, 98 is even, 97 is not divisible by an even number, 3, 5, 7, 9, 11, or 13. Since we have checked all factors less than 13, and 17 × 13 is greater than 99, we do not need to check any more numbers.

97

3 30 apples and 45 oranges need to be placed in baskets so that each basket has the same number of fruits. What is the greatest possible number of baskets needed?

Factors of 30: 1, 2, 3, 5, 6, 10, 15, 30
Factors of 45: 1, 3, 5, 9, 15, 45
15 baskets

4 Mateo was supposed to multiply a number by 7. Instead he divided the number by 7 and got an answer of 8.5. What should the correct answer be?

8.5 × 7 = 59.5
59.5 × 7 = 416.5
416.5

5 Which of the following have a value greater than 1 but less than 10?

| 0.96 × 9 | 17.8 ÷ 2 | 3.79 × 3 | 12 ÷ 5 | 40.6 ÷ 4 |

6

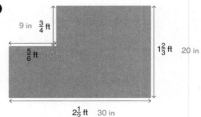

(a) Express the perimeter of the figure in inches.
100 in
(b) Express the area of the figure in square inches.
510 in²

7 A rope $5\frac{1}{4}$ m long is cut into 5 pieces. 4 of the pieces are $\frac{5}{8}$ m long. How long is the fourth piece? Express the answer in meters as a mixed number in simplest form.

$4 \times \frac{5}{8} = \frac{20}{8} = 2\frac{1}{2}$

$5\frac{1}{4} - 2\frac{1}{2} = 2\frac{3}{4}$

$2\frac{3}{4}$ m

8 Antonio paid $26.85 for 2 towels and 3 wash cloths. A wash cloth cost $2.55 less than a towel. What was the cost of 1 towel?

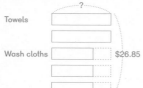

$2.55 × 3 = $7.65
5 units ⟶ $26.85 + $7.65 = $34.50
1 unit ⟶ $34.50 ÷ 5 = $6.90
$6.90

9 Measure each of the marked angles.
Measurements may vary by a few degrees.

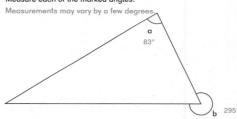

10 (a) Draw an angle that measures 28°.

(b) Draw an angle that measures 280°.

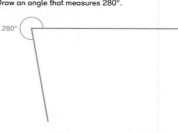

11 Complete each figure so that the dotted line is a line of symmetry.

(a)

(b)

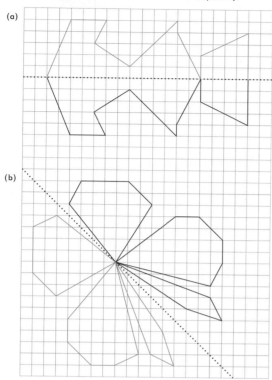

12 The figure is made up of squares, each with 3-cm sides. What is the perimeter of the entire figure in centimeters?

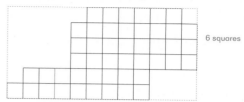

6 squares

12 squares

6 + 6 + 12 + 12 = 36
36 × 3 = 108
108 cm

13 The weights of different groups of objects are shown below. How much does the cone weigh?

0.8 × 2 = 1.6

□△ = 4   □△□ = 4.8   □□△ = 4.2

                4.8 − 4 = 0.8   4.2 − 1.6 = 2.6

2.6 kg

14 The figure shows two different faces of the same cube. In the net of the cube, draw the missing ■ and ◯.

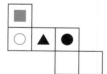

15 This figure is made from three identical overlapping squares. Find the measure of ∠a.

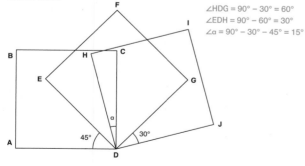

∠HDG = 90° − 30° = 60°
∠EDH = 90° − 60° = 30°
∠a = 90° − 30° − 45° = 15°

Blackline Masters for 4B

All Blackline Masters used in the guide can be downloaded from dimensionsmath.com.
This lists BLMs used in the **Think** and **Learn** sections.
BLMs used in **Activities** are included in the Materials list within each chapter.

Blank Hundredths Grid	Chapter 12: Lesson 3, Lesson 4, Lesson 8
Conversions of Measurement	Chapter 10: Lesson 4
Decimal and Fraction Number Line	Chapter 12: Lesson 1
Drawing Perpendicular and Parallel Lines	Chapter 16: Lesson 3
Grid Paper	Chapter 11: Lesson 2, Lesson 5
Large Cuboid Net	Chapter 17: Lesson 3
Net of a Cuboid	Chapter 17: Lesson 2
Nets of Cubes	Chapter 17: Lesson 2, Lesson 3
Paper Circles	Chapter 15: Lesson 1
Pool and Patio	Chapter 11: Lesson 3
Quadrilaterals	Chapter 16: Lesson 4
Shapes	Chapter 16: Lesson 5
Symmetrical Figures	Chapter 16: Lesson 6